# SLEEPWALKING

# TO

# APOCALYPSE

## RON NASH

### BELVOIR VALE PUBLISHING

First published in 2016


Copyright © 2016 by Ron Nash


Ron Nash has asserted his right under the Copyright, Designs and
Patents Act 1988 to be identified as the author of this work.


First published in the United Kingdom in 2016
by Belvoir Vale Publishing
49 Fairway, Keyworth, Nottingham NG12 5DW


ISBN 978-0-9562826-1-3


Printed by York Publishing Services Ltd

# ACKNOWLEDGEMENTS

Thanks to:-

Gwyneth M Donaldson – for her enthusiasm, computer work, attention to detail and patience.

Tim Hughes – for his artistic ability, comments and the Cover Illustration.

Eileen – for tolerance, patience and help while I was working on this book.

Dan Roberts – for his valuable observations and comments.

Margaret Wainer – for her proof reading, Editing and attention to detail.

SLEEPWALKING TO APOCALYPSE          R. NASH

# CONTENTS

| CHAPTER | | PAGE |
|---|---|---|

# INTRODUCTION

This book is written as a wake-up call. The Apocalypse, predicted and described, is based on four interacting factors. Three of them are real, ongoing and inescapable. Only the fourth – the Alpha HIV is fiction. I have added that as a trigger, a catalyst, to precipitate a final, massive disaster that drastically slashes the human population of the Earth over a relatively short timescale, basically to create a readable book.

However, even without the HIVa, the three primary factors, coming together, are more than enough to create a human, global disaster of totally unprecedented proportions. The Holocaust described in the book, totally devastating but of relatively short duration, may not happen. Instead there could be a long drawn out correction, lasting 150 years or more, with endless financial and economic upheavals as raw material supplies run out; with droughts, famines, flood disasters devastating various parts of the world at different times; with the world partially recovering from one disaster only to be shattered again by the next. With millions of people dying of famine in one country while the rest of the world looks on, unable to help because they hardly have enough food themselves. With murderous minor wars and conflicts because billions of people want to migrate north, out of the heat, and billions of people already in the North want to stop them.

This could go on for a very long time but, all the while, the correction slowly taking place and the numbers of human beings on this planet gradually being reduced.

I don't know which would be worse – the short sharp hell described by this book or several hundred years of prolonged conflict, famine, disease and misery. As I have said – three of the four factors are real. Let us consider them carefully.

1. <u>The Human Population Explosion</u>

In my mind this is the fundamental problem – the root cause of the second and third factors which are Global Warming and Resources Depletion. In the days when Julius Caesar walked the Earth it is believed there were only 180 million people on the entire planet and now, in 2015, there are 7¼ billion, roughly forty times as many.

Surely, it must be obvious, that if there were only 180 million people on the earth now, despite having had the Industrial Revolution, there would not be the dangerous levels of $CO^2$ emissions, there would not be the over exploitation of the seas, the excessive stripping and depletion of the world's metal ores and mineral resources, the over-cultivation of the land leading to soil impoverishment and salt contamination.

The Earth can take a substantial extra release of $CO^2$. The forests, the other land plants, the plankton and algae in the sea, can all soak up $CO^2$. If there were only 180 million of us the earth could cope with our extra emissions and there would be little or no rise in atmospheric $CO^2$ levels. But there are limits. The fact that measured atmospheric $CO^2$ levels have been steadily increasing for the last hundred years shows the biological systems that absorb $CO^2$ are being overwhelmed.

As it is, at 7¼ billion, there are already far too many human beings on this earth.

We are over polluting the planet. We are impoverishing the seas and the land, stripping earth's metal and mineral resources. Excessive population, first and foremost, is the root cause of our problems.

At the time of writing (Jan 2015) not only is the world population at 7¼ billion but it is increasing at the rate of 90 million additional people per year, which is 246,000 every single day. Twenty years ago, a group of optimistic scientists were telling us not to worry – the world population would rise to 9 billion by 2100 and then stabilise. My own calculations, at that time, suggested we were likely to reach the 9 billion figure as early as 2035 and, at the present rate of increase, we are well on the way to doing just that.

Those scientists have now had a rethink and are now predicting 12 billion by 2100. This is possible but it would still need a substantial reduction in the birth rate to achieve it.

In this book I have worked on the premise of 13.1 billion by the year 2100 and 15.2 billion by 2130 which I consider to be realistic and reasonable possibilities. If we carried on at the present rate of increase of 90 million per year then the numbers would be 14.9 billion by 2100 and 17.6 billion by 2130. However, let us not forget, that as you double the number of people on this earth you increase the number of people producing children for the next generation. In actual fact, therefore, to prevent the population going over the 15.2 billion I project for 2130, there would have to be a very considerable fall in the birth rate from what it is now. To prevent the total population of the earth from ever going over 10 billion – which I regard as the absolute maximum if we are going to avoid the sort of disaster described in this book, would require a massive and sustained worldwide birth control awareness and implementation program starting <u>now</u>.

## 2. Global Warming

Can any reasonable person now doubt that Global Warming, which affects human beings through the related climate change, is real and on going. The evidence is overwhelming. The seas are measurably warming. The glaciers are shrinking, the arctic ice cap is rapidly reducing. The arctic tundra areas of the world have warmed by an amazing 2°C to 3°C over the last 70 years, leading to melting of the permafrost as never seen before in human memory. The ice cap on Greenland is warming, leading to a speeding up of the glaciers and a vast increase in the release of icebergs into the sea.

People have argued that global warming is a natural phenomenon – not generated by human activities. However, we cannot deny the evidence – from numerous ice core and sea bed deposits – that, in the past, high atmospheric $CO^2$ levels have always been associated with a period of global warming. And there is now no question – human activity has increased $CO^2$ levels from 280 ppm before the Industrial Revolution to 400 ppm today in 2015. The Inter-Government Panel on Climate Change scientists have said that, if we can control $CO^2$ emissions – if we can prevent atmospheric $CO^2$ going above 450 ppm we can hold global warming to no more that 2°C above pre-industrialisation figures.

"Is this really possible?" Let us look at the facts.

At the present time more coal than ever before is being burned. More oil than ever before is being burned. More natural gas than ever before is being burned. More cement – for concrete – than ever before is being made. (Making cement produces large quantities of $CO^2$ apart from the fuel that is used).

This is all because there are more people enjoying and demanding a higher standard of living than ever before.

The developed nations are cutting down on use of coal, oil, and gas. They are building wind farms, solar panels and energy conservation systems. Increasing the fuel efficiency of transport systems – introducing electric cars and so on.

But their efforts are more than counterbalanced by extra fossil fuel use by developing countries. China, for instance, has recently overtaken the USA as the greatest greenhouse gas producer on Earth. The Chinese are not irresponsible. They are working hard to introduce wind farms and solar panels. They have introduced strict emission limits on personal cars. They are doing what they can. However, the Chinese economy is still growing rapidly. They have 1,300 million people clamouring for improvements in their standard of living. To do this needs energy.

America has recently announced it will cut $CO_2$ emissions by 20% by 2020. China has stated it hopes to reach peak emissions by 2020. In other words China expects their emissions to increase 30% or so before the peak is reached. I also think the Chinese estimate is optimistic. Although Chinese emissions have just overtaken America's the amount of emissions, per person, in China, is less than a quarter that of an average American. (There are 1,300 million Chinese as against 300 million Americans). Is it likely, do you think, that the Chinese will settle, permanently, for a standard of living vastly below Americans? And then there is India – with 1,100 million people. They too are rapidly industrialising. Their people too want a high standard of living. And South East Asia, Indonesia, South America and Africa. They all want to modernise and industrialise and have a high standard of living.

Economists and Scientists accept that, in general, energy use and GDP (Gross Domestic Product) go together. i.e. An increase of 30% in GDP goes with around 30% increase in the use of energy. At the present time, especially in Europe, we have a situation where a number of countries have very low growth or zero growth in GDP, some have even contracted. Energy use has followed the trend so it is not too surprising the European countries have managed to reduce $CO_2$ emissions. However, other countries have been growing rapidly – China and India being prime examples.

Overall – world GDP has been steadily growing by about 3½% over the last 30 years and is highly likely to keep doing so. Because of compounding, if the world GDP continues to grow at 3½% it means world GDP will double in just 21 years, quadruple in 42 years and, if growth can still be maintained, increase eight times by the year 2078.

How can anybody reasonably suggest that the total human world production of greenhouse gases is going to be reduced in the next 40 to 50 years? Not only that, but greenhouse gas emissions are already so high that, to hold $CO^2$ levels at or below 450 ppm would require current levels of emissions to be slashed by at least 75%.

Also – we have the indisputable fact that two positive feedback events have already kicked in – to exacerbate global warming.

The most important is the warming and melting of the Arctic Tundra.

Remarkably, and for some reason that is not yet understood, the Arctic is warming much faster than the rest of the planet. Whilst the world, on average, has only warmed ¾°C in the last 80 years, the Arctic Tundra areas have warmed 2°C to 3°C. The Tundra areas of the world – Siberia, Canada and Alaska are remarkable for the vast quantities of peat (trillions of tons) incorporated in the permafrost. Permafrost used to be what its name implies – permanently frozen ground, so we are talking of trillions of tons (a trillion is a million, million) of permanently frozen peat.

This is now changing. In summer the permafrost is melting. The thawed out peat begins to rot and as it rots it emits $CO^2$ and methane. Methane is at least 20 times more powerful a greenhouse gas than $CO^2$. Fortunately, methane is more short lived in the atmosphere than $CO^2$ but its effects are still very important in the short term.

So we already have large, extra, emissions of $CO^2$ and methane over and above human emissions – and this will get worse as the tundra warms further.

Another powerful positive feedback effect that has already started is the extra warming effect resulting from the reduction of the Arctic ice cap. Ice and snow reflects 95% of the energy of the sun's rays back out into space, whereas open water absorbs 90% of the incoming radiation. Arctic summer sea ice area has already drastically reduced from what was the norm just 80 years ago. (In 2007 the summer ice area was down over 30% from what was the norm a few years ago).

A satellite, capable of measuring the area of the ice and also the thickness, showed that, in 2014, the volume of Arctic sea ice was down 13% from that recorded in 2013 – a 13% reduction in volume in just one year. Extrapolating from these figures suggests that, in 10 to 20 years from now, the Arctic ice cap will, in summer, totally disappear for a time each year.

This means that a massive extra input of solar radiation (which converts to heat) into the Arctic sea is already occurring and is going to get worse.

Why scientists keep saying they are afraid of positive feedbacks occurring, later in the century, is beyond me. Positive feedbacks have already measurably and indubitably kicked in – probably starting at least 20 years ago. In this book I have assumed a modest and reasonable rate of increase of $CO^2$ levels in the atmosphere occurring in the next 115 years. The present rate of increase of $CO^2$ is about 2 ppm per year and climbing rapidly. I have assumed the average rate of increase for the next 115 years to be 3 ppm per year. (Don't forget – population increasing. World GDP quadrupling or more and $CO^2$ emissions from the tundra increasing) I think 3 ppm per year to be an optimistic average projection over this period. Reality could, very easily, be very much worse.

The conclusion must surely be – that Global Warming – at least as bad as outlined in this book – is just about inevitable. Only an earlier massive calamity, drastically affecting the human race, would be likely to change these projections to any degree.

3. Depletion of Resources

In order to fuel the Industrialisation of Nations and Improvement in the Standard of Living of everyone on Earth, the natural resources of the planet have to be exploited.

America can be taken as an example of the most modern and industrially developed nation – with one of the highest standards of living. To achieve that requires massive exploitation of earth's natural resources. Here are a few basic statistics.

At the present time, the average American, living the average lifetime, consumes, indirectly, over 500kg (1,102lbs) of copper, 300kg (660lbs) of lead, 300kg (660lbs) of zinc, 40kg (88lbs) of nickel, 100kg (220lbs) of chromium and so on. You may think these figures look high but stop to think how many cars, televisions, washing machines, refrigerators, lawn mowers, etc you yourself have owned and scrapped in your lifetime, not to mention bottles, beer cans, bean tins, etc.

Also, think of all the grain and animal feed required to produce the steaks, the meat, the burgers the Americans so love. It is true the Americans are over consuming, but they set the standard. They are the ones whose lifestyle is seen most on films, TV and computer screens.

A few years ago the Chinese people simply survived. They lived on a bowl of rice and a few bits of fish or chicken a day. But not now! They are industrialising fast. They too want cars, fridges, TVs, computers, mobile phones and all the modern trappings. They too, prefer a diet with plenty of meat and veg. Consumption of beef, chicken and fish has rocketed in the last ten years. (Roughly ten pounds of feed is required to produce a pound of beef and 3lbs of grain to produce a pound of chicken meat).

Soon Chinese GDP is set to overtake Americas. Already annual $CO^2$ emissions have exceeded the USA's. But there are 1,300 million Chinese and only 300 million Americans. The Chinese still have a long way to go to catch up the Americans in GDP per capita. Their National GDP would have to increase over 4 times to do that. However, they are working on it – and they are not going to stop.

Next door is India with a population of 1,100 million. They have the same ambitions. So too have Pakistan, Bangladesh, South East Asia and Indonesia. They all have the same ambitions and dreams. To the North they can see the Chinese succeeding, and Japan and South Korea, who have already succeeded.

Looking further, we see the countries of South America – from Argentina to Mexico. They can't industrialise fast enough. And Africa – another 1,100 million people.

Previously I quoted the figures for Americans consumption of raw materials. There are 24 times as many people on this earth as there are Americans.

How long do you think the supplies of copper, zinc, chromium, lead, etc are going to last? Sure! They will find new deposits, open new mines, find copper in Greenland or wherever. But they will have to find a hell of a lot of it. And it won't be long before they cannot find enough. What happens then?

The nations of the Earth consume, between them, 90 million barrels of oil a day. We have seen that a shortfall of only 2 or 3 million barrels a day makes the price rocket – from 50 dollars a barrel to 110 dollars a barrel or more. That is – despite the fact there are plenty of alternatives to oil. We can even make oil from gas or coal if we have to – and there are vast reserves of coal.

What happens when there is a shortfall of copper or zinc or lead or tin or any of the scores of essential raw materials. Not a shortfall of 2% or 3% as per the oil but, say 20% or 40%. The prices will go sky-high.

We will find substitutes – you say. And in some instances – no doubt we will.

The best metal to use, as a conductor, in electric motors, is silver. We don't use it because it is relatively rare and too expensive. So we use copper – the next best thing. When the copper runs out – we can use aluminium. But aluminium is nowhere near as good and you need to use lots of electricity in order to make aluminium.

So – when the copper starts to run out – and the price rockets, it throws a spanner in the economic cog wheels – the same as it does when the oil price rockets. At some point in the future, the economies of the Nations of the World are in for a very bumpy ride.

As I write, in early 2015, the oil price is plummeting – down 50% in the last 6 months. The Americans solved the shortfall – by exploiting shale oil deposits. Saudi Arabia decided it wouldn't cut production – just to please other OPEC members – to create a shortfall and keep the price high, so the oil price is in freefall.

But what happens when the Earth's supply of raw materials and resources starts to really run out – from copper and zinc to say beans and wheat, rice and fish? The economists will tell you – when demand exceeds supply – the price goes up. Everything goes to the highest bidder.

One of the disturbing facts that come out – if you study the history of the Great Irish Potato Famine – is that half the people who starved to death did so, not because there was no food available at all, but because they could not afford to buy what little food there actually was still available.

For the entire world population of 7¼ billion to have the same standard of living as the Americans do now, you would have to increase production of oil, copper, zinc, chromium and so on by more than four times. And when the world population is 14½ billion you would need to double it again. Do you really think that is possible?

In this book I have been optimistic. I have assumed there will be no serious food problems for 100 years. I also assume they will keep finding new sources of raw materials and introduce substitutes to keep the economic wheels turning for 100 years. I assume the human race can survive and live in ever hotter countries for at least most of the next 100 years. I assume the human race will 'muddle through' until there are 15 billion human beings on the planet.

And then – I have wondered what will happen next. This book spells out one of several possibilities – none of them pleasant. We could solve the population problem – if we tackled it head on. If we all dedicated ourselves like the Allies dedicated themselves in World War 2. We would need to mount a massive World Wide propaganda campaign. Devote massive financial funds to the program. Make films showing what sort of hell we could create if we don't control our numbers – and the heaven we could create if we do. We would need to keep hammering the message home – ad nauseam. Talk to and pressure the Pope and the Roman Catholic Church to change their stance. If necessary – apply sanctions to States that didn't co-operate – and give benefits to those that did.

We should set targets – to try to stop world population going over 10 billion (9 billion is not practical – we are as good as there) and then try to get it down to 6 billion in the shortest possible time – and after that gradually down to a figure the world can support – forever. I have written this book in hopes that somehow, somewhere, someone with influence and power may be provoked and shocked into thinking about the situation and taking the lead.

However, I am a realist. With the political and economic systems that exist on the Earth at the present time, I expect that things will carry on as usual. Everybody will continue to enjoy their holidays, prefer to laugh than cry, push nasty thoughts of Global Disaster away as they cuddle their grandchildren. Therefore, I expect the world population to grow to at least 12 billion and, possibly, far more.

I expect Global Warming to continue; the developed countries to continue to make efforts to reduce $CO_2$ emissions (providing it doesn't upset the economic applecart too much), the undeveloped countries to carry on developing, increasing their $CO^2$ emissions while making excuses and making token $CO^2$ cuts and I expect atmospheric $CO^2$ levels to keep on rising for the next 100 years at least.

I expect over exploitation of natural resources to continue and I expect everyone on the planet to go about their business, enjoy their dinners, worry about their future and the kids' futures – what school shall they go to? What career shall they work for? Where do we go for this years Holiday? But never, ever worry about the world population. No point in worrying about that is there? And who wants to read Doom and Gloom anyway.

So I expect everyone to happily carry on – as before – sleepwalking to Apocalypse.

# APRIL 2647 – GREENLAND

Daniel Kealey waited his turn, then stepped off the great ship on to the gangway. He shuffled along in the queue, down corridors and along escalators, until, eventually, he came to a great hall. There was a large sign

IMMIGRATION
WELCOME TO GREENLAND
European Contingent No 5
April 2647

He took a deep breath. "Well! I finally made it!"

---

Ten minutes later he was in a cafeteria sipping a cup of coffee and munching a few biscuits. He let his mind run back to his parents in Britain.

Only 10 million people lived in the British Isles now and that was still too many for two small islands. There were only 500 million people on the whole planet now – and two thirds of them were in Siberia, Canada and Alaska. They said that, back in 2120, there had been over 100 million people in Britain. Incredible! However, at that time the whole world was overcrowded – with over 15 Billion on the Earth. Everything must have been on a knife edge, with population at its limit, billions desperate to move North, as Global Warming began to make the tropics unbearably hot. Food production critical, with aquifers failing and droughts devastating food producing areas. Natural Resources failing as oil, gas, copper and all the other minerals began to run out.

And then, to top it all, had come the hellish Alpha HIV.

HIV had been known for years – but this was different. A cross between HIV and the common cold. It spread like wildfire – all over the globe – and was far more virulent. People developed AIDS in one year – not ten.

World wide – the old Civilisation collapsed. Thirteen billion people died.

So – now – here he was on Greenland, at the University of New Copenhagen.

A new world, in a new Age – a New Civilisation.

---

1

# 2025 USA/RUSSIA CONFRONTATION

In 2025, Trouble in Ukraine flared up again. Previously, in 2014, Pro-Russian factions, in the eastern part of Ukraine had rebelled against the west-leaning Government in Kiev. Russia, still paranoid and fearing attack by NATO and the USA, supported the rebels. They secretly supplied the rebels with arms and equipment and even sent Russian Special Forces troops to assist them. Fighting flared, the rebels advanced and, for a time, it appeared the rebels might take over the whole of Ukraine. However, at this point NATO and USA stepped in and supported the Kiev Government. Piqued, the Russians then annexed the Crimea area of Ukraine on the pretext of protecting their interests in the Black Sea ports.

Fighting continued, sporadically, for the next two years until an uneasy truce was declared. East Ukraine, although granted some degree of autonomy, still continued to be ruled by the Kiev Government. The situation, however, was unstable. The Kiev Government still resented the annexation of Crimea and the East Ukrainians still resented being ruled by Kiev. In 2025 fighting began anew. The Russians had, again, been secretly supplying weapons and equipment, including tanks and anti-aircraft missiles, to the East Ukrainians.

On the tenth of September, 2025 the rebels attacked in force and rapidly advanced west. Recognising that this was a Russian sponsored and supported attack – intent on removing and replacing the Europe oriented Kiev Government – NATO sent in aircraft, in daylight, to support the West Ukrainians. They were met with a barrage of Surface to Air Missiles which destroyed most of the aircraft sent in. At this point, America flew in two squadrons of their latest 'stealth' fighter bombers to help the west Ukrainians. Stealth planes were especially designed to be invisible to Radar detection systems. They flew at night and attacked their targets using laser guided bombs and missiles. However, to do so, they had to fly over the targets in clear air conditions. Otherwise, their laser spotting and guidance systems would not work. Two days after arrival, when air conditions were suitable, at night, a complete squadron of stealth planes was sent out to attack and stop the advancing East Ukrainians. They were promptly blown out of the sky. Not a single stealth plane returned to base.

There was enormous shock in America – particularly in the Air Force. The USA had spent billions of dollars developing stealth technology and now, the entire force – fighters, fighter bombers and heavy bombers, was rendered impotent. It was discovered the Russians had developed a new aircraft detection system – LADAR, which used lasers to find and track the planes instead of RADAR which used short wavelength radio waves.

The stealth planes were almost totally invisible to radio waves but, as anyone who had been to an air show could testify, they were perfectly visible in daylight. LADAR worked by shining a high powered, pencil thin beam of coherent light into the sky and, using computer controlled equipment, scanning the entire sky in a minute fraction of a second. The instant the beam touched a target it immediately 'locked on', marking the target with a very small, high intensity glowing spot of laser light. Also, in a fraction of a second, computers calculated the targets range, height and speed and programmed the guidance computers of laser seeking missiles. With a stealth plane overhead, from the time the seeking laser was switched on, to the time a missile was launched, was less than one second.

The first warning the stealth plane received, be it a manned or an unmanned drone, was when its missile attack threat warning operated. Twist and dive as the stealth plane might, it was impossible to throw off the laser beam. And the laser seeking missile could manoeuvre faster than the plane could.

America was shocked – and humiliated. They had been humiliated in what was nothing less than a direct confrontation with the Russians. Enraged, they put all their nuclear missile systems on full alert. The Russians did the same. They had, to a great extent, rebuilt their nuclear capability. Way back, in 2005, under President Putin, they had become disillusioned with the behaviour of the West. The 'friendliness' with the West, that had briefly blossomed, after the collapse of the old Soviet Union, had gone. Now Russia was a very dangerous nuclear power again.

For a few days the world teetered on the brink of a disastrous nuclear war. A time reminiscent of the Cuba Crisis of 1962 when the USA's President Kennedy and Russia's President Khrushchev threatened and dared each other.

Fortunately, in 2025, as in 1962, the sheer devastating power of nuclear weapons was so fearful that, after a few days, both sides agreed to back down and de-escalate the conflict. It was agreed, eventually, to split Ukraine into two separate states. East Ukraine and West Ukraine and, by this means, the conflict was finally resolved.

It is interesting to note that, at a later date, during investigations into the LADAR system, it was found that a private Engineer in the West named Nash had independently and separately, invented the LADAR system, many years before – way back in the year 1994, but, despite the fact the system, if it had been patented, would obviously be worth millions of dollars, had, nevertheless, kept it secret for, over twenty years. Very late in his life, when questioned, he said. "When I first learned of the stealth planes – purely as a mental exercise – I asked myself – is there really nothing that can be done to stop stealth aircraft? And, after some thought – I came up with the LADAR system. However, the stealth planes were operated by the USA – the 'good guys' and I had no wish whatsoever to help their enemies, so I kept it secret. No Notes. No Drawings. No Sketches. No talk – until I felt sure – since it seemed so obvious to me – that other people than myself must have also invented it."

Basically, it could be said that the extremely dangerous USA/RUSSIA Nuclear Confrontation of 2025 was Russia's fault. They should have warned the USA – either directly or in a more subtle way, that they had LADAR. However, traces of the old 'Cold War' paranoia and desire to humiliate and discredit the USA still lingered – even in 2025, and the Russians could not resist taking the opportunity.

Way back, in 1960, during the early 'Cold War' days, the Russians had, very successfully, humiliated America and, particularly President Eisenhower, by shooting down (with a missile) an American U2 spy plane, on a clandestine flight over central Russia.

Before doing so, Russia's Premier Khrushchev, had goaded and deliberately enticed President Eisenhower into denying that secret spy flights over Russia were taking place. Having induced Eisenhower into making a clear statement that no such flights were taking place, Khrushchev, having been assured by his scientists that they finally had a missile capable of shooting down a U2, proceeded to prove Eisenhower a total liar by shooting down the next U2 flight.

Up to that time the U2 had been thought untouchable, because it flew at the then unprecedented height of 70,000 feet. In actual fact, the missile only just succeeded, barely reaching the U2 and blasting a hail of shrapnel at it from below. Only a couple of pieces of shrapnel touched the U2 but it was enough to cause sufficient damage to ensure the U2 could not fly long enough to return to base from the centre of the USSR. The plane descended to a lower altitude and the pilot – Gary Powers – baled out and was captured.

Although Powers had been given a suicide pill to take in such emergencies, he declined to do so, and was later paraded on Russian TV, as was the wreckage of the downed U2. So Khrushchev and the Russians had the pleasure and satisfaction of embarrassing and humiliating Eisenhower and America but, in actual fact, it was a very stupid and dangerous thing to do. It created much resentment and hatred in America and, when the Cuban Missile Crisis erupted, later, it greatly increased the risk of all out nuclear war.        And now, in 2025, the Russians had basically repeated the same trick – by blasting a whole squadron of America's latest 'stealth' planes from the sky and proving, to the whole world, that America's, much vaunted 'stealth' fighter and bomber force, costing untold billions, was virtually useless.

To do this – to a nation with the greatest nuclear capability on Earth was incredibly stupid, to say the least. It speaks volumes for the terrifying power of modern nuclear weapons that the Second Major Nuclear Crisis between USA and Russia was, again, peacefully resolved.

The Chinese, being, it appears, a much more thoughtful and less impetuous people than the Russians, gave, in 2007, a demonstration of how such things should be handled without risking nuclear confrontation.

Following the debacle of the U2, the Americans produced another spy plane – the SR71 which flew even higher and a whole lot faster.

The SR71 flew at 80,000 feet (15 miles) altitude and at a speed of over 2,000 miles per hour. When it was introduced, no fighter plane and no anti-aircraft missile on Earth could reach it or threaten it on its reconnaissance missions. For years the SR71 carried out reconnaissance missions along the Northern coasts of Russia (where the most important military installations were). It flew just off the coast (from where it could see hundreds of miles inland) but not directly over Russia. It also did the same along the coast of China (another nuclear power) and did reconnaissance missions directly over the city of Hanoi – the capital of North Vietnam which, at the time, was involved in a nasty war with South Vietnam, including some 50,000 American troops fighting in support of South Vietnam. The Chinese, at that time, supported North Vietnam and supplied weapons, including anti-aircraft missiles. However, to do its job, the SR71 had to fly at an exact speed (2,050 mph) and height (80,000 feet) on an exact straight course. This was necessary to allow its super precision cameras to be precisely co-ordinated to follow the apparent movement of the ground as the SR71 flew over. Now – to a missile engineer – that is the perfect target situation. A computer, once the radar has picked up the target, could precisely predict where the SR71 would be, to within feet, for a considerable time, as the SR71 over flew its target.

If we consider an Earth Satellite, in low Earth orbit – we have a similar situation. The satellite is travelling at an exact speed, at an exact height in an exact direction. A computer can work out, exactly where the satellite will be, to within feet, at an exact time. The difference with the SR71 is that the satellite is doing 17,000 miles an hour at a height of 170 miles.

The Chinese improved their missiles and, there came a day when they fired a missile and blew one of their own satellites to smithereens. Satellites, of course, are very much smaller than SR71's.

The Americans got the message. Took the SR71's out of service. They were able to claim that the SR71 had been an outstanding success (which it had), had never been successfully attacked by a plane or missile (which was true) and now, their reconnaissance satellites were so good, they didn't need SR71 anymore. So – the Americans kept face. The Chinese got respect. Nobody was killed. Nobody was humiliated. How much more sensible than the Russian approach. What a pity the Russians didn't learn the lesson too and not make a stupid mistake again in 2025.

# 2036 AL-QAEDA ATTACKS NEW YORK AGAIN

The four men sat in a cramped little room on the 7th floor of one of the massive multi-storey, reinforced concrete, apartment blocks that characterised the bleak city of Murmansk on the Northern coast of Russia's Kola Peninsula. A few miles away were the docks, housing many of the ships and submarines of the Northern Fleet. To the South were several military airfields, scattered with big Mil 8 helicopters and, dispersed around the perimeters, several of the giant 'Bear' reconnaissance planes and the smaller 'Backfire' supersonic bombers. Dispersed over the whole of the peninsula, hidden in the pine forests, were innumerable inter-continental missile silos.

The men looked like four ordinary, bored, Russian working men, having an ordinary conversation and drinking vodka in an ordinary apartment room on an ordinary grey cold day in Murmansk. But their conversation was anything but ordinary.

"I tell you – if we can succeed we will strike the greatest blow that Islam has ever done against America. We might even trigger a war between Russia and the USA. What an achievement that would be!"

"Do you really think the Major is ready for us to move that far?"

"I think so! If it ever came out he had supplied us with Army stores and Kalashnikovs he would be for Siberia or a firing squad anyway. How could he refuse?"

"I hope you're right."

---

The four men were, in fact, a Muslim terrorist cell, affiliated to Al Qaeda. By birth – Chechens – but they had lived in Russia from childhood when their parents had migrated North. They had taken Russian names. Had served their time in the Russian Army; moved north to the Murmansk area ostensibly to find work. One of them – Igor Jansky – had found work in a garage/ repair workshop. The other three – in the shipyards and warehouses of the Navy Yards. Igor was a wiry-ferret like, little man but very astute. Boris Ulanov – a great bear of a man – was the leader of the group. He was a stac-truck driver, ferrying components, ammunition, weapons around the Navy stores complex. Then there was Peter Benkovsky, a studious intellectual, slightly short sighted, always wearing glasses, who had managed to get himself a position as a clerk, checking records and inventories in the documents office. Finally there was Vladimir Berenkov who had started off as an electrician, became an electronics man, in the Army and was now a systems engineer, working on maintenance on helicopters and transport planes at one of the nearby airfields.

They had successfully kept their Chechen background and Muslim loyalties secret for over 20 years and had gradually made contacts and friends. They had also become involved in a few black market operations. Smuggling cigarettes and vodka, to and from Norway – the border was only 150 kilometres away.

Peter had gradually cultivated a friendship with the Russian Major in charge of the military stores. First he had got him some Western cigarettes. Then inveigled him into joining a vodka smuggling enterprise – running illicit vodka across the Norwegian border. The Major had been involved in bribing the Norwegian border guards. Finally he had talked the Major into helping to smuggle a lorry load of Army stores. (Including 50 Kalashnikov rifles) across the Norwegian border. The Major was now on the hook! The lure of extra dollars and roubles was very strong. The Major was also in charge of some serious weapons stores. Some with various kinds of guided missiles – mainly anti aircraft and also, most importantly, a store containing cruise missile warheads – both high explosive and nuclear. These were for cruise missiles for use by submarines and surface ships.

In accordance with usual Russian practice, their cruise missiles were larger, longer range and had more powerful warheads than their American counterparts. Whether they were as accurate or as reliable was another matter.

The only times cruise missiles had actually been used in anger (by the Americans) they had been fitted with conventional high explosive warheads. These had no more power than a medium sized conventional, aircraft carried, bomb but were often very effective because of the precision with which the warhead was delivered.

Less well known was the fact that, in a really serious war, these cruise missiles could be fitted with a small but highly efficient nuclear bomb.  A small hydrogen bomb, to be exact, of 150 kiloton yield.  In other words, in a nuclear war, just one cruise missile was capable of wiping out any of the largest cities on Earth.

The Russians of course, were not to be out done.  Their cruise missiles, in addition to being larger and with longer range could carry an even more powerful H Bomb of 200 kilotons power.

In a bunker, in the complex near Murmansk, was a bomb store containing no less than 150 of these weapons.  The cruise missile nuclear warhead itself was remarkably small for its power, and looked like an oversize, elongated artillery shell about 40 centimetres in diameter and 1 metre long.

Al Qaeda had been interested in obtaining a nuclear bomb for many years and still nursed the dream of destroying one of America's major cities.  A strike that would make the 9/11 attacks pale into insignificance.

For a long time they had plotted and planned and the Chechen group in Murmansk was, as a secret militant Muslim group, affiliated to Al Qaeda.

After a number of years, a message finally reached the higher echelons of Al Qaeda that the Chechen group now knew where there was a store of small H bombs and even had speaking contact with some of the Russian personnel involved in handling the bombs.

Al Qaeda had always had access to immense funds and a massive sum was rapidly earmarked for use in a possible nuclear operation.

Six months later and they were ready to move.  When Peter Benkovsky finally approached Major Yuri Kraschenko with the proposal to steal a nuclear warhead, Yuri was stunned.  He was viciously anti-American it was true but he had never anticipated anything like this.  Gradually it dawned on him that he had been carefully 'set-up' and he was now trapped.  Yuri Kraschenko may have been greedy but he was not stupid.  He did a lot of careful thinking before he agreed.

In a garage in Murmansk, a thin steel dummy of a nuclear warhead was carefully prepared.  One night a lorry pulled up at the perimeter gates of the weapons store, which were opened smartly, on the major's orders.  The lorry drove in.  The major climbed aboard and after driving to the bomb store and talking to the Guard Captain, the main doors were opened and the lorry entered.  The major directed the lorry to the back of a store where there were several long rows of warheads.

Each warhead sat on a heavy duty wooden pallet, covered by a tarpaulin. They were spaced 4 metres apart and the rows pitched at 5 metres so as to give all round access to each weapon and allow free movement of fork lift trucks.

Kraschenko directed them to drive to the middle of the back row and slightly to one side. The men opened the truck doors and carried out the dummy which they laid to one side.

The tarpaulin, on one of the bombs, was pulled away, a fork lift brought up and the bomb gently and carefully lifted and transferred to the lorry, where it was strapped firmly in position then covered and camouflaged under a mass of small crates that were already in the lorry. The dummy was then transferred to the pallet, strapped down and the tarpaulin replaced.

Ten minutes later the lorry was out of the gate and on a road leading to the Norwegian border.

At the border the guards made a perfunctory inspection of the lorry contents and waved it through. A wad of money had already changed hands. They probably thought it was simply another load of Vodka being smuggled.

After they were safely through into Norway, Boris Ulanov reflected on how easy it had all been. It was amazing what could be done if you had enough money.

A few hours later Major Yuri Kraschenko sat in the cab of a truck and carefully considered the situation. When he had been entrapped and realised what a deadly dangerous game he was involved in, he spent many hours thinking long and hard. It was a firing squad for sure if he was ever caught. But the prize – enough money to set him up for life – was very attractive. In any case they already had him trapped. His previous misdemeanours – the minor bribes – the Army stores – the Kalashnikovs – were already enough to get him 15 years in a Gulag. For a moment he began to sweat, then got a grip of himself. He had been married for 15 years. He and his wife had long since become bored with each other. Fortunately there were no children. What did he have to lose?

He had told the Chechen leader he was prepared to go ahead but wanted paying in gold and diamonds, delivered into his hands. Nothing else or the deal was off. He also told him he knew how to check the gold and diamonds were genuine. At first the Chechen argued but Yuri was adamant and, after a short discussion it was agreed.

Kraschenko had decided the only thing to do, after the deal was completed, was to disappear. Disappear completely. There would have to be a complete cut off from all his contacts. A completely separate new life. No contact with his wife, relatives or friends whatsoever, for the rest of his life, otherwise they would nail him.

He had decided it was worth it and looked forward to the challenge of a new life. He didn't have an option anyway.

A few days later the Major was reported missing. A search was made but there was no trace. Then a fisherman reported seeing a small Army truck going over a cliff and into the sea. Divers inspected the truck but no body was ever found.

It was three months later before the fake bomb was discovered. Several genuine weapons had been moved and, when a sergeant came with a fork lift truck, to shift the next one, he took off the tarpaulin but it was only when he unstrapped it and came to move it he found the difference. For a moment he could not believe it, but the casing was light and, when he tapped it, rang like an empty oil drum. As the implications flooded into his mind he decided to tell no one about it except the chief.

The Colonel sat stiffly in his chair. His hand shook slightly.

"Are you trying to tell me, Sergeant, that one of our Mark 38 nuclear warheads has gone missing?"

"Yes Sir! It had been replaced by a clever, sheet metal fake, strapped in place on the pallet and covered in the tarpaulin. Everything looked normal."

"Have you told anybody else about this?"

"No Sir! I thought it best to come directly to you!"

"Very Good! That was very sensible!"

The Colonel pondered for a while.

"Sergeant! Tell absolutely nobody else. If this comes out – both you and I could end up in a Siberian labour camp."

He then outlined what should be done.

A week later a truck turned up carrying a genuine Mark 38 warhead. It was offloaded, placed on an empty pallet, waiting for it, and covered in a tarpaulin.

After talking to the Colonel, the sergeant had returned to the depot, obtained oxy-acetylene cutting equipment and had gone back to the bomb store, cut the fake up into small pieces, and dropped them in a scrap bin.

A few days later, there was a most unfortunate happening. A recruit, fiddling about with his rifle, accidentally shot and killed a sergeant.

---

Two months later, a small Norwegian freighter, loaded with high quality sawn timber, eased into the dock in New York harbour. Hidden in the hold, under tons of timber, was the Mark 38 warhead.

At the rear of the bullet shaped warhead was a small electronics package. This consisted of a computer, several small electronic components and a large capacitor. In normal use, in the cruise missile, the computer accepted signals from the missiles navigation system and, finally, triggered the impulse to the capacitor that detonated the bomb. An important feature of the computer was that it was programmed so that the final detonation signal would not be released until the safety code had been entered. Normally, this would be entered and transferred from the ships computer when use of nuclear weapons had been authorised and confirmed. The nuclear weapon would, therefore, only have the code entered just before launch. Finally another safety system would ensure that the capacitor could not fire and initiate detonation until the missile was on its last few seconds of flight.

One of the ship's crew, Yusuf Almedi, was an electronics expert. He knew what the bomb was, and, roughly, how it worked.

During the voyage Yusuf had accessed the bomb, through a tunnel in the timber, and cut the wire which would take the final signal to the capacitor and connected it, instead, to a simple clock type timer. He had also ensured that the capacitor was fully charged.

In addition to the clock timer there was a parallel wired switching circuit with wires running to a hidden switch on the top deck of the ship, fairly near the bomb. This would be safer, they had decided, than a radio operated link. Radio could be jammed or there could be interference. If necessary, this would be a suicide mission.

Just before going into the harbour Yusuf went down into the hold, shifted the camouflage timber, and accessed the bomb, setting the timer and starting it so that it would detonate the bomb at 9am the next day; a very busy time in the City.

Later, as the ship moved towards its berth, Yusuf was in the wheelhouse with the Captain when they noticed a small launch pull out from a jetty and head for them. They could see there were several uniformed men aboard, either customs officials or police.

Yusuf looked at the Captain. The Captain compressed his lips, then spoke. "This looks like trouble. We can't take any risks. If they come aboard, go to the override switch and manually set off the bomb. We are in the harbour anyway."

Yusuf left the wheelhouse and began to walk steadily along the deck towards the place where his override switch was hidden. The launch came alongside and a group of men came aboard. They brought with them an Alsatian dog – probably a sniffer dog. It was on a leash but as soon as the men were on deck, one of them bent to unclip it.

"Dogs must be psychic!" thought Yusuf. He noticed that the dog had its eyes fixed on him, even before its feet touched the deck. Yusuf was now within yards of the switch. He covered the distance with a few quick paces, fumbled under the rail, found the switch. He looked back. The dog was sprinting for him. It would be on him in a few seconds. Yusuf looked around him – at the sky – the harbour – the New York skyline. Fear surged through him. He understood the hellish power of the bomb in the hold. If he pressed the switch he wouldn't just be killed – he would be totally vaporised – reduced to his component atoms. A ghastly thought came in his brain. If that happened – could he really hope for an afterlife in heaven. He steadied himself. "With Allah – all things are possible." The dog was on him. Instantly it leaped for his arm but the switch was in his fingers. Yusuf took a deep breath; screamed "Allah is great!" and pressed the button.

There was a massive explosion and an enormous fountain of flame, fragments and broken timber flew into the air. Being close to the bomb, Yusuf and the dog were instantly killed. Further back, along the deck the wheelhouse was crazily askew – half wrecked by the blast wave. Groggily, the Captain tottered to his feet. His dazed mind registered that something was wrong.

He clutched at a stanchion to steady himself, shook his head and slowly his mind cleared.

He saw the pall of dust and smoke rising into the sky – and pieces of broken timber still raining down into the water. But, beyond that, he could still see the harbour and in the background, the New York skyscrapers, unchanged.

Realization surged through him – and anguish. If the bomb had gone off properly there would be no ship, no harbour and no New York skyline. He and the ship would have been vaporised.

Two of the men who came aboard were unharmed – stunned but unharmed. He saw them getting to their feet and realised that – for him – there could be no escape. He knew that, if he was captured, they would interrogate him. Take him somewhere secret and they would not rest until they had dragged every scrap of information from him. Ever since they had sailed from Norway he had kept a loaded pistol in his jacket pocket. Now he pulled the pistol out and, without hesitation, placed it to his temple and fired.

A great cloud of smoke billowed into the air and then slowly drifted, on the westerly wind, out towards the sea. A fire started and rapidly took hold. The harbour fire service boats were there within minutes, started their massive pumps and rapidly overwhelmed the fire with their enormous sprays.

Only one of the custom's men had died in the explosion, but, two days later, two of the men fell ill, with sickness and vomiting. The following day, with the symptoms getting worse, a doctor was called in.

The Doctor was puzzled. Something didn't seem quite right – not like ordinary food poisoning. He spoke to a colleague – an older man of wide experience. He came and looked at the patients, then turned away. His face was grave.

"I hate to say this" he said "but it looks very like radiation poisoning."

---

The Secretary of State eased himself into a chair.

"Mr President" he said "I am afraid I have some very disturbing news.  Terrorists have exploded a 'dirty' bomb in New York harbour."

For a moment the President froze – as though he couldn't believe his ears.

"A dirty bomb!  My God!  George!  "A dirty bomb?  Isn't that where they have radio-active material and a high explosive charge to spread it?"

"Yes Sir.  That is exactly right."

"In the harbour – you say!  How bad is the contamination?"

"Fortunately the terrorists were spooked into detonating the bomb prematurely – at least we assume so – because the wind was westerly and much of the contamination had drifted out to sea.  If they had let it off when there was an east wind, then half of New York would have been contaminated.  We have been very lucky."

"Where the hell did they get the radio-active material?"

"We don't yet know but we have experts from Los Alamos at the scene, with special equipment and I expect a report from them in the next few days."

"OK – George!  Keep me informed!"

———————————

Four days later the Secretary of State was back in the Oval Office.  He had a sheaf of notes in his hand and his face was grave.

"Mr President!  I am afraid I have some extremely disturbing and serious news.  The device exploded in New York harbour was not a simple 'dirty' bomb as we had assumed.  The people from Los Alamos have reported they found plutonium, not uranium as expected, and also traces of lithium, deuterium and tritium."

"What does that mean, George?"

"It means, Mr President, that the device that was detonated was, in fact, a hydrogen bomb.  It failed to detonate as it should but if it had done so it would have been capable of totally obliterating New York."

"My God!  George.  Do you know what you are saying?"

"Yes!  Mr President.  I most certainly do."

The President sat there, silent for a minute, and then said.

"I think, George, we should keep the fact it was an H Bomb secret, at least for the time being, if we can, and stick with the 'dirty' bomb story. Do you think we can do that?"

"Yes! I think we can. I realised you might want to do that and told the Los Alamos people their info was classified, at least for the time being. Incidentally, we have been extremely lucky. Most of the fall out went out to sea. The ship did not sink and we can tow it away. The harbour is contaminated to a degree but we should be able to handle that."

"Nice work George! How the hell is it the bomb didn't go off properly?"

"That is an interesting question Mr President and I have a Doctor Bernstein, from Los Alamos outside, waiting to explain that to you. Shall I call him in?"

"Please do. George!"

Five minutes later Doctor Joseph Bernstein took a chair in the Oval Office. After introductions he got straight down to business.

"Mr President! This is indeed a terrifying and most puzzling affair. But the reason that the bomb did not detonate as it should is very simple. The weapon brought into New York harbour was not a viable device. It was not possible for it to detonate properly."

"I don't understand. Can you explain?"

"I can Mr President, but I will need to go into details of the bombs construction, and a little nuclear physics, to do so. I would guess it will take about half an hour, if you have the time."

"Please continue Doctor Bernstein."

"Yes Sir! I will simplify as much as I can.

A Hydrogen bomb consists of a Lithium Hydride fuel container, which, in the explosion, produces 95% of the power. This is set off by the heat and pressure produced by the detonation of a small, plutonium fuelled, atomic bomb. It is the atomic bomb which is the key to the misfire. A modern atomic bomb contains a small sphere of plutonium, surrounded by high explosive. The plutonium sphere is slightly less than the critical mass. Critical mass being the mass that would spontaneously detonate. However, critical mass depends also on the density of the plutonium assembly. For instance, a hollow sphere would have a larger critical mass than a solid sphere. At this point, Mr President, it is necessary for you to grasp that nothing in this Universe is truly solid. Everything can be compressed into a smaller volume, given enough pressure.

So, in an atomic bomb, a slightly sub-critical spherical mass of plutonium is surrounded by a thick shell of high explosive. When the explosive is detonated, the shockwave produced has such tremendous power it is capable of crushing the solid plutonium ball down to a small fraction of its original size. In this state the plutonium is way over the critical mass. However, it doesn't have time to spontaneously detonate because it is only in this super dense state for a very short time – less than a millionth of a second, in fact. Spontaneous detonation depends on the natural fissioning of a plutonium atom producing neutrons which will initiate a chain reaction. The time the plutonium is in the super critical state is so short that the chances of spontaneous detonation is extremely small.

You will appreciate that, if the plutonium does not produce a chain reaction in the micro second it is super critical, it will then rebound violently and, simply by its inertia and momentum, explode like a hand grenade, pulverising the plutonium and scattering it in the form of radio-active dust.

To make the plutonium bomb detonate properly, the designers have to build in an initiator. This is a small ovoid that sits in the middle of the plutonium sphere. It consists of a small assembly of two substances – Beryllium and Polonium 210. Polonium 210 is extremely radio active but produces only alpha radiation, which only penetrates short distances into solid material, not like gamma radiation, which can penetrate more than 18 inches of solid steel. Beryllium has the property that, if it is bombarded with alpha radiation it will produce a flux of neutrons in proportion to the alpha input. In the initiator, in the centre of the plutonium core, the polonium is separated from the beryllium by a thin metal foil which, despite being thin, is enough to stop the alpha radiation from reaching the beryllium.

When a bomb is detonated, the shockwave from the explosive blasts inwards, crushing the plutonium ball and, lastly, just when the plutonium is at maximum density, crushing the little polonium/beryllium initiator and exposing the beryllium to the alpha radiation from the polonium. The beryllium then produces an instant and massive blast of neutrons and it is these neutrons which set off a chain reaction in the plutonium. This all works so fast that a substantial part of the plutonium fissions before the super compressed plutonium ball has had time to rebound. Are you still with me Mr President?"

"I think so Doctor Bernstein. But what causes the misfire?"

"I'm coming to that in a moment. Please bear with me! You will remember I said the Polonium was intensely radio active. So radio active, in fact, that it has a half life of only 147 days. That means that in 147 days the radio-activity has fallen to just half of what it was originally. And in another 147 days it will be down to a quarter and in another 147 days, down to an eighth and so on. What this means, in practice, Mr President is that if you keep a plutonium bomb in store for five years and try to let it off it won't work. We have to keep tags on all our plutonium based bombs and, every so often, strip them down and fit new initiators. So – in this case in New York harbour – either the terrorists have got hold of a bomb and stored it somewhere for a number of years or, which I think is far more likely – they have been sold a dud."

"Fascinating! Doctor Bernstein! That leaves a lot of scope for speculation and investigation. Would it be possible, do you think, to determine the place of origin."

"Yes! Mr President! In fact we have already run a number of tests and, at this stage, we are 90% sure the bomb was of Russian origin."

"The bastards!" muttered the President.

"If you will excuse me. Mr President. I think I must point out that the Russian Government may well be totally innocent. There are tens of thousands of nuclear bombs, in stores all over the world. Sooner or later it was almost inevitable that terrorists would get hold of one. We shall only be really safe when all nuclear bombs are abolished."

"Thank you, Doctor Bernstein! Thank you! That will be all!"

And, with that, Bernstein was dismissed. However, his last comment had not failed to register in the President's mind.

———————————

Two days later details of the blast were released through the media. The headline on the TV News Channel was.

RADIOACTIVE 'DIRTY' BOMB EXPLODED IN
NEW YORK HARBOUR
BY TERRORISTS.
PENTAGON SAYS – CRUDE DEVICE.
CONTAMINATION MINIMAL.

That afternoon President Abraham Lewis spoke to an Aide.

"Set up a top priority 'hot line' conversation for tomorrow with President Kurchakov. I will need at least an hour."

---

Gregori Kurchakov sat in his office and pondered. He had, of course, been fully informed of the explosion in New York harbour. "Nasty business!" He wondered where the terrorists had obtained the radio-active material. The thing that puzzled him a little was that the device had been set off while there was a westerly wind. Presumably the terrorists had been forced, by fear of imminent discovery, to let the bomb off prematurely. If they had waited until there was an easterly wind they really would have created a mess. Presumably President Lewis wished to fill him in with some of the details.

At 5pm a security man signalled that the secure 'hot line' was live and President Lewis was waiting to speak to him. In Washington it was 9am and Lewis glanced at his notes and began the conversation. They exchanged formalities and then Lewis pressed on with little preamble.

"Gregori! You will have been informed of the explosion in New York harbour. What I am about to say may come as a shock to you. Our nuclear experts have analysed the 'fall out' from the bomb and say that it was not a crude and simple 'dirty' bomb as initially thought. It was, in fact, a medium yield fusion device – an H Bomb – in other words – probably in the 200/400 kiloton range – that failed to detonate properly. Furthermore, additional tests have revealed that it was of Russian origin – probably a cruise missile warhead."

Kurchakov was stunned.

"Are you sure? This is incredible!"

"Of course we are sure. Gregori! Or I wouldn't be talking to you now." Kurchakov began to bluster but was cut off.

"Gregori! If necessary we can tell you which one of your reactors actually produced the plutonium."

Kurchakov was silent.

"Gregori. The reason we have kept silent and issued the story of the terrorists 'dirty' bomb to the media is that we are convinced you have more sense than to, knowingly, participate in such a plot. Will you please now listen carefully to what I am going to say.

If that bomb had gone off as intended and wiped out New York and contaminated half of New York State, the pressure to retaliate in kind against Russia would have been overwhelming. Nobody would have believed your protestations.

Even if the true facts got out, and people knew it was a failed H Bomb, there would be demands that there should be some form of retaliation – sanctions or a trade embargo at least. They would argue that you were in collusion with the terrorists or at least, criminally negligent.

Having thought about this and discussed it with my Secretary of State I have a serious proposal to make.

In the 1980s, we had a situation where the USA and Russia had over 35,000 nuclear weapons between them. This was totally insane. Fortunately Presidents Reagan and Gorbachev recognised the fact, got their heads together and signed a treaty which reduced nuclear stock piles to the levels we have today – where we have a few thousand each. I now suggest that you and I get together and announce to the World a new treaty where nuclear weapons are again slashed from thousands to a few hundreds. I further suggest that we call an International Nuclear Arms convention to do this and call on every nuclear equipped nation to join the Convention and to declare, and make available for inspection, the exact number of nuclear weapons they possess.

Gregori! You and I would go down in history as two far sighted leaders who showed the world the way. We would confound the terrorists and there would be enhanced friendship between our countries, with great benefits in contacts and international trade. The alternative – I leave to your imagination. What do you say?" Kurchakov was silent for a minute.

"I think Mr President! You are blackmailing me."

"Yes Gregori! I think I am. But it is in a good cause."

"Let me think about it Abraham! And come back to you."

Back in Washington President Lewis put down the phone – and noted that, for the first time, Kurchakov had used his Christian name.

A few months later President Abraham Lewis of the USA and President Gregori Kurchakov of Russia were filmed together, smiling and shaking hands. It was announced that they had got together and agreed to slash the number of nuclear weapons in their armouries from thousands down to a few hundred. A massive reduction. Furthermore, they were calling on all nuclear armed nations to join the Convention and make similar binding commitments. It was all for the good of humanity. Failure to do so would, of course, result in a nation being a pariah state – and there might also be sanctions.

---

In a nice little Hacienda in Uruguay, Major – or should we say ex major Yuri Kraschenko – now Luigi Fernandez – relaxed on his veranda and sipped a vodka (he still preferred it to the local alcohol) and pondered. "One never knew quite what might happen – when you made a decision did you!"

He remembered the night, back in Murmansk, when his stomach had rebelled at the thought of incinerating a city of millions. Sure! He really hated the Americans but that was too much. They were human beings – after all! There would be millions of innocent women and children. So! He had made his decision – and had knowingly and deliberately sold the Chechens a dud. There were three rows of bombs, all stencil coded. The first row were up to date, recently refurbished, totally functional warheads. The second row were two year old weapons of questionable reliability and yield. The third row were well past their 'use by' date and were earmarked for refurbishment before being transferred to ships or to storage row No.1.

Yuri smiled as he watched a video of Presidents Lewis and Kurchakov embracing and smiling for the cameras.

"Now he knew he had made the right decision!"

# 2043 – MEGA HURRICANE

In the summer of 2042, an unusual weather situation occurred.

It had been discovered, in the late 20th Century, that weather patterns, in the Northern Hemisphere, depended, to a great extent, on the vagaries of the Northern Jet Stream. The Jet Stream – a great river of air, flowing West to East all around the world at high altitude (30,000 to 35,000 ft), was created by atmospheric circulation patterns brought about by differences in temperature between hot equatorial air and cold polar air.

The Jet Stream acted as a barrier between cold arctic air and warmer, mid latitude, air. It also spawned high and low pressure areas, generated by vortices coming off the sides of the flow. When it was first discovered, and until the end of the 20th Century, the Jet Stream was a fairly stable flow forming a complete ring around the globe. It rippled occasionally and drifted north or south sometimes. Normally it blew over the UK and its erratic north/south fluctuations accounted for the unpredictability of the British weather.

However, in the early 21st Century, there was a change. The Jet Stream became far more erratic, developing enormous U shaped and inverted U shaped deviations north and south. This resulted in great masses of cold polar air following the swings south and masses of warm air following the swings north. The deviations might stick in one place for a few days and then move or become locked in place for weeks or even months at a time.

A northerly fluctuation in the summer of 2013 resulted in one of the hottest heat waves ever recorded over Europe and around 40,000 people are reckoned to have died from the heat. A southerly fluctuation over Canada and the USA, in the winter of 2014/15, resulted in one of the coldest, most blizzard ridden winters in the history of the USA.

In the summer of 2042, another freakish happening occurred. The Jet Stream swung south over the USA then north in an enormous inverted U encompassing the whole of Greenland. A vast pulse of warm, subtropical air, followed the Jet Stream north. This massive fluctuation then 'locked in' and sat there for most of the summer. The result was the greatest melt of the Greenland ice cap ever seen.

Temperatures over the entire ice cap were not just above freezing; they were ridiculously high, 10°C or more.

The entire surface of the ice sheet began to melt rapidly. Enormous quantities of surface water were created, which poured through holes in the ice (called Grabens in Scandinavia) and made its way down to the rock bed, thousands of feet below. (The ice cap on Greenland is up to a mile thick or more).

Planes, flying over, saw great blue lakes of melt water on top of the ice and enormous rivers, plunging into the grabens. As the water descended it generated additional heat, which melted yet more ice, particularly at the base, so that the glaciers began to flow more rapidly into the sea.

The increased flux of icebergs was all too obvious from the air but the great rivers of fresh water flowing below the glaciers into the sea were not. The glaciers projected into and at the surface of the sea but the rivers entered the sea below the ice and could not be seen. However, their presence could be deduced by ships, around the coast, taking water samples. It became obvious that an enormous volume of fresh water had entered the Arctic Ocean and, because of its lower density, (saline water is 2½lbs per cubic foot heavier than fresh water) floated on the surface. The icebergs also contributed more fresh water as they melted.

It also happened, that same summer, that 2042, was the year the polar ice cap – that great floating mass of ice around the North Pole – finally and completely disappeared by late August. It had been expected for a long time. In 2015, it had been predicted the first Arctic Ocean ice free summer would be as early as 2030. However, with the perversity of Nature, it had defied the experts and global warming trends and hung on. Although it had shrunk, to less and less area each summer, it had never totally disappeared until the summer of 2042.

---

In the Met Office at the Woods Hole Oceanographic Institute in Massachusetts, at 2.43pm on 28th August, 2042, Nathaniel Greenbank downloaded a picture from the polar orbiting Geosat satellite and shouted to his friend.

"Joe! Joe! Come and look at this!"
Joe Carmino walked over, looked at the picture and whistled.

"Nat! I reckon that's the second most amazing picture of the Earth ever taken. Second only to the Apollo astronauts' picture of Earth Rise, taken on the moon."

The satellite picture showed the entire Arctic Ocean free of floating ice. Blue grey water, all the way to the North Pole. The first time in human history – and the first time in over a million years. There was white around the coast of Greenland, of course, and to the south. But that was floating icebergs – not sea ice.

"By the way! Joe! There's something else I intended to tell you. When the satellite passes over Greenland, it uses a laser to check the altitude of the ice below it. Feeding the data into a computer, we can monitor the drop in the ice surface levels and thus the rate of melting of the Greenland ice field. The satellite reveals that, over the last four months, the surface of the ice has fallen over four metres, on average, over the whole of Greenland. That is an absolutely unprecedented amount."

"It also represents a hell of a lot of melt water" said Joe. "There must be some very big rivers flowing under those glaciers."

---

The following year – 2043 – there was another unusual happening – connected to the strange weather of 2042 – but no less surprising for all that. The Gulf Stream – that massive, warm, ocean current, that flowed north east, from the Caribbean to Scandinavia and beyond, slowed.

Normally, the gulf stream carried enormous amounts of heat northward. Heat, picked up in the tropics and carried north eastward. So great was the amount of heat that it greatly modified the climate of Ireland, Great Britain, Northern Europe and Scandinavia. The gulf stream flowed steadily and continuously, all year round. Without the gulf stream, the natural climate of Great Britain, for instance, would be at least 6°C colder.

Now – the gulf stream had slowed.

The Gulf Stream was part of a worldwide system of ocean currents called the Thermo-Haline Circulation System. Basically, in conjunction with Atmospheric air movements, it redistributed the solar heat, accumulated in the tropics, to other, cooler, areas of the World. You could say – these currents helped cool the tropics and warm the more northerly and southerly latitudes. Disruption could play havoc with the world's weather patterns.

Normally, cooler water rose to the surface near the tropics, picked up heat from solar radiation and flowed northwards. As it went, a lot of evaporation took place at the surface of the sea, increasing the salinity and density. The warm saline water flowed north, gave up its heat to the atmosphere and finally cooled at the start of the Arctic Ocean. The cooled water, already carrying an excess salt load, became even more dense and sank to the ocean floor, where it then ran south. The whole system worked like a conveyor belt. Warm surface water running north, delivering its heat, falling to the ocean floor, returning south, rising to the surface, reheating and so one, endlessly. That is how it worked, normally.

However, in 2042, vast amounts of fresh, salt free, water had flowed into the northern sea from Greenland. Also, when the floating ice of the Arctic ice cap had melted there was another enormous introduction of fresh water. (When saline water freezes, salt is ejected and ice is, apart from trapped pockets of salt, fresh water). Also, a large part of the hitherto permanent ice cap has been formed from snow, falling on the ice cap over a period of years. All this fresh water, being much lighter than brine, tends to float and gradually mix in the surface layers of the sea.

The Gulf Stream, coming north, is a surface current and, when it arrived, tended to also mix with the fresh water. The mixture is then less dense and, when it cools sufficiently, will begin its fall, more slowly, to the sea bed.

There is a critical point where enough fresh water, mixed with the saline gulf stream water, will reduce its density to the point where it is no denser than the underlying seawater and will not fall through it to the sea bed.

In practice, there is enough momentum in the millions of tons of moving water to keep the system going for a time and, if the fresh water eventually gets flushed away, the system can return to normal. However, if the influx of fresh water was maintained, if, for instance, the Greenland ice cap continued to melt at the same rate as it did in 2042, then the gulf stream might stop flowing altogether.

---

At Woods Hole, in July 2043, Nat Greenbank was worried.

"Joe! You know how I have been monitoring the surface sea water density off Greenland and the Gulf Stream flow. The latest data suggests the fresh water is not being flushed away fast enough. Although the summer of 2043, on Greenland is a lot colder than last summer, there is still too much fresh water on the surface in the North Atlantic. I have been worrying about it for months and now, the latest data shows the Gulf Stream has drastically slowed. The rate of flow is down more than 50%. I hate to think what will happen if it stops completely. And another thing! We have equipment monitoring the surface seawater temperatures in the Atlantic further south – specifically between the African coast and the Caribbean areas. Because the Gulf Stream has slowed, it is not carrying the tropical heat away. The surface seawater temperatures in the tropical areas are now several degrees warmer than has ever been recorded before."

Joe Carmino studied the charts and the figures and pursed his lips.

"Nat! Maybe you are worrying a bit too much. Greenland is cooler. The Gulf Stream has not stopped. Soon the excess fresh water in the North Atlantic will be flushed away. The Gulf Stream will speed up again and will be back to normal. Leave your charts and come down to 'Jerry's Bar' and have a drink."

"OK! Joe! But I hope you're right."

Two weeks later Nat was checking the satellite photos and noticed a large tropical storm developing, just off the coast of Africa. Three days later it had grown and was beginning to track west.

Nat again spoke to his friend.

"Joe! There's a nasty looking storm off West Africa. Could be the beginning of one of your specialities – a hurricane."
Joe came over and looked at the photographs. He looked up and his face was grave.

"You're right! It does look very much that way. If so, this could turn very nasty, with the sea surface temperatures being so hellishly high, from Africa to the USA. As you know, Hurricanes pick up their energy from the surface of the sea. A lot depends on where a hurricane tracks and how fast it moves, as to how much power it can develop. We'd better cross our fingers on this one."
A day later, Hurricane Beta, as it was now known, was steadily tracking west and growing very rapidly. Joe spoke to Nathaniel again.

"Nat! this is getting to be very disturbing. Beta is only in mid atlantic and already it is a full blown hurricane. It's difficult to predict where it will go, at this stage but, if it tracks to the Caribbean, some of the islands are going to take a hell of a caning."

A day later, Beta had tracked further west and was noticeably larger. The satellite photos showed an enormous rotating disc with a large central hole – the eye – in evidence.

"Joe! According to the satellite data we have already got maximum wind speeds of 150 mph. I would like to put a drone down into the eye and check the 'baro' pressure. Can you arrange that?"

"OK! Nat! But it will take at least 24 hours."
Twenty five hours later, a long range drone had been flown out and descended, in the eye, down to just above sea level. The barometric pressure it relayed back via satellite was stunning.

"Nat! I don't believe this. The lowest barometric pressure ever recorded in a storm or hurricane is 870 milibars. The drone recorded 854 milibars. Hurricane Beta is also now 700 miles across and satellite data suggests wind speeds up to 210 mph."
The hurricane had now swung slightly north and was tracking between the Bahamas and Bermuda.
"I've never seen anything like this before" muttered Joe. "The worst thing is – the sea surface, all around that area and up the east coast of America is at the highest temperatures ever recorded. It's because the Gulf Stream has slowed. If it strikes the American East Coast it will be devastating."

---

A hundred and fifty miles south west of Bermuda the oil tanker Antares III was steadily ploughing her way north westwards towards Norfolk, Virginia, to bring supplies to a massive new oil refinery that had been built there. She had loaded up at Kuwait, one of the few places on Earth which still had oil to sell. The Antares III had a gross weight of 470,000 tons, carrying around 400,000 tons of crude oil. She was over 1,000 feet long and, like all oil tankers, was a long low vessel with the only superstructure right at the stern. After tracking through the Strait of Hormuz and around the Cape of South Africa, she had sailed north, through the Atlantic, and was now on the last lap to Norfolk. Her skipper, Suleem Vassan, was weary of the trip and anxious to get his cargo to port.

He was not pleased when the Mate, Norhan Dashti, came to him.

"Sir! This hurricane 'Beta' to the south! The reports are that it is intensifying and could possibly track northwards. Do you think we should divert, northwest and hold off for a few days?"

"Norhan! This ship is built to take rough weather. If we keep going we can be in port in two days. If we hold off we could lose a week or more. Do you know how much it costs, per day, to run a ship like this? We will stay on course! If it gets really bad we can reconsider."

Twenty four hours later they were only 500 miles from Norfolk. Norhan came to him again.

"Sir! The reports are very bad! The hurricane has turned north. If it maintains its current track, in 6 hours we shall be directly in its path. Already the wind is picking up and there are heavy swells."

Suleem looked at the displays. He knew Norhan was right. If the hurricane continued on its track at its present speed he could not escape. If he carried on to Norfolk he would be caught. If he turned around and headed east, he would still be caught. The hurricane was now 750 miles in diameter.

He looked at the displays. He looked at Norhan – and made his decision.

"We shall take a hammering, Norhan, either way. It will be just as bad, if we turn back, as if we go on. We will carry on to Norfolk. Please check that everything is secured."

"Aye Sir!"

The wind was building fast and the great ship already lurching and rolling on the swells. Six hours later and the hurricane was on them. Suleem had never seen anything like it. The wind rapidly rose to over 100 miles an hour. The swells were becoming vast. Forty feet from trough to crest. The trouble was the ship was a gigantic weather vane. The superstructure, right at the stern, caught the wind, which was directly easterly, pushing him towards Norfolk. But, with the wind from behind, and of such force, the ship was difficult to handle.

"Norhan! We must turn the ship, while we still have control. Put her nose into the wind."

The ship turned slowly. It seemed to take forever to get her bow into the wind. When she was sideways on she rolled horribly, sluggishly,

Suleem breathed a sigh of relief when she was round. The weather vane effect now worked with them, stabilising the ship. The wind built rapidly. It became almost unbelievable. The instruments indicated a wind speed of 150 miles an hour, gusting to 170. The swells became immense. Fifty feet from trough to crest. Also the distance between swells increased. Suleem stood at his window, watching the giant swells approaching, felt the ship shudder as they hit the nose, watched the swell track down the ship.

He noticed that they were so far apart now that, as a new swell lifted the nose of the ship, the previous one was lifting the stern. She was creaking and groaning with the passing of each enormous wave, almost like an animal in pain. He looked along the long deck, with its great array of pipes and valves. For a moment he could have sworn he saw the deck move.

An enormous swell hit the bow. The ship juddered. The bow began to lift. The ship groaned. As Suleem stared, the great mountain of heaving water moved down the ship. Just before it reached where he was standing he saw the pipe work tear apart and, unbelievably, the deck buckled upwards and there was a fountain of oil. A great roar and scream of tearing metal and the Antares III broke in two. A few seconds later and the back end of the ship, torn away from the main mass, but containing the massive engines and the weight of the super-structure, upended and rolled slowly backwards. Water smashed the windows and poured in to the wheel house. Thirty seconds later the rear third of the ship disappeared beneath the waves.

The front two-thirds, still containing roughly 300,000 tons of oil in compartmentalised tanks, continued to float, driven towards the American coast by the howling, roaring wind.

---

Before the Antares had gone down, the cruise ship 'Princess of the Seas' had left Bermuda. She had been cruising the Caribbean, moved north to Bermuda and was now on her way back to New York.

The ship looked less like a ship and more like what she really was. A great rectangular block of a ship. A multi-story floating hotel.

She weighed nearly 180,000 tons, had fifteen decks, swimming pools, gymnasiums, entertainment centres, dozens of restaurants, snack bars, coffee bars, lounges and so on. She was carrying 4,372 passengers and 2,234 crew. This wasn't the largest cruise liner that had ever been built but she was certainly top rank. It cost half a billion dollars to build and was one of the most luxurious, opulent ships of all time. She had cruised the Caribbean for six weeks and was now heading for her home port of New York.

However, her captain was not happy. Somewhere the ship had picked up a bug – a stomach bug, and far too many of his extremely wealthy passengers were lying in their beds in their apartments (you could hardly call them cabins) feeling very sorry for themselves.

"Damn it!" thought Captain Josh Harrison. "We can do without this! There's nothing worse for putting people off the idea of cruising."

The doctors had told him the bug was nasty and very catching. "Norovirus" they said. The sooner they got back to New York the better. However, they had used up a lot of fuel in the last few weeks and the tanks were pretty low. He decided to proceed back to New York at cruise speed.

Twelve hours after leaving Bermuda the First Officer, Sean Connors approached him.

"Sir! Reports say that hurricane Beta, to the south, has enlarged, rapidly intensified, and is heading north. Should we turn back to Bermuda or continue?"

Captain Harrison mulled it over for a minute.

"We don't know which way that storm will go. It could well hammer Bermuda. The New York area has only very rarely been hit. Also we have a load of sick passengers aboard and not much fuel. Continue on course for New York."

"Right! Sir!"

Twelve hours later the wind began to rise. Rapidly it began to build. Fortunately the wind was behind them, helping to push them towards New York.

Six hours later they were hit by the full force of hurricane Beta.

The wind rose to unbelievable levels. Instruments showed 160 miles an hour gusting to 180. The waves became mountainous. The stabilisers couldn't cope with seas like that and the ship began to roll and pitch in a most ungainly fashion. Hundreds of passengers rapidly became sea sick.

High up on the bridge Captain Harrison looked at the mountainous waves, felt the ship shudder. "Hell! This blasted hurricane had speeded up, passed between the mainland and Bermuda and come right at them. Couldn't have been worse!" But his decision to continue to New York had been valid, in the circumstances. "Nobody could have foreseen this – could they?"

Two hours later conditions were even worse. The great ship was rocking and rolling in unbelievable fashion. The scream of the wind was incredible. By a miracle the engines kept going. The strain on the engine bolts and supporting structures must have been enormous, when the ship pitched and rolled so violently – but they held.

An hour later Josh Harrison was still on the bridge, watching the enormous waves approaching and wondering when it would all end.

Then something caught his eye, way over to port. For a moment he stared, then his stomach contracted in a tight knot; a ball of fear. He had heard of them before, but never experienced one. They were the stuff of legend. Old sailors used to tell unbelievable tales.

Closing in, from the left, was a rogue wave. A freak caused by the interaction of smaller waves. Only rarely did it happen, but, when it did it created the greatest waves ever seen on this planet. Closing in, from the left, was a colossal wall of water. A rogue wave at least a hundred and twenty feet high.

Harrison stared in horror. There was nothing he could do. He just stood there – paralysed. As the wave reached the ship, the sea seemed to fall away into a great cavity. The Princess of the Seas hung there a moment, then rolled into the cavity, heeling over to a 45 degree angle. Then the wave hit. Pounding down on top of the ship. Hundreds of thousands of tons of water.

The windows came in on Captain Harrison. Water roared into the gangways, the walkways, the swimming pools, the entertainment centres. Portholes and windows were smashed. The top part of the ship was pulverised. It had never been designed to take an impact such as this.

As the giant wave passed, the Princess of the Seas was on its side. As the next, normal waves came in, and they were 40 to 50 feet high, more water poured in. Slowly the great ship capsized, tipped down at the stern and sank.

From the first impact of the rogue wave to the ship disappearing was no more than 3 minutes. Not a single person survived. The loss of the Princess of the Seas, and everyone on board was far greater than the loss of the Titanic. It was, in fact, the greatest maritime disaster in the history of mankind.

––––––––––––––––––––

Captain James Lachlan was fuming as he finally taxied the plane to the north end of runway No. 1 at New York International Airport.

"Nothing but damned hold-ups!" he told himself.

For ten years he had flown massive transport aircraft for the US Army. Then he had left and landed a job as Captain, flying A380's for South East Asia Airlines. The plane he was sitting in now was one of the latest models – the A380X a 'stretched' version of Airbus's giant, double-decker, A380 passenger plane. The A380X was the largest airliner that had ever been built, capable of carrying 1,020 passengers ten thousand miles.

Today he had 930 on board plus a crew of 34 including himself and the co-pilot – Harry Lesnovitch – another American. They would be flying to Bahrain and then on to Singapore. For half an hour they had been waiting to take off and the wind had been building all the time. Lachlan knew all about hurricane Beta, coming up from the south and wanted out before it got any closer.

Ten minutes ago the Tower had reported a wind speed of sixty miles an hour gusting to 75. Direction – North, North East.

Lachlan knew he could take off in that but he didn't want to hang around. The sooner he got away the better.

The A380X was a modern plane with the latest in computers and avionics. The plane was perfectly capable of taxying, taking off, flying to its destination, landing and taxying all the way to the disembarkation bay without the Captain lifting a finger. But passengers liked to know there were experienced professional pilots in the cockpit.

James Lachlan liked to fly planes. He didn't want to just sit there and let the plane fly itself. The computer was programmed with all the necessary information – fuel load, passenger load and distribution, cargo load (passengers always seemed to travel with mountains of luggage), atmospheric pressure, temperature – everything. If he wanted to, he could push a button, sit back and enjoy the view as the plane took off. Instead he punched in a code and the displays lit up. He and the co-pilot would fly out in the old fashioned way. He knew if he made a mistake the computer would correct it anyway but he liked to feel he was doing the flying.

They sat on the runway another three minutes. The previous plane had also been a 'heavy' – a Boeing 747-600 and there was a mandatory time gap between one take off and the next – to allow the vortices from the wings to clear. Even the mighty A380 would stagger if it ran into them.

Finally he got the 'clear for take off'. The co-pilot pushed the four throttle levers slowly forward and the engines built up thrust. The A380X was powered by four massive Rolls Royce Trent 1100 engines, each capable of delivering 110,000lbs of thrust.

Brakes off! The plane began to accelerate down the runway. The co-pilot monitoring the engines and the air speed indicator. Lachlan held the control column gently but firmly with his left hand and steered the plane with his right hand on a small lever which controlled the nose wheel steering, keeping her centred down the runway, until the speed exceeded 45 knots. At 50 knots he released the lever, took hold of the column with both hands and steered with the rudder pedals. He had to hold her hard against the pressure of the side wind. As the speed built up they could feel the plane shake and buffet with the turbulence of the gale. They were well down the runway when the co-pilot called "Vee One". V1 was the speed at which a plane is committed to take off. The speed at which it becomes impossible to abort. To try to abort, after V1, would mean the plane would run out of runway before it could stop.

As the speed increased towards take off speed they felt the plane stagger under a heavy gust. She smoothed a moment, then the co-pilot called "Vee Two." Lachlan pulled back on the control column and the nose began to lift. Two seconds later the wheels left the runway.

At that moment the plane lurched, struck by a heavy sideways gust. The great Trent engines, at full power, were pulling in enormous quantities of air. At this point it is essential that airflow into the intake is smooth and clean. The furious gust of wind cut across the front of the engines and disrupted the airflow.

Immediately, the two engines on the starboard wing stalled.

Lachlan felt the plane stagger and the starboard wing began to drop. She was just seventy feet above the ground.

Desperately he kicked the rudder and turned the yoke on the control column to counter the roll. But it was impossible. The A380X was capable of flying on two engines – even with two on the same side. But in this condition, just after rotation, at the climb, and just above 'take off' speed they had no chance.

The wing continued to dip. The tip touched the ground. The tip crumpled but the wing held. With the wingtip dragging the ground, the great plane slewed, turned to the right. The end of the wing folded. The outermost engine struck the ground and exploded. The mid part of the wing tore apart and the blazing engine ripped off. The inboard engine struck the ground and a fuel tank ruptured. A great roaring smear of flame dragged behind the inboard engine and then the whole wing was gone.

The enormous body of the plane struck the ground, careering on like some gigantic missile, sliding across the ground until it slammed into some of the airport buildings. It ploughed half way through the buildings before finally coming to rest. A hundred and ninety tons of aviation fuel created a gigantic blazing pyre.

---

At Woods Hole, Nat Greenbank and Joe Carmino were still monitoring the hurricane. Their colleagues were issuing bulletins every hour.

Nat showed Joe the latest data and satellite photographs.

"This is one hell of a hurricane!" said Joe. "Unbelievable! Twenty four hours ago it was 850 miles across. Now it's down to 760. It's actually tightening."

"Yes!" said Nat. "It's tracking up the American East Coast. The 'eye' is still over the sea, fifty miles from shore. The sea surface all along the coast is excessively warm. Only one third of the hurricane's area is over land. It's still gaining power. It's hammering New York and Boston now."

The hurricane had tracked between the mainland and Bermuda, closed on the land and then swung north, with the eye 50 miles from land and running north, parallel to the coast.

Most of the hurricane was over the sea. The screaming wind was forcing evaporation. Sucking energy from the warm sea. Vast quantities of water vapour lifted from the sea surface and mixed with the air. Water vapour is lighter than air. The water vapour and air mass rises to the stratosphere, creating a massive and intense low pressure area beneath. Air rushes in from around the hurricane to replace the rising air, causing yet more evaporation and perpetuating the situation. As long as the hurricane keeps moving over a warm sea surface it will persist. Only if it tracked over land or a cold sea surface would it weaken and dissipate. Coriolis forces cause the mass to rotate.

In the last 24 hours it had tightened. It had actually become smaller in diameter, not larger. Like a skater who spins, arms outstretched, and then draws their arms in, the hurricane winds had speeded up.

"Joe! We are now recording sustained wind speeds of 190 miles an hour, gusting to 220."

"God help the poor devils within a hundred miles of the coast" said Joe. "This is going to be a full scale disaster."

---

In a departure lounge at Boston International Airport, Pete Henshaw sat, gloomily, looking out of the window. He had expected to be halfway across the Atlantic by now, on his way to London. But all flights had been suddenly cancelled. The wind was rising, to be sure, but he had flown before, in worse conditions than this. Somebody said there had been a crash at New York. Something about an A380. "Not an A380, surely!"

Nevertheless, he had to admit, the wind was building fast. There was a fluctuating roar of wind. The windows in front of him kept flexing with the change of pressure as the gusts passed. Ten minutes later the roar increased. The building began to shake. "Maybe they had been right to end the flights!"

Five minutes later the wind was screaming. He looked out across the Airport and his mouth fell open. In the distance he saw planes, lifting off the ground, flipping on their backs, some cartwheeling, others end over end. It struck him they looked like leaves tumbling along in an autumn breeze. He also noted, in a daze, these were not light aircraft but large, intercity Jet passenger planes.

Suddenly there came a massive roar. The windows in front of him bowed and exploded outwards. His dazed mind noted they exploded outwards; pulled out by the massive suction on the downwind side of the building. He heard a terrible rending screeching noise behind him, turned and looked up. Just in time to see the roof peel away. Two seconds later he was looking at the sky. Instinct made him run and cower at the base of a stanchion. All around him was chaos.

Five hundred yards away a Boeing 747-400 was parked outside a maintenance bay. She was there awaiting an engine change. All the bays inside were full so, for the moment, she had to wait. There were, of course, no passengers or crew on board. No luggage and her fuel tanks were only 20% full.

A mechanic, inside the maintenance bay, walking back from a restroom, glanced out of a window, looked at the Jumbo and paused. He could have sworn he had seen the massive plane move. The wind was roaring around the building and he didn't think he had ever heard it quite this bad. He paused and watched. "Must have been a trick of the light." After all, even an empty 747 weighed over 140 tons.

The building shook. Unbelieving he watched as the giant plane's nose and wings lifted. Slowly it reared, rocked back on its tail and lifted to an incredible 50° from the horizontal. For a moment it hung there, then another gust hit it and it was over, flipped onto its back. He stood there, gulping, trying to catch his breath.

Two minutes later, the roof of the maintenance building, too, was gone.

Most jet planes, from the smaller, twin engine, intercity planes to the largest inter-continental 'Jumbos', fully loaded, had a take off speed from 150mph for the smaller to 180mph for the largest, heavily loaded, planes. It is no wonder that gusts of 200 miles an hour lifted and wrecked scores of massive but lightly loaded passenger planes, parked on airports, all down the East Coast of America.

There were over twenty major airports, all handling large, international jet transports, from Norfolk to Boston, devastated by hurricane Beta.

---

All the major cities and the smaller conurbations as well, along the US East Coast were savagely damaged. Trees and power lines were down. Rooftops ripped off houses. Lorries and vans overturned. In the Appalachian Mountains it is reckoned over 2 million trees were flattened.

In New York there was a massive storm surge and much flooding. However, the bridges and skyscrapers survived – though not unscathed. Although the skyscraper structures had been robustly designed, nobody had designed windows to stand 200 miles an hour gusts.

On the windward side of the buildings the windows took the full pressure and many of them caved in. This allowed the pressure of the wind to get inside the buildings. At the same time the windows on the leeward side were subjected to massive suction. The combination of suction and internal pressure was too much and most of the leeward side windows blew out. Rain and wind then swept through the buildings causing much internal damage.

The hurricane tracked north, hitting Nova-Scotia and Newfoundland. As the hurricane passed over land and cooler seas it gradually lost energy. It then tracked across the North Atlantic, dissipating as it went.

When, a week later, it struck Great Britain, the winds were down to 110 miles an hour. Even this was enough to flatten trees, disrupt power lines and cause three billion pounds worth of damage. Hurricane Beta would never be forgotten.

The following year Nat and Joe discussed the situation.

"Well!" said Nat. "You were right! Joe! The gulf stream is starting to speed up again. Temperatures over Greenland and Europe have dropped – primarily because the gulf stream slowed – so the Greenland ice cap is not thawing so fast. A small Arctic ice cap mass has reappeared. So we are unlikely to get a repeat of Hurricane Beta – for a while."

"No!" Joe replied. "But global warming continues. And it is getting worse. In fifty or a hundred years time global temperatures will be much higher. The freak high surface sea temperatures we experienced in 2043 will become normal. Hurricane Beta will become just an average hurricane."

"Ye Gods!" said Nat. "I hope I'm not around to see it."

"You say that – but I think you might well be!  Pass me that weather chart – will you?"

# 2050 – PRE-CRASH CONDITIONS

By 2050, things were getting difficult. The world population had climbed to 9.6 billion. Global average temperature was now 1.5°C above pre Industrial Revolution temperatures. This equated to a rise of 5.0°C over Arctic land surfaces and 2.9°C over tropical land masses such as India. The temperature rise in India made the summer heat waves even more exhausting, but just about bearable, and crops could still be grown – aided by the efforts of the Genetic Engineers.

The 5°C rise over the Arctic land masses meant that it was now becoming feasible to grow crops as far north as the Arctic Circle, especially since the Genetic Engineers had created frost resistant potatoes and other crops. The growing season was short but the short season was compensated for, to some degree, because of the extended daylight hours; non stop daylight in fact, in midsummer, above the Arctic Circle.

The downside, of course, was the increased melting of the permafrost; the warming and defrosting of the tundra peat, leading to increasing releases of $CO^2$ and methane from rotting of the peat and, in many areas, a heavy release of methane from decomposing methane hydrate, just under the peat layer.

Substantial releases of methane were also seen in the sea, along the Siberian coast and also in other parts of the world, such as off the coast of Alaska, the Canadian north coast, the coast of North East USA, off Japan and even off Scandinavia. These methane releases were entirely due to the decomposition of methane hydrate deposits. These Arctic releases of greenhouse gases acted to offset worldwide efforts to reduce human greenhouse gas emissions and ensured that the measured levels of these gases in the atmosphere continued to rise.

In the first half of the 21st Century, the Polar ice cap had steadily continued to reduce in area until, by 2050, it was not unusual for the ice cap to disappear completely during August/September months. This, of course, meant there was an additional massive direct input of solar energy into the Arctic Ocean, independent of the input due to greenhouse gases. The Greenland ice cap continued to melt but the amount of ice, and its thickness, was such that it would probably take a thousand years to completely melt off the bulk of it. Sea level rise, by 2050, was not sufficient to cause any serious concern.

However, a number of other problems were becoming noticeable by 2050. The most important was fresh water supplies. Early in the 21$^{st}$ Century, massive exploitation of underground aquifers was taking place. It had been found that, in many parts of the world, enormous deposits of water had accumulated in the porous rocks and sand formations underground. Some of the deposits were found to be millions of years old – sometimes referred to as fossil water. Other aquifers were more recent, regularly replenished in areas of frequent rain, by water slowly percolating down through the ground. It was found there were vast aquifers under the Sahara Desert. Most of it dating back to the time, thousands of years ago, when the Sahara was a more fertile area with low but fairly regular rainfall. These aquifers, which, incidentally, were the source of the small, fertile, Oases dotted about the desert, began to be exploited by the Arab nations in the early 21$^{st}$ Century and the water mainly used for irrigation of crops.

In many areas of the USA there were found to be large aquifers of sweet water. (The term 'sweet' is used to denote 'salt free'). Boreholes were drilled and these supplies tapped. In the south west USA, enormous quantities of water were taken from the giant Ogallala Aquifer and used for crop irrigation.

In India many large aquifers were found. In the 20$^{th}$ Century there had been a lot of trouble and disease associated with poor quality and contaminated drinking water. When the aquifers were discovered, many boreholes were sunk in villages all over India. The incidence of bacterial disease was drastically reduced and the borehole water was hailed as a life saver. Unfortunately, for some reason, the water was never checked out, originally, as thoroughly as it might have been. The fact that it was sweet and free from dangerous bacteria was deemed enough. Later, after a number of years, it was found that much of the Indian borehole water contained minute traces of arsenic. Not enough to cause any immediate problems but, unfortunately, arsenic is a cumulative poison and, over a period of years, people began to develop definite symptoms of poisoning.

Australia, too, had vast aquifers under some of its desert areas but again, much of the water had some degree of mineral contamination. The water could be drunk by cattle and even humans but it was unsuitable for crop irrigation. The interior of Australia, therefore, largely remained arid.

By 2050, most of the sweet water aquifers of the world were either exhausted or drastically depleted. Even those that were naturally replenished by rain percolation were greatly depleted because extraction was far greater than the rate of replenishment. Often the water had to be pumped from deeper and deeper down, which, of course, greatly increased the cost. With climate change, due to global warming, becoming noticeable in many areas of the world, the south western and central parts of the United States were particularly hard hit. Rainfall reduced, leading to drought on the Great Plains and lower river flows in California. Because of reduced rainfall and depletion of rivers and aquifers, the great agricultural areas of Southern California were affected very badly and agricultural productivity reduced.

In North Africa and the Middle East, with steady population increases, more and more drinking water, and water for general domestic use, had to be produced by desalination plants using water supplies from the sea; a very expensive reverse-osmosis process, needing a lot of high pressure pumps and equipment.

So, by 2050, the world wide fresh water supply problem was becoming difficult – but not insuperable.

Another problem that was developing, by 2050, was the problem of soil impoverishment, leading to reduced crops and poor productivity. In order to produce crops in the most efficient manner possible, most farmers, across the world, had adopted high intensity farming techniques. This involved massive use of fertilisers, herbicides and pesticides, heavy and sustained production of mono culture crops and, in drier areas, sustained and intensive irrigation techniques. This undoubtedly led to high productivity, but many farmers were worried. They knew that, back in the Middle Ages, in order to maintain soil fertility, farmers used a rotation system, where different crops were planted in successive years and it was normal to let the land lie fallow i.e. plant no crops, every fourth year. Modern farmers could not afford to do this because of the intense competition of modern times. If a farmer could not or did not produce efficiently and cheaply enough – he went out of business.

A rich, healthy soil contains a lot of humus – which is fine organic material accumulated slowly over a period of time. Soil that is intensively farmed gradually loses its humus. Without humus the soil becomes very friable and dusty. It does not hold water as efficiently. Also the soil loses much of its secondary nutrients – still essential for healthy plant growth.

So – to make the plants grow – the farmers apply more and more of the basic fertilisers and, because the fertilisers are applied from above – and the soil below has lost its humus, the plants form more and more shallow root structures, which then make them more drought prone. Hence – more and more need for irrigation. Unfortunately, the water used for irrigation contains various salts, to a greater or lesser degree. Salts can be found in both river and aquifer water. Since the farmer, using irrigation, normally uses the minimum water to do the job, there is no run-off. The water applied to the crops eventually evaporates into the air, one way or another, leaving behind, in the soil, any salts it had contained. The result, over a period of years, is that the soil gradually accumulates toxic salts until the plants can no longer cope. The only way to prevent this is to irrigate the plants, occasionally, with an excess of water so that the salts are dissolved and are taken away with the 'run off' water. Since irrigation is most often carried out in areas with very little rain fall and water must be carefully conserved and not wasted, then using an excess of water to carry off salts is simply not done. It is believed some of the Cities and States in ancient Mesopotamia failed and disappeared because of soil impoverishment and salt contamination which made it eventually impossible to grow crops on the surrounding land.

# 2056 – GEO ENGINEERING – COOLING THE PLANET

In 2053 it had become obvious that it was not going to be possible to completely stop the continuing rise of $CO^2$ in the atmosphere. It was now 511 parts per million – way above the 450 ppm once thought to be the maximum target level to limit global warming. Despite massive efforts to convert to 'green energy – with wind farms, solar panels, wave power, and efforts to capture $CO^2$ at coal and gas fired power plants, compress it and pump it underground, $CO^2$ levels inexorably continued to climb. It would have climbed much faster, of course, if these efforts had not been made.

The fundamental problem was population. More and more people, demanding a higher standard of living, inevitably meant more consumption, more power, more burning. By 2055 the world population was just over 10 Billion. With the Politics that existed then, and the attitude of most of the people on the planet, it was not possible to impose any drastic form of population control. So the population continued to rise – but at a slower rate than previously. The steady improvement in the standard of living – and consequent increase in average life span – also contributed to population increase. So – in 2055 – at a world Climate Control Convention – it was finally decided that the Worlds largest nations should take positive action – Geo Engineering – to control the global temperature – and bring it down 1 or 1½°C if possible.

It had been known for many years that large volcanic eruptions often acted to cool the planet, and the Earth might be cooled as much at 1°C or more for the one to two years following a major eruption. When some types of volcano erupted there was, in addition to the lava and dust, a great outpouring of steam, $CO^2$ and Sulphur Dioxide. It was the sulphur dioxide, injected into the stratosphere that caused the cooling. In the stratosphere it converted to sulphuric acid and, somehow, acted to reflect solar radiation back into space. After a few years the sulphuric acid dissipated, most of it washed out of the atmosphere. Unfortunately the $CO^2$ also produced by the volcano, persisted. So – immediately following a major eruption – the Earth cooled. This was, later, followed by a smaller amount of warming, caused by the more persistent $CO^2$.

Armed with this knowledge some scientists said – "We could cool the planet simply by injecting sulphuric acid into the upper atmosphere." At the 2055 Convention it was decided to go ahead and do it. There was plenty of sulphur available. Every coal fired power station produced lots of it.

Some scientists pointed out the irony of the situation. Originally the first coal fired power stations had allowed the sulphur dioxide to go up the chimneys together with the $CO^2$ but, in the late $20^{th}$ Century, legislation had been passed to force installation of equipment specially to remove the sulphur. Vast quantities of lime were used to react with the sulphur to produce calcium sulphate (Gypsum) and there was quite a problem getting rid of it.

The reason the people in the $20^{th}$ Century decided to eliminate the sulphur from the power stations was because the sulphur dioxide, released from the chimneys, stayed at a fairly low altitude in the atmosphere. It was then rapidly washed out of the air by rain, usually a few hundred to a thousand miles down wind, the $SO^2$ converting to sulphuric acid. This produced acid rain which started killing forests. As an example, in the late $20^{th}$ Century – Scandinavia complained to Britain that acid rain – caused by Britain's coal fired power stations – was destroying their pine forests. The British reluctantly conceded and fitted sulphur extraction equipment to all their coal fired power stations. "That won't happen this time!" said the experts – in 2055. "The sulphur will be injected at high altitude – at least 30,000 feet and will stay in the upper atmosphere for years".

So – equipment was installed at power stations and the sulphur extracted. $SO^2$ was converted to sulphuric acid and transported to selected airports where it was pumped into the tanks of enormous transport planes – similar to the old KC135 fuel tanker planes – and flown to 33,000 feet altitude, where it was sprayed into the atmosphere in ultra-fine droplets. When the system was fully operational, tanker planes operated a shuttle service, continuously, day and night.

Over several years, millions of tons of sulphuric acid were sprayed into the upper atmosphere. It was expensive, of course, but the cost, shared out between the nations, was acceptable. And – it worked! After 3 years there was no doubt about it. The average global temperatures had reduced. The satellites showed it and people could tell, in their daily lives – it was cooler. But then came snags.

The sulphuric acid particles did not stay in the upper atmosphere for ever – as they didn't after the volcanic eruptions. Scientists reported that the sea was becoming more acidic. They said – "If we keep this up for 100 years – and to keep the Earth cool we must keep it up, because the $CO^2$ is not going to go away, then there will be a disaster. The Oceans will be ruined. And the land is being damaged as well. We simply cannot keep up this sulphur injection for ever. Sooner or later we have to stop. Let's face facts – and do it now – while the damage is not too great".

In 2061 sulphur injection into the upper atmosphere was terminated. By 2065 there was no doubt – Global Warming was back – and worse.

# 2062 – THE GREAT NORTHERN PINE FORESTS BURN

One of the features of the late 20th and early 21st Century, as Global Warming gradually acted to modify eco-systems, was the shifting of species to different parts of the planet. Often this was made possible by human activity, sometimes deliberate, more often accidental.

In the mid 20th Century, a bark boring beetle, which normally lived in parts of America, was accidentally introduced, (in a consignment of timber), to Europe. Unfortunately the beetle brought with it a disease – Dutch Elm Disease – to which the European Elm trees were particularly susceptible. The warmer winter conditions allowed the beetle eggs to survive and beetle populations exploded. The beetle fed on the leaves and thin bark of the growing shoots and then burrowed under the thick bark of the main tree trunk to lay its eggs. The disease agent itself – a type of fungus, which did not affect the beetles themselves, was transmitted into the sap – the life blood of the tree – where it multiplied and accumulated until it blocked the capillaries so the sap could no longer flow. In Britain 99% of all elm trees were destroyed in a few years.

At the end of the 20th Century, in southern Alaska, it was noted that great swathes of the native pine forests were dying. The cause was the effects of another bark boring beetle – which acted in a similar way to the Elm beetle – but which attacked pine trees. This beetle, which, previously, had been confined to warmer areas in the south, where there were fewer pine trees, had been unable to move north, previously, because the beetle eggs could not stand the cold of the harsh Alaskan winters.

A noticeable feature of the early stages of Global Warming was the fact that the Arctic areas warmed much more rapidly than the rest of the planet. Alaska, Northern Canada and Siberia warmed several degrees C by the end of the 20th Century when the planet, as a whole had, on average, only warmed ¾°C. So – Alaskan warming had allowed the beetle to move North. Thirty years later the pine bark beetle was in the Siberian Taiga – the gigantic pine forest – stretching from the Ural Mountains to the Bering Sea in the East. It was also in the Canadian pine forest.

People in planes, flying over, saw large brown patches amongst the green. Even live green pines, full of resin, can burn fiercely in forest fires. A patch of brown, dead, pines is a tinderbox. It was only a question of time.

In 2062, in Northern Siberia and the Taiga, it was an exceptionally hot/dry summer. No one had ever seen anything like it. And then there came some summer storms. A few lightning flashes and the Taiga erupted. Vast areas blazed, uncontrollably. So great was the burning that the smoke rose into the upper atmosphere and circled the world. There were spectacular sunsets. Views from space satellites, at night, showed vast areas were ablaze. Large areas of tundra peat also caught fire. Surprisingly – some people said "Maybe this is a good thing! We shall soon need to clear large areas in the North for cultivation – the same as they did in the Amazon area of South America in the late 20th Century."

The following year, large areas of the Canadian and Alaskan pine forests also burned.

---

Ivan Bronsky walked slowly between the trees, on the lower slopes of a hill near his home. Slung over his shoulder was a small wild boar piglet. Roasted, it would make a very nice supper for him, his wife and two children.

He had come upon the boar family a couple of hours ago. A boar, his mate and a grunting little tribe of piglets, rooting in the underbrush. Fortunately he was down wind and he had been able to take his time, choose one of the piglets and fire a single, accurate, shot. The boar had been enraged and had charged at him. Ivan fired a couple of shots in the air and the boar, fortunately, although in a fury, was not stupid and stopped. Then he grunted and took off, following his mate and the other piglets, deep into the forest.

Ivan gave a sigh of relief. He had not wanted to kill the boar and he knew, if he didn't drop the charging boar with a perfect shot, the wounded animal could be very dangerous. As he walked back, heading for the log cabin alongside the little stream in the valley, he noticed that more of the pine trees were weeping. The trunks looked as if they had been blasted with a shotgun, with the holes slowly weeping resin. Nearby was a group of totally dead trees, the needles on the branches brown and lifeless.

He had heard it was something to do with beetles that bored into the tree and, somehow, killed it. He had only noticed this in the last few years. There had been nothing like it in his youth. "Something to do with this Climate Change, no doubt." The Taiga was steadily getting warmer and warmer.

He shrugged and continued his walk. Then he paused. Momentarily he seemed to have caught a faint whiff of smoke. For a moment he stood still, sniffing. But there was nothing. He continued his walk. A minute later – there it was again – and there was no mistaking it this time. There had been a brief storm in the night. Nothing to worry about – and it had soon passed over. There had been a few flickers of far-off lightning and a few faint rumbles – that was all. But now – he felt a twinge of anxiety.

The wind was not blowing from the log cabin. He sniffed the smoke again and made up his mind, turned away and headed up the hill. It was not a high hill but it rose a few hundred feet above the surrounding forest and, at its top was a rocky accumulation – probably a relic of some ancient volcanic activity, and a small crag, where he had occasionally gone, to look out and ponder the vastness of the great Taiga forest.

Fifteen minutes later he was on the crag, puffing heavily. "Maybe he was not as young as he used to be." The crag gave him a view, over the tops of the trees, in almost every direction. If there was a forest fire, he should be able to spot it and, knowing the direction of the wind, could judge whether there was any danger or risk to his local area.

He straightened up, caught his breath and began to scan the horizon. An icy knot began to materialise in his stomach. In the distance, in every direction he looked, there was a pall of smoke on the horizon. Beneath the smoke, in several places, he could just make out the red glow of flames.

Ivan walked down the hill and through the forest to the cabin. His wife met him with a smile of delight when she saw the piglet and took it from him. His little girl, scarcely more than a toddler, came to him for a cuddle and a kiss. The boy, seven years old, smiled and leaned against his knee. Ivan had decided, on the walk down from the hill, to say nothing. "Wait and see!" The fires were a long way away.

Later, they had the piglet for supper. His wife had roasted it to perfection. Nevertheless, she noticed her husband was quiet – a bit withdrawn. Maybe he was just tired.

They slept through the night. Ivan a little fitfully perhaps. He woke, in the darkness, sniffed. Smoke! Probably just the remains of the cooking fire – or imagination.

In the morning he arose early, put on his hunting gear, took the rifle and went out. His wife would think he was simply being keen.

He headed for the hill and puffed his way to the top. Half way up, he paused for breath and thought he could hear an unusual noise – a faint rumbling and crackling. He hurried to the top, climbed his little crag and looked around. His stomach knotted in horror. All around, just a mile away, on all sides, the forest was a wall of flame, advancing rapidly. Ivan rushed down the hill, through the trees and to the cabin, arriving gasping horribly. His wife looked at him in alarm and the children were scared.

"Ivan! Ivan! What is the matter?"

"The forest!" Ivan said hoarsely. "The forest is on fire!"

"Where? Which Way?"

"All around!"

"Surely. Ivan! It can't be all around? There must be someway we can go!"

"I don't know! Let me think. Let me think."

The stream, running past the cabin, was only a trickle – but enough for their needs. The main river was several miles to the North. To the West was a lake but, again, that was miles away.

Desperately Ivan racked his brains. He went outside. He could plainly hear the roaring and crackling now, and, as he watched, a wraith of smoke drifted across the little clearing. All around were the massed pines of the forest, many over 100 feet tall. There could be no escape – in any direction. Paralysed he stood there. The roaring increased. He saw the first flash of fire as a treetop exploded into flame. The fire was rushing through the forest – as fast as a man could run. Ivan knew now, with complete certainty. They could not escape. He went back into the cabin, seized his rifle. His wife looked at him, wide eyed with horror. He pointed the rifle at her and fired. The little boy was crying now, cringing in a corner. Ivan pointed the rifle and fired again. With a sob he went to the little girl, in her cot.

He could hardly see to shoot, through his tears. And then he placed the muzzle of the rifle under his chin and pressed the trigger. Ten minutes later the cabin was an inferno.

# 2070 – DROUGHT – COLORADO USA

Hank Jefferson climbed out of the light plane he had hired, stepped on to the dusty ground and stared at the ruins of the family homestead. This was the place where he was brought up as a kid, with his two brothers. He remembered it as a bustling lively place, with his brothers, his Ma and Pa and a couple of hired hands. There had been several groves of trees, near the house, probably planted as windbreaks. He remembered playing around these, and looking out over an endless green expanse of growing corn, taller than he was. The corn seemed to go on for ever – or so it seemed to him. There had been barns, grain silos and a simple, fan like, wind pump creaking away near the barn, pumping water from a borehole for the house, and a few cattle and pigs. There was also a small, fenced off garden, where they grew vegetables and fruit for their own use. Basically the farm was an arable farm, growing maize corn and soy beans, 2,000 acres of fertile prairie.

It had been a good life. They had friendly neighbours on the other nearby farms and there was a little town about 20 miles away. Sometimes they would all pile into their ancient truck and go for a night out. He loved the country and western singing and dancing.

Hank sighed. Maybe it had been a mistake to come back here. Better to keep the old memories and not see what it had become now. The house was a derelict mess. The paint all gone and peeled off. Doors hanging off the hinges. Shingles gone off the roof. All the trees had disappeared. The barns gone. The grain silo was now a heap of twisted, flapping, rusted, metal. The wind pump long since gone – replaced, later, by a more efficient electric borehole pump, powered by a diesel/electric generator – to provide water for irrigation as well as the house.

As he grew up – he remembered – it gradually became dryer. The rains seemed less and less. Something to do with climate change – a friend had once said – an adjustment of the Hadley cells or Ferrell cells or something like that. He hadn't understood it at the time. All he knew was it seemed to be getting dryer year by year, and his father had, gradually, become more and more dour and withdrawn.

His father was a trier. He did not give up easily. They installed a monstrous irrigation system – multi wheeled things a quarter of a mile long that slowly rotated about a central pivot,

51

spraying the crops as it turned.  It seemed strange to have enormous circular fields instead of rectangular ones.

The water came from a creek about a mile away, fed from the snow capped mountains of the Rockies, a hundred and fifty miles to the west.  They also pumped irrigation water from the aquifer that lay beneath the ranch.  Gradually the water in the creek, in the summer, reduced.  Other farmers were pumping from it too.  And, in the distance, the snow cover on the mountains, seen in the fall, grew less and less.

There came a day when the old man died.  They called him 'the old man' but he wasn't old really.  Some said he died before his time.  After his father died Hank had a chat with his brothers.  He decided to leave – to head for California and see what he could do there.  His two brothers said they would stay – and run the farm; do their damnedest to keep it going.  For a few years they carried on.  Gradually the snow on the mountains disappeared.  The little creek became a raging torrent in the winter – and dried up in the summer.  The two brothers still did not give up.  They built a large, plastic lined, reservoir and pumped it full of water, from the creek, every winter.  They changed their crops.  They ditched the wasteful spray irrigation system and changed to a trickle feed system with a network of pipes feeding water directly to the plant roots.  The reservoir had to be supplemented by water from the aquifer.  The water level in the aquifer slowly went down.  They had to pump from deeper and deeper – increasing the cost.  Their mother died.  By 2060 they were barely eking out a living.  They could hardly afford hired hands to help them with the harvest.  There was no chance of selling the place.  Eventually they just gave up and walked away.  There came a point where farming this country was just impossible.  They caught a train and went East.  Got jobs somewhere in Baltimore.

So now Hank had come back for one last look at the place.  He walked around the remains of the house, pushed through a collapsed doorway into what had been the old living room.  Remembered the joking and banter that used to go on there.  He came out and walked to where the clump of trees used to be.  Scuffed the parched and dusty ground with his foot, paused for a few moments then started to walk slowly back to the plane.  Although it was a calm day, a stray puff of wind scoured his face with dust and grit.  As he climbed into the cockpit he reflected.  Nothing ever lasts.  Nothing ever stays the same.  And got ready for take off.

# 2074 – IMMIGRANT PROBLEMS – FRANCE

It was June 2074, and the Comte de Tassigny stood at a window and stared out gloomily. A screaming mob of children tore across his lawn and flower beds, ripping up the precisely trimmed little box bush hedges, that surrounded the beds, as they went. Beyond that, two hundred metres away, was what looked like the beginnings of a shanty town.

He and his family were constrained (imprisoned would be a more suitable word) in just four small rooms at one corner of his magnificent Chateau. All the other rooms had been commandeered by the French Government and made available to house some of the immense flux of immigrants from Africa and the Middle East.

In the last six months the Chateau had been just about wrecked. What with rampaging children and thieving and looting adults. They had even smashed up some of the priceless furniture, to fuel their fires.

There was nothing he could do. When he complained to the local police, their chief had simply shrugged and spread his hands. There were still a couple of loyal servants and a few gardeners – but – what was the point? When he noticed his favourite fancy carp had gone from the ornamental pond near the front entrance and mentioned it to his valet, the man had replied with one word. "Eaten!"

He also asked about the peacocks that had mysteriously disappeared.

"Monsieur Le Comte" said the valet "Even in Louis the Fourteenths time, roast peacock was considered a delicacy."

"And the deer?"

"Barbecued!"

So now the Count stared out of his window. "This is a Revolution!" he thought "The Second Revolution. What is the difference?" And then – bitterly, "Oh! Yes! There is a difference. This time I am allowed to keep my head. The first time – some of my ancestors lost theirs."

––––––––––––

Jules Lafarge cursed under his breath. He and his wife lived in a very desirable detached house, with a substantial garden, on the outskirts of Paris. At least, it had been desirable – until recently. Now – it was hell on Earth.

The children had grown up and fled the nest. Jules and his wife had settled down for a relaxed, peaceful, retirement. And then the Police had come – with documents.

"According to our records, your house has five bedrooms and seven other rooms. The house is now occupied by just the two of you. According to the new Legislation, you must accommodate two immigrant families, in addition to yourselves. I shall return in seven days time with the two families. You have seven days to make arrangements."

Jules had protested. His wife had broken down in tears. The Policeman was adamant.

"I'm sorry! But that is the Law!"

The Policeman was back, a week later. The families he brought with him both had young children, between three and six years old, and also babes in arms. The adults didn't even speak French.

At first it had been bad enough. The children ran riot, shouting and screaming. The babies bawled. And then the two families fell out with one another. They weren't even from the same tribe. The adults began shouting at one another – with threats. Jules and his wife talked about leaving. But where could they go? They were willing, even, to completely abandon the place. They had some money, put aside. How they wished they had down sized, when the children left, to a small cottage, just for two. But it was too late now. It was the small cottage – just two up and two down – a peasant's cottage – that was the Des-Res now.

# 2074 – MEXICO/USA BORDER FENCE

Jose Ferrera looked across the valley to the vastness of Mexico city; the great metropolis – built on the site of Tenochtitlan – the ancient Aztec capital city where the great Mocteczuma had, in 1519, fatefully met Hernan Cortes and his doom. The entire valley was covered in a pall of smoke. Some of it from the numerous burning buildings and the rest from the giant funeral pyres. – A grim and ominous foretaste of what was to come, half a century later.

He had narrowly escaped with his life. The city was teeming with marauding bands of scavengers. Millions had come in from the south, hoping to, somehow, keep migrating north – to cooler, more forgiving climes. But the Americans had been adamant. The border was closed – and would stay closed.

———————

By 2060, Mexico was in difficulties. The population had escalated and the climate was steadily getting hotter. However, the countries to the South – Guatemala, Honduras, Nicaragua, Panama and the northern countries of South America – Colombia and Venezuela, were in far worse condition with massive over population and suffocating heat.

People from these countries began to move north, hoping eventually to get into the USA. Some actually made it and sent encouraging messages to their relatives back home.

The trickle became a flood, with millions moving north through Mexico to infiltrate into the USA.

The whole of Mexico was seething with people. Mexico City, alone, had more than two million refugees from the south, mainly living in shanty towns around the city. As the numbers of refugees crossing into the USA increased to a flood – and the existing border controls were overwhelmed, the American Government found it increasingly difficult to cope with the influx.

When the American Population passed the 500 million mark and the flood of refugees was still rapidly increasing, there were strident calls, from all over the USA, that action must be taken. Accordingly they had decided to hold a National Referendum – on whether the USA should, at least for a time, totally close its border with Mexico. Although over half of the total population of the USA were now Hispanics, the vote had been overwhelming. 73% had voted to close the border.

Mexico had protested most strongly. The other nations had demanded that the people of the south must be allowed to migrate north – into the USA, Canada and Alaska. With Global Warming continuing to increase it would not be long before the tropics would be too hot for people to live there. They <u>must</u> be allowed to migrate.

But America was decided. The border must be closed – at least for a time – to allow the existing influx to be assimilated. Most people, however, suspected it would be permanent.

Having made the decision the Americans worked fast. By 2073, the new border fence was complete. It worked. Immigration into the USA was cut off – almost overnight.

The effect on Mexico was devastating.

Millions were continuing to come up from the South. They simply would not believe it was no longer possible to enter the USA. "Their relatives had managed to get in. Why not they?" So, Refugees still flooded into Mexico – like flood water surging against a newly erected barrier.

Enormous camps sprang up everywhere. Millions of refugees lived in squalor and on the brink of starvation. Eventually frustration and disappointment gave way to rage and anger. Rioting broke out. Armed mobs surged into the cities – burning and looting. In Mexico City, with the Capital on the brink of chaos, the Government finally ordered the Commander of the Armed forces to restore order and authorised him to use whatever force he deemed necessary.

Some people said it was a mistake.

The Army went into the city and, after confrontation, fired on the dissidents. The dissidents fired back and a pitched battle developed. Enormous numbers of disaffected refugees became involved. The battle escalated and raged out of control. Hundreds of buildings were fired.

By the time order was finally restored, no fewer than 30,000 refugees had been killed and thousands of troops. Mexico was in total turmoil.

In the North a few people still tried to get into the USA.

------

The Robot Sentry 116A sat on its parking plot atop a low hill. 50 metres away sat its sibling 116B and, another 50 metres further away, sibling 116C. The sentries were always deployed in threes – in case of breakdown or action by determined, would be, migrants – such as a missile.

The sentry was a squat, tank like vehicle, with wide, rubber treaded, tracks. It had twin 7.62mm machine guns in a low turret, a quick firing 20mm cannon and several missiles. Its computer would select the type of weapon to be used, depending on the information the computer received from its sensors. It had taken several years to construct the border defences but now America was sealed off. Over 1,800 miles of defences that made the old Soviet Union 'Iron Curtain' across Europe look child's play. Firstly, on the Mexican side, there was a low fence, free from any weapons or sensors. Every few yards, on this fence, was a large sign

BEYOND THIS POINT
EXTREME DANGER OF DEATH
AUTOMATIC WEAPONS
ANTI PERSONNEL AND ANTI VEHICLE MINES
ARMED ROBOT SENTRIES

Twenty yards further back was a tall fence, its top strung with barbed wire and with black sensor boxes at intervals along the top of the fence. Ten yards further back still, was a tarmac roadway, 15 feet wide, which ran the whole length of the fence. Ten yards beyond that was another low fence which marked one boundary of a 20 yard deep minefield. The minefield also ran the whole length of the border fence or was supposed to. The big secret was that the minefield didn't actually run from coast to coast. They existed only in a few key areas. Otherwise the number of mines needed would have been astronomical. It didn't really matter. The sentries were very capable.

---

Carlos Ramirez, and the remains of his family crept closer and closer to the great border fence. They were ill and emaciated and had escaped, when their village was raided by a large band of scavengers, only by a miracle, although his two sons had been mercilessly shot down. He had concluded that their only hope of survival was to go North and get across the border into the USA.

He had been warned about the fence – told about the black sensor boxes every few yards on top of the fence. He had also been told about the minefield – that it didn't really exist – except in a few particular places – which meant – if you tried it, right out in the wilds, you might stand a chance. He was not warned about the sentries.

So – just after dawn – Carlos, with his wife and daughter, were lying flat on the desert sand just 150 yards south of the border fence. He had brought wire cutters and his old .303 rifle, fitted with a 'scope and a bipod. He set up the rifle and peered through the 'scope. He saw the black sensor boxes on top of the fence, but decided to read the sign on the low fence. 'Armed Robot Sentries' – what the hell did that mean? Nobody had warned him about that! But it was too late to turn back now. And what did they have to lose?

He shoved a cartridge in the breech and pushed the bolt forward and down. Then he settled the rifle on its bipod, put his cheek against the stock, squinted through the 'scope and lined the cross hairs on one of the sensor boxes. He took several breaths, relaxed his body, held his breath, set the cross hairs on the centre of the box and slowly squeezed the trigger, keeping the cross hairs centred. The rifle kicked and the sensor box disintegrated.

He repeated the performance until there was a 150 yard gap in the sensors in front of them. They crept up to the fence. There were no alarms so he started work with the wire cutters. After quite a while he wiped the sweat from his face and pulled a two foot square section of fence away. Big enough for them to crawl through. He went first and then helped the others. Holding them back, he scanned along the tarmac road in both directions. Nothing!

So, cautiously, they crept across the tarmac road and headed for the second fence and the minefield. What he had failed to notice was a small unobtrusive sensor, mounted on the inside face of a fence post – which would have been quite invisible to him when he was in his sniping position. They negotiated the second fence and started across the minefield. A twinge of fear went through him. "What if?" So he told the others to wait and, very gingerly, began to move forward on his belly, gently probing the sand with his fingers.

Seven kilometres away, 116A stirred. Its silenced engine purred. It moved down the slope and along the connecting track to the main tarmac road running along the fence and turned East. It accelerated rapidly and, in seconds, was speeding east at 70 miles an hour. One minute before, as it sat on its platform, a signal had come in to its computer. Something was happening at fence post 116/743. Three and a half minutes later 116A slowed, almost to walking speed. Its infra-red sensors were on and, half a mile ahead, three bright infra-red images stood out. One, in the middle of the minefield area. 116A stopped, assessed the situation, selected the small calibre machine guns. A laser flicked, checking the range. Sensors checked, windage, temperature, air pressure, humidity. The turret moved, the guns adjusted slightly. A robot has no compassion, no consideration, no sympathy. The guns blazed briefly.

116A rolled forward, closed the gap to the targets. Sensors operated. Checked for signs of life. There were none. 116A turned, accelerated up to 40 miles an hour and trundled back to its parking position. It automatically refuelled, moved a little and then went into stasis.

--------

Sixty miles away in the monitoring station, Ed Sullivan had just finished his coffee when a monitor bleeped. He scanned the screen then shouted across to another soldier sitting at a nearby desk.

"Hey! Sarge! Looks as if we have had some action on section 116. 116A has expended some seven six two ammo." Sergeant Garcia winced.

"Sounds as if some poor devils were trying it on. You better go and check the fence in the morning. Make sure those damn machines are switched off."

"OK! Sarge!"

Sullivan went for another coffee, then sat down again. Those robots gave him the jitters. They shredded everything and everybody that didn't show an IFF signal. He'd make very sure they were inactivated before he went near that fence. And double check his IFF transmitter was working. When he was repairing a fence he was always scared stiff one of those hellish machines would appear on the horizon.

"And don't forget the body bags!" the sergeant threw back at him, in a ghastly attempt at levity.

"As if he could!" Sullivan thought, grimly.

His elongated repair/recce vehicle had a large, built in, body bag/storage compartment.  He glanced out of a window where he could just see the squat sinister silhouette of the incinerator building in the distance, and let out his breath in a long slow sigh.

# 2075 – THE BRITISH STOP IMMIGRATION

In 2075, when the British Population had reached 87 million, it was finally decided that something drastic simply had to be done to curb or stop immigration – at least for a time – to allow the country to assimilate and absorb the current influx.

Back in 2014, some Civil Servant had calculated that the total population of the UK would be around 72 million people by 2075 and 77 million by the turn of the century.

However, although at the beginning of the 21$^{st}$ Century, the original native populations of Great Britain tended to have small families (at or below replacement levels), the immigrants tended to have larger families. Also, the steadily increasing populations of tropical areas of the world, allied to climate change effects in those areas (heat and drought) served to greatly increase immigration pressure. By 2020, net immigration to the UK (i.e. those coming in less those going out) was around 200,000 per year. This had escalated to 300,000 per year by 2040 and 500,000 by 2060. Then, as climate change became more noticeable, this rapidly escalated, until, by 2075, it exceeded 1 million immigrants per year.

So, in 2075, instead of the anticipated 72 million the UK found itself with 87 million and climbing rapidly.

Hospitals, Social Services, Housing, food supply, Benefits, Infrastructure – all were at critical levels – close to breaking down. The UK needed a pause – a chance to sort itself out. Time to build more houses, create infrastructure, re-organise. The Government was desperate. They were in danger of losing control – of the Economy – of Law and Order – of Social Cohesion.

Eventually – somebody suggested a total block of further immigration for five years and then, perhaps, a review. At first, there was Parliamentary uproar. Heated debate followed on heated debate. Britain had always been a haven for the homeless, the dispossessed, the asylum seekers. But the fundamental facts, the brutal truth – the desperate situation, could not, forever, be denied. Eventually, reality was faced and hard and painful decisions taken. The British would clamp down on immigration. No One – not already a Registered and Certified British Citizen would be allowed in the country, to stay, for the next five years, at least. Action would be taken, to stop and turn back, shiploads of immigrants. Action would be taken to intercept, interrogate and deport anyone, not authorised to stay, who arrived in the UK by any means of transport whatsoever.

The British tackled it in a typically old-fashioned way. A blockade, or should we say – a reverse blockade. Manned ships, and fast patrol boats monitored the English Channel. A chain of RADAR and LADAR stations was set up along the coast, to keep an eye on anything moving on or above, the Channel. Since Britain, as a massively over-populated Island, was so dependent on imports of food and raw materials, it was found to be impossible to impose a 100% control of immigration. It was too easy to stow away, hide in the cargo or simply bribe members of ships crews. So – although the Control of Immigration Law sounded Draconian, in practice it was not and around 100,000 immigrants per year still managed to get in. They were often aided and abetted by related family members already here. The British Government, pragmatic as ever, pretended the embargo was working perfectly and turned a blind eye, settling for the fact that, at least, immigration was drastically reduced. The British Public, realistic as ever, knew perfectly well the controls were not working as the Government said they were and, as ever, resignedly accepted the situation.

# 2077 – EUROPEANS STOP IMMIGRATION FROM AFRICA

By 2070, immigration into Europe, from Africa and the Middle East, had changed from a steady flow to a flood. What with the effects of Global Warming, the associated climate change, and the massive increase in populations in Africa and the Middle East, a vast number of people were becoming desperate to move north.

In the early 21st Century, in Britain, economists had been predicting a British population of 75 million by the end of the century. However, the great flood of immigrants that occurred after 2045 was such that by 2074, the population had reached 85 million and was climbing rapidly. The flood was increasing week by week.

In early 2075 a decision was taken by the British Government to call a halt. A total halt. Time was needed to assimilate and accommodate the extra millions that had arrived in the last few years. European and other countries were told – No Immigration to Britain, whatsoever, would be allowed in the next five years. After that there would be a review. The 'No Immigration' Policy would be backed up – by force, if necessary.

The other European countries, already struggling under their own massive immigration problems, found their load increased still more. By 2076 European immigration problems were becoming intolerable. The entire infrastructure was overloaded.

In order to accommodate some of the population overload, Draconian action was taken by Governments. All properties that were not permanently occupied were confiscated and became Government Property. Holiday homes, second homes, week-end chalets, even empty caravans were requisitioned. When this was not enough then a survey of all occupied houses was undertaken. Any unused or unoccupied rooms were allocated to immigrants. The owners of fancy Chateaux, in France, suddenly found their stately homes awash with swarms of immigrants.

In addition to these actions it was necessary to create enormous tent cities and, finally, large shanty towns began to appear on the perimeters of major cities. Problems of feeding, transportation and sanitation were enormous. All over Europe, Public services were stretched to the limit. Everything was on the brink of collapse.

Finally it was decided. A conference of European Nations was called and a decision taken. Immigration must be stopped – totally – for a minimum period of five years. Europe must follow Britain's lead, or total anarchy and chaos would ensue. It was realised that, to completely stop Immigration into Europe, drastic and even brutal action would have to be taken. However, there was no other way. Maybe, after five years or so, restrictions could be relaxed, but, for the present, it had to be total. For the time being – even world respected standards of humanitarian behaviour would have to be shelved. With the decision made – the problem of how to actually enforce the ruling was handed over to the military and the planners.

The influx in large ships and planes could be stopped easily enough. In effect, Africa and the Middle East would be blockaded. If ships refused to turn back they would be boarded, control taken over, and sailed back to the port of origin. No ship load of immigrants, whatsoever, must be allowed to get through. People must be convinced that to attempt it was futile.

The treatment of aircraft could be similar. All planes containing immigrants would be refuelled and flown back to their Airport or airfield of origin. However, aircraft would not be a great problem. All the old Major Airlines had long since gone out of business. Only smaller, commercial airlines still existed.

The real problem was how to stop the myriads of smaller, sea going craft; ranging from holiday cruisers, trawlers, fishing boats of all sizes, down to dinghy size craft, that flooded across the Mediterranean. How could you stop those?

The military pondered this and finally made a decision. The only way that could possibly work was to adopt a completely ruthless and brutal policy, backed up by a massive propaganda campaign all along the North African/Middle East coastal area. People must be convinced that, to attempt to cross the Mediterranean and enter Europe would be simply suicide. Only when they were convinced there was no chance whatsoever would they desist.

After much discussion it was decided to adopt a maritime version of the American system on the USA/Mexico border. A robotic system as far as possible. So that transgressors, or would be transgressors, would know there would be no sympathy, no humanity, no human weakness involved. There was no question in the designers' minds. To make the system work, horrific as it undoubtedly was, - some people would have to be murderously killed; brutally slaughtered – until people learned. Nothing else would work. Half measures would certainly fail.

What they came up with was a picket line of robotic ships – spaced along the full length of the Mediterranean and beyond. In some areas the ships would be widely spaced. More densely spaced where there were known migration routes. The ships were very squat, ugly, cumbersome looking things, with oversize fuel tanks. They were fitted with several thrusters – fore and aft and were capable of maintaining their position, to within a few yards, for six months or more without refuelling.

When in position, each ship deployed a small, hydrogen filled, elongated and streamlined balloon, anchored to the ship by a thin, but extremely strong, Dacron cable. Under the balloon was a small gondola which contained high definition radar and other sensors. Communication, from balloon to ship, was by radio – similar to a small mobile phone. Power was normally supplied by solar panels, incorporated in the upper surface of the balloon, charging high capacity batteries in the gondola.

The balloon was normally winched up to 300 metres altitude but it could be raised to 1000 metres if required. Each ship carried an automatic, radar and laser guided Gatling gun for close range self protection and a number of short range missiles. The ship would fire on any vessel – large or small – that approached within a critical range without giving a coded IFF signal.

For long range – up to sixty miles – the ship had a number of medium size drones which could be catapulted off and, on return to the ship, retrieved by a net capture and retrieval system. The drones were normally armed with six, very small, but quite lethal, short range, laser guided missiles. The drones also incorporated a loud hailer system.

Drones were normally used to intercept and interdict small to medium boats. In addition, the ships incorporated a bank of eight larger, longer range (130 miles) heat seeking missiles, capable of destroying a large ship and providing coverage if one of the guard ships should be, somehow, disabled or destroyed.

Legitimate trade transport ships were checked out, gathered into convoys and, periodically, escorted through the picket line by naval vessels using the coded IFF signals to neutralise the picket boats. The picket ships (50 in all) were deployed in a chain from the Bosporus to the Straits of Gibraltar and beyond, to a hundred miles out into the Atlantic. Normal spacing between the picket ships was 100 miles but more closely in areas of high risk.

If the ships sensors, on the balloon, detected a small boat or ship approaching the forbidden zone – a 50 mile wide band – 20 miles to the African side of the ships and 30 miles on the European side – then a drone was despatched. Intercommunication between adjacent ships computers was maintained to prevent duplication of response. Upon reaching the target, the drone would overfly at close range and, using the loud hailer, inform the trespassers, in several languages "they must turn around and go back to Africa. If they proceeded another ten miles towards Europe then – "they would be attacked, without further warning, and the boat sunk. They were being monitored by a robot defence system which would operate totally automatically. Turn back – or be destroyed." If, during this procedure, a drone should be fired on and destroyed, another drone would be despatched and would attack without further notice.

———————————

The sun had just set on 11<sup>th</sup> May, 2078, and it was time to go home!

Mohammed Yussuf wearily pulled in the nets for the last time that day. His friend Achmed was glum and they looked despairingly at each other as the last net came aboard. Nothing! Unless you counted the three miserable little fish tangled in the last meshes. In May, 2078, the Mediterranean was now almost a barren sea; its fish stripped by humanity's endless and desperate search for protein. They had fished all day and their total catch was no more than would feed half a dozen families for a day. There was nothing for sale on the market. Nothing to bring in some money so he could buy essentials for his young wife and their beautiful little baby daughter, let alone a few baubles and bangles that his wife so loved.

Mohammed stowed the nets away and set sail for the North African coast and home. Home was a little mud brick building in one of the coastal villages. The house had been half wrecked a month ago in one of the murderous fire fights between rival factions. Rioting and endless violence seemed to have been the rule – forever. As they sailed slowly back they were too morose to talk and he let his mind wander.

He remembered his father, years before, describing how, as a young man, he had once gone to the West Coast of Africa, when there were still fish to be caught, and helped in some of the fishing boats. He had described the nets coming in, so loaded with fish that it was impossible to get them all in the boat. The boat, which was quite sizable, with half a dozen men on board, would have sunk if they had done so. And they had had to call in other boats, to take some of the catch before they could, finally, get the nets aboard.

His grandfather had even wilder tales to tell. About how he had gone to Sicily and been involved in the great annual 'Matanza' when great shoals of enormous bluefin tuna, migrating around the coast, were driven into great nets along the shoreline and massacred. He had described how, after the nets had been closed, a hundred men had heaved and, gradually, forced a vast shoal of hundreds of massive tuna to the surface. Each fish was from two to two and a half metres long, weighing from seventy to a hundred kilos each. When they finally pulled the thrashing giants to the surface, half the men grabbed massive boat hook like tools, hacked the ends into the sides of the fish and hauled them out. Often it took two strong men to haul one fish out of the net. It took many hours to finally clear the great net. Then there was celebration and drinking. The Matanza had gone on every year for many years. Gradually the numbers and size of the fish had reduced. But nobody ever thought of allowing any of the fish to escape. They were too valuable.

Mohammed sighed. There was nothing anywhere in the Mediterranean now. The sea was almost barren – stripped from end to end. The fish driven to extinction.

Eventually they reached the little harbour and tied up the boat. He shared the few fish he had with Achmed, then walked along the dusty street and down an alley to the place he called home. His wife – Alisha – was there, huddled over a small fire, cooking. He gave her the small sling of fish and embraced her. She gave him a wan smile and motioned him to a corner of the room to pick up and cuddle his baby daughter.

Later that night, the shooting started again. It was the same every night. And, sometimes, when the shooting was close, he pulled Alisha to him – and felt her trembling with fright. He lay there, in the darkness, wondering what he could do and, finally, made up his mind. He would take her, and the child and sail North West. See if they could possibly get into Europe – and a better life. They said it couldn't be done – but he must try!

The next morning he talked to Alisha and explained what he was thinking. At first she was hesitant – but they both knew there was no future where they were. Life was becoming impossible. After a while she agreed. He went out and checked the conditions. The weather was hot but not unbearable. The sea, quiet with a light breeze. The skipper of a larger boat – with a radio – confirmed the weather should stay settled for a few days. They collected what little food and water they had and loaded it in his little fishing boat. Then he managed to get Alisha and the baby safely on the boat and settled in the front. He cast off and jumped aboard, sat in the stern and sailed, slowly, out of the harbour. For some reason his mind wandered and he reflected that, in other parts of the world, you had to wait for the tide to be right before you could sail. But not in the Med. There was no tide worth mentioning. You could sail anytime.

They cleared the harbour and he turned North West. With the wind in this direction he would have to tack a few times to reach his destination but there would be no real problem. The little boat sailed well and Spain was less than a hundred and sixty miles away. He checked that Alisha and the child were comfortable then settled himself for the long pull.

They sailed through the evening and through the night. During the night the wind lessened and changed slightly so he had to tack a little more often. Progress was not as good as he expected but, by the morning, he judged they had covered fifty miles.

It was a clear and pleasant morning but he was anxious now. He had heard that there was some sort of defensive system to stop immigrants getting into Europe. But his was only a little boat – with just three people – and one of them a baby. Perhaps they would send a boat, to challenge him – and try to send him back. But they wouldn't harm them – would they? A gentle fisherman – with his wife and baby. No! Of course they wouldn't! But would they let them in? That was the question.

A few hours later, he changed course again and scanned the sea. Nothing! Then, he caught a glint of something in the sky, low on the horizon. It resolved itself into a small, peculiar looking plane. A slab sided ugly body with a bulbous nose. There didn't seem to be a cockpit. Just bulges and bumps here and there and two pods at the end of stubby wings. As it came closer it made a thin hissing whining sound which Mohammed guessed was its propulsion system. It flew over the boat at about 100 metres height then came back and swept low, over the boat and began to circle. Mohammed was astounded when a loud booming voice issued from the machine, in a language he did not understand. Then it came back and repeated the performance in his own language. The machine said he was to turn around and sail back to Africa. To continue was death. If he proceeded another twenty kilometres towards Spain the boat would be attacked and destroyed.

"Turn back! Now!"

Mohammed had heard about these small flying machines. Drones they called them. He was told they were remote controlled. They had cameras and, many miles away, a man sat in a little cubicle, controlling it.

As the little plane circled he told Alisha to stand up and hold the baby out – so the man in the cubicle could see there was only a man and his wife and baby. She was scared now.

"Mohammed! – We must go back! We must go back!"

But Mohammed had made up his mind.

"Go back to that hell? Never! Better to risk death than go back to those conditions."

The little plane flew away and disappeared over the horizon – to the West. Mohammed set his sails and continued – North West. Alisha was quietly sobbing now.

"Courage my love! Courage! They won't harm us!"

For several hours they sailed. Nothing appeared. He became more confident. Then, suddenly, the little plane was back, low over the water. He told Alisha to stand again, with the baby. Almost before she did so he saw a streak of light – just over the water. Seconds later – the boat exploded.

# 2082 – AFRICA TAKES LAND BACK FROM THE CHINESE

Around the end of the 20th Century, China began seeking to secure its food imports from overseas. They negotiated with a number of African States and contracted to buy or lease large areas of Savannah and bush land, in Central and Southern Africa, to be converted into arable land – with the intention of growing food specifically for Chinese consumption.

They paid for the land in cash and in the development and construction of large infra-structure projects such as roads, railways and electrical installations in the involved African nations. It was also suspected, by some, that substantial sums of money had found its way into the Swiss bank accounts of a number of African leaders and Government officials. In addition to the payments, it was also believed the Chinese would employ many native Africans in the agricultural businesses that would be created i.e. field workers, truck drivers, factory managers, etc.

Deals were done and the Chinese moved into Africa. The Infrastructure was built, payments were made and land cleared. Crops were grown, processing factories set up, shipping facilities arranged and everything progressed nicely. China secured large, regular, supplies of food and everybody was happy. Well! Almost! A number of Africans complained, mostly lower echelons, that the Chinese were not employing native Africans as expected. Instead they shipped in thousands of Chinese field workers, Chinese Overseers, Chinese truck drivers, Chinese factory workers. The entire labour force was Chinese. A few cynics said "Perhaps the Chinese were looking ahead" and, maybe, they were. However, all went well for many years. The Chinese were efficient, courteous and diligent and did not upset anybody.

For a long time the situation remained stable. The Chinese prospered, Africa prospered and, because Africa prospered, the population exploded. In the 21st Century, Africa was one of the areas of the planet with the greatest population increase. By 2082, the population of Africa had reached 2.7 billion.

China had been around 1.3 billion back in 2014, when they abandoned the One Child Policy experiment. They, too, had

71

prospered – exceedingly well in fact. Their industrial output had soared in the early 21$^{st}$ Century and they had matched and overtaken the United States of America as the greatest industrial power on Earth. After abandoning their Population Control Experiment the population had again started to rise, although not as rapidly as expected, and was now 1.8 billion.

Unfortunately, the generation of sufficient power to achieve their industrial expansion had been, to a large extent, created by the burning of immense quantities of fossil fuel, mainly coal, and the discharge of correspondingly large amounts of $CO^2$ into the atmosphere which offset, to a great degree, the efforts of much of the developed world to reduce emissions. By 2080, Global Warming was beginning to noticeably affect the climate of most areas on the Earth. Droughts were far more frequent. Rainfall patterns were changing.

In 2081, the whole of Southern Africa suffered drought conditions. Food became very scarce, reaching famine conditions in some areas. Unfortunately, most of the rest of the world was also suffering that year and most of the available excess food, from those countries that had a surplus, was snapped up by China and India. China was still, of course, importing large quantities of food from its leased territories in Africa. In 2082, the African famine really took hold, as food stocks were diminished, and millions of Africans were starving, many in areas immediately adjacent to the Chinese controlled land.

Massive unrest and rioting broke out and thousands of half starved Africans swarmed into the Chinese leased territories and ransacked food stores. Agitators were filmed claiming the Chinese were stealing food from the mouths of African babies and children and demanding the Chinese be thrown out and ejected from Africa completely.

The key moment came when a large mob of Africans stormed a major food processing factory, near a shipping facility on the coast. A number of Chinese Police, considering it their duty to defend the installation, panicked and opened fire, killing a number of rioters. The next day, more rioters appeared, this time armed to the teeth. They over whelmed the police guards and burned the entire installation to the ground. Rioting then erupted everywhere.

The Chinese Government recognised the gravity of the situation, and realised the exploitation of African land could no longer continue.  Ships were organised and a mass evacuation of all Chinese personnel arranged.  Since the situation had deteriorated to such a point that a vicious confrontation occurred whenever groups of Chinese and Africans met, the Chinese, full of fear and resentment, decided to torch, destroy and disable everything they could not take away.  Farmsteads were burned, agricultural equipment wrecked, road transport torched, fuel installations, processing equipment, storage facilities – all destroyed.

The Africans had their land back – but it was of practically no use to them.  Within three years, the land that had been so carefully cultivated was back to Savannah, desert and scrub.  Fortunately, in Africa, the following year, the weather improved, rains came and the food crisis resolved.

In China – it was not so good.  China continued its trend to become hotter and drier.  Living conditions were becoming more and more difficult.  Food supplies were becoming less and less secure.

# 2086 – SINO/RUSSIAN WAR

It was the 3$^{rd}$ of October, 2085. The Supreme Council of China was in emergency session. China had just suffered the worst drought for 40 years. Crops were badly down and it was estimated more than a quarter of a million people had died from the effects of the last heat wave alone.

Global warming was badly affecting China, and, indeed, all South East Asia and India. Atmospheric $CO^2$ levels were now over 600 ppm. The seas were noticeably warming. Ocean currents changing. Atmospheric circulation patterns disrupted. The monsoon had failed. Many Chinese were, once more, on the brink of starvation.

---

Lee Sung paused, straightened up and wiped the sweat off his face. The heat was oppressive. His eyes swept over the terraced hills. Tier after tier of small paddy fields, seemingly glued to the hillsides. The rice was high, just developing the kernels. He knew this heat would ruin the crop. Rice had always been sensitive to heat. It still was, despite the efforts of the Genetic Engineers. A few degrees of excessive heat at the wrong time could halve the yield. All that back breaking work for nothing. Rice was still very labour intensive. It was almost impossible to use machines on the myriad terraced fields. So – most of the work was still done by hand. Planting and harvesting. It was one of the snags that one of the major food plants of the world was a water plant – basically a reed. (Wild rice still grows along the margins of some lakes in Canada).

Wearily Lee Sung shut off the trickle of the water supply to his little plot, noting that the trickle was less than it had been, and headed down into the valley for the evening meal. Reaching the valley floor, the heat was almost unbearable.

As he approached what was basically still a peasants hut (house was hardly a realistic description), a little girl came running, arms outstretched. He swept her off the ground and saw that her face was wet with tears.

Dada! Dada! Grand momma is dead!

---

The Government of China had decided to call in the Scientists, the Meteorologists, the Agronomists even the Sociologists – to try to get a grasp of what the future held in store.

What the experts reported was not good. The Scientists reported that, despite all the efforts, human $CO^2$ emissions were still rising, not falling. In addition, large quantities of $CO^2$ and methane were being released from the Arctic Tundra as the permafrost continued to melt. Sea and land temperatures were likely to continue rising for the next 100 years at least. Changes in the world's ocean currents and weather patterns would continue. The tendency for droughts in China would continue and probably intensify.

The Meteorologists confirmed – weather patterns, - all over the world were indeed changing. Ocean currents and air circulation cells were measurably shifting. Things were definitely likely to get worse – not better.

The Agronomists said they had done their best – but there were limits to what could be done even with the most modern Genetically Engineered crop seeds and cultivars – with the levels of heat and drought that was being experienced.

The Sociologists said that things were becoming dangerous. People were getting disgruntled, disaffected, rebellious and blamed the Government. "They were in charge – weren't they? Why didn't they do something?"

Heat made people bad tempered. Drought made them rebellious. Starvation made them dangerous.

So. Now the Supreme Council of China had called this meeting – to thrash out what, if anything, should be done.

---

Chairman Lee En Lai, called the meeting to order and spoke – summing up the situation.

"As you know, we are in great difficulty. Climate change is affecting China very badly and we can only expect things to get worse. China's population is now 1.8 Billion and the world total has just exceeded 12 Billion. With the droughts we have been experiencing, China can no longer feed its population. Other areas of the world are also stressed and the availability of food for import is reducing year by year.

Three years ago we lost our back-up food supplies – from the leases in Africa.

The question then, very simply, is – what, if anything, can we do about it?"

For a while, very little was said.

Someone suggested extending the pumped irrigation schemes using the Yangtze water but that had been pushed to the limit already. Another suggested cutting down what remained of the bamboo forests and replacing them with crops.

When this was shouted down, Yang Lou, the Defence Minister, said thoughtfully.

"I would point out there is a substantial area of land to the North that is relatively undeveloped and could undoubtedly, be used to produce more crops. I refer to that area of Siberia that used to be Chinese territory before it was so blatantly annexed by Russia in 1860 when China was at its weakest and being assailed by several foreign nations."

There was a deadly silence.

Lee En Lai, coughed and slowly said "You are not suggesting we invade Russia and try to take it back by force are you?"

There was an immediate hubbub.

After a while Chairman Lee called for order and things quietened down.

The Agriculture Minister Chin Tzu indicated he wished to speak and Lee signed for him to proceed.

Chin spoke slowly, quietly and carefully.

"Yang Lou has raised a very interesting question. Let us consider our situation very carefully.

Fundamentally, the way things are going, we are headed for disaster. If we face the facts we realise that, in another 50 to 100 years, South East Asia, China and India will be unliveable, what with the heat and drought. Putting it bluntly – if we stay where we are we die.

To the North, we have the vast area of Siberia. I do not mean the ex-Chinese area annexed by Russia. I mean the entire land mass from the Ural Mountains to the Pacific Ocean. This vast area, which is warming up and will soon become eminently suitable for human habitation, is sparsely populated and controlled by a nation with only 400 million total inhabitants.

What if we had the courage to challenge Russia head on. Demand the release of Siberia – from the Urals to the Pacific. We could claim that we were not demanding it for ourselves but for all the people of South East Asia, indeed – all the southern Nations from Indonesia to the Red Sea. We could claim, rightly, that the habitable areas of the world are changing. Humanity must move north.

If we tackle it carefully we could, perhaps, get the psychological support of the rest of the world. In effect we would have to state, quite bluntly, we were prepared to go to war with Russia over the issue. And, we would have mean it – 100%. Half hearted threats would not do. We would have to be prepared to commit ourselves to full scale war, including nuclear war, if necessary. If we gave the Russians a simple choice – Release Siberia or face total nuclear annihilation we might just get them to give up Siberia without actually having to fight a full scale war."

"This is ridiculous and very dangerous thinking" said the Minister of the Interior – Li Peng. "The Russians would fight. They have always defended their territory – and they would do so again – even if we only claimed the territory they annexed from us in 1860."

Chin Tzu spoke again "I would point out, Mr Chairman, that in 1962, when faced with all out nuclear war with the United States – in the stand-off over nuclear missiles on Cuba – the Russians did back down. Even the belligerent, bombastic Kruschev balked at the prospect of all-out nuclear war. Why? Because they were totally convinced the Americans were not bluffing. And that, Mr Chairman, is the key to Siberia. If we can convince them that we are deadly serious and are prepared to go to full scale nuclear war over Siberia – even if it results in the annihilation of both China and Russia, then we present them with a classic choice – lose everything or concede and keep a good part of what you have – and your lives. Given this – there is only one logical course of action. They must concede.

However, to convince the Russians we must first convince ourselves. We must be totally committed. The slightest hint of hesitation or indecision and we are lost.

We must make our minds up. Is Siberia worth the ultimate gamble or not?"

There was a babble of voices and then Lee En Lai stepped in.

"Gentlemen – Comrades (using the old term). I think Chin Tzu has probably put his finger on our Salvation. To follow his proposals, however, would be a momentous decision. I propose to adjourn this meeting for a week. We will re-convene at the same time next week. Think very, very carefully on Chin Tzu's proposals. Next week you will be asked to vote on a decision that will affect the future of China forever."

---

The following week they all sat, once more, at the long table. Twelve very quiet, very sober, very serious men.

Lee En Lai called the meeting to order.

He summed up the situation and the proposals in detail. Informed them that China's finest psychologists rated the chance of success at no better than 55/58%. Then he took the vote. The vote was 8 to 4 in favour.

The die was cast.

Yang Lou spoke. "In the last few days I have given these proposals considerable thought. To optimise our chances of success I propose that this discussion remains top secret. If we are to proceed I propose that we do so in six months time and, during that time, we secretly overhaul and bring all our long range missiles up to perfect working order. We also, secretly, refurbish, firstly, all our high yield fusion warheads and as many fission weapons as possible. When we are ready, we announce to the entire world our intentions and reasons and that we will invade Russia at an exact time and exact date only 10 days from the date of our announcement."

Chairman Lee En Lai interrupted. "But surely, such a move would throw away the element of surprise, so vital to success in modern war?"

Yang Lou raised his hand. "It will indeed. But I point out that we will not be trying to win a war. We will be trying to wrong foot the Russians, get the world on our side and pressure the Russians into conceding. When we go ahead and invade, it will cost us in men and equipment but it will make a powerful statement. I further propose that we use all the strength at our disposal, short of nuclear arms, to smash through the Russian defences and then we stop. Call a unilateral cease fire, then announce to the world we do not wish to fight a full scale war – which would undoubtedly escalate to the use of nuclear weapons but we are determined Siberia must be released for international colonisation. Therefore, we are pausing for ten days to give Russia and the world time to consider our proposals and then, if no action is taken and Russia does not concede, at an exact time on an exact date we recommence hostilities and, this time we are prepared to use all nuclear weapons at our disposal.

I would point out that if we are successful in keeping our nuclear weapon preparations secret for six months we may enhance our chances by not giving Russia time to make similar preparations. We might well catch them with only half or less of their missiles and bombs serviceable.

I propose that no overt preparations or mobilisation of conventional forces be made whatsoever, prior to our announcement. If we do, the Russians will find out. Secrecy on our missiles and nuclear weapons is just about possible. In any case we can, in ten days, mass far greater conventional forces on the northern border than Russia can. If we get this right, we could have Russia both at a moral and a military disadvantage and so enhance our chances of success.

When we make our initial announcement and when, after ten days, we go ahead and invade Russia, the world will call on us, as the initial aggressors, to stop and reconsider. When we are resolute and demonstrate our commitment, the world will have a rethink, realise we are right and will call on the Russians to concede."

Lee En Lai raised his hand. "Yang Lou has obviously thought this out very carefully and, what he says, makes sense. I propose we vote on adopting his proposals." The vote was taken – and passed with only one dissention.

---

It was the 26th of May, 2086. Mikhail Konstantin Tupolev, President of the Russian Federation sat on a long luxurious couch, cuddling his youngest daughter – Natalya – in his dacha a few miles outside Moscow, suffused by the warm glow that comes of having eaten a good meal and imbibed a couple of glasses of fine wine. A small glass of Benedictine was on a little table nearby. There was a broad smile on his face and little Natalya was in a tickly, giggly mood.

An Aide approached and, after a short pause, said "Mr President. You are wanted on the phone!"

"Not now! Vitaly. Not Now! Tell them I am indisposed!"

"I'm sorry Mr President but this is a triple A – Top Priority – call."

Mikhail frowned briefly "What the hell could justify a 'triple A' call. Everything was fine wasn't it?" But he felt so good the smile returned and he heaved himself off the couch, detaching his hand from the little girl's clutching fingers and made his way to a small room, off to one side.

He sat down at his desk and punched in his code, placed his hand on the scanner and waited for the screen to light up. Authorisation was confirmed and the screen duly lit up but remained blank.

He put an old fashioned pair of headphones in place, pushed a button and said "Tupolev!"

As he listened, the last vestige of a smile faded and his face hardened. There was a long pause then he said "When was this announced?" He pushed a button, on one side of his desk and, when Vitaly came in said grimly "Vitaly! Call an Emergency, Priority One, Council Meeting for tomorrow morning – 10 o'clock."

As he stepped out of the Secure Communications Room he reflected on the almost unbelievable information he had just received. The Chinese had openly stated – they would invade Russia.

They announced that, in 10 days time, their armies would cross the Chinese/Russian border and move north with the intention of occupying an area of Siberia.

This area had, originally, been Chinese territory anyway before it was annexed by the Russians in 1860. However, they announced that that was not the point. In their opinion it was madness for a group of just 400 million human beings (the population of Russia) to claim ownership of a vast area of northern territory which, because of the progress of global warming, was now becoming eminently habitable, while billions of other human beings were starving and dying in overheated southern areas.

The Chinese, therefore, demanded that Russia release and make available all northern land, from a line 200 miles east of the Ural Mountains to the Pacific Ocean. The Chinese were not demanding this area for themselves but for all the southern nations from Indonesia to the Arabian Sea.

It was time, in the interests of humanity in general, to scrap all antiquated ideas of sovereignty and national borders and redistribute the worlds landmasses as best for the overall benefit of the human race. To this end the Chinese would, on 5th June, 2086 take action to bring the redistribution about.

China hoped and believed the Russian Government would see the sense and necessity for redistribution, agree to it and co-operate to ensure the peaceful and organised migration of the people of the South into Northern Lands.

If this was done it might be possible to arrange some form of compensation, so the Russians, to the west, would see some benefit from the new arrangement.

Should the Russians refuse this undertaking then the Chinese would go ahead anyway and were prepared to take military action – all the way to full scale Nuclear War if necessary. Even in this scenario, the Chinese had nothing to lose. If they stayed passively south, in China, most of them would die anyway, sooner or later, from heat, starvation and disease, along with billions more in the other Southern Nations.

---

The eleven members of The Supreme Russian Council were spaced along the long Council table when Mikhail Tupolev strode in and took his place.

He wasted no time, called the meeting to order and spoke.

"You have all been made aware of the exact details of the Chinese communiqué that was issued to the World last night. Briefly – we are here to discuss exactly what our response should be." He signalled the Secretary of Defence.

"We fight of course. We have always fought anyone who invaded our territory." Several heads nodded and spoke in assent.

"Igor – what do you think?"

Igor Spassky, Minister of the Interior and by far the oldest man in the group, steepled his fingers on the table, pursed his lips for a moment. "We must think this out very, very carefully before we decide our response and choose a course of action. Let us bear in mind the Chinese have bluntly stated they are prepared to go all the way to full scale nuclear war. Also – that since the Soviet/ American Accord in 2028 our nuclear capabilities have been drastically reduced and, at the present time China has more large Intercontinental missiles than we do."

"But they can't be serious!" said the Minister of Defence. By announcing the exact time and date of the attack they are giving us time to prepare our response, draft in reinforcements and even go for a pre-emptive strike. No Nation, in history has ever announced a full scale attack, in advance, like that. Every officer, in every Army, from the Generals down to the Lance Corporals, knows that surprise is the key element in achieving Victory in battle."

"Surprising!" said Spassky. "But this manoeuvre is to try to get the World on their side. You must admit – they have got a point. Siberia is a vast area – with an extremely low population – ripe for development now that it is warming through Climate Change. And China, South East Asia, India and so on are gradually becoming impossibly hot places to live. The World is likely to be on their side, not ours."

"Surely! You are not suggesting we just give in to this blackmail – are you?" The Minister of Defence looked incredulous.

"No!" said Spassky. "But we must tread very carefully. I think a pre-emptive strike is out. Maybe they are bluffing. Let us state that we will defend. Let us put in plenty of reinforcements and weapons – for everyone to see. Maybe they will back off. And if they still attack – let us defend."

Finally, if they still come forward – if they overcome our defences – and they can if they wish, muster far greater forces there than we can – then" Spassky pondered for a moment – "We could even let off a battlefield nuclear weapon – not to kill – but as a warning that we are prepared to go nuclear. If they still come on – after that – then, Gentlemen – we really do have a problem."

At first there was a hubbub. Then rational discussions took place for the next two hours. Eventually, a vote was taken and a decision made.

Spassky's suggestion would be adopted.

———————————————

As the details of the Chinese Announcement spread all over the globe the World was stunned. On top of all the other existing problems and disasters, the Chinese were now threatening a massive Nuclear War which, if it went ahead, would kill hundreds of millions, devastate what was left of agriculture and wreck the world's economy.

The United Nations held an immediate emergency session and, almost unanimously, demanded that China cancel the proposed invasion and withdraw the threat of Nuclear War.

The Chinese response was blunt. They were going to go ahead, come what may, for the ultimate progress of the World and the benefit of the human race.

For two days there was no response from Russia. Then they issued a Communiqué.

Russia, they said, had always resisted invasion of its territory and would do so again – if necessary, with all means at its disposal.

In the next few days, thousands of Russian troops, with supporting tanks, guns and missiles arrived on the Russia/Chinese border. Bombers, fighter planes and drones were moved to airfields in the area.

The Chinese were undeterred. At 8am, on the 5th June, massed tanks supported by infantry smashed through the Russian border defences and advanced North. Attempts by the Russian Air Force, with planes and drones, to attack the Chinese ground troops and tanks were met by a devastating barrage of missiles.

---

Yuri Borodin and Boris Zhinsky were standing outside their bunker on the Russian/ Chinese border, sipping coffee. Yuri's head ached – from too much Vodka the night before. He winced and popped an aspirin into his mouth. This was a hopeless, boring place to be stationed, he thought. Stuck out in the middle of nowhere. Nothing ever happened.

Years ago, there used to be occasional 'flare ups', with the Chinese firing a few shots across the border and the Russians firing back. Some Chinese obviously still resented the fact that Russia had annexed some of their territory – back in 1860 – but there had been no trouble to speak of in years.

Yuri reflected – "It hardly seemed necessary to have troops out here. Then again – if he wasn't in the Army he might be slogging his guts out felling trees somewhere in Siberia."

When the news came through of the Chinese Announcement, Yuri and Boris were utterly stunned. They were told the Chinese weren't just demanding the return of the old annexed territories. They were demanding the whole of Siberia – from the Urals to the Pacific. After the shock wore off, Yuri and Boris raged.

"Who the hell do these Chinese think they are?" said Boris. "Don't they read the history books? Russia always fought – and had seen off every invader in history including Napoleon and Hitler.

Damnation! We'll see off the Chinese as well – if they try it on!"

Yuri and Boris knew the anti-tank gun in their bunker was old fashioned by modern standards. But it still fired a hyper velocity tungsten shot that could knock out any Chinese tank. "Let them come!"

---

"This doesn't make sense" said Yuri. "No invader ever states the exact time and place of an invasion. Surprise is the essence of military success. Surely they must know that Russia always defends its territory – to the last drop of blood if necessary."

Boris shook his head. "They are giving us time to prepare and bring in reinforcements. Crazy! It must be some sort of a bluff."

In the following week the entire planet was in turmoil. Every News Channel on every radio and TV was full of nothing else.

Two days after the Chinese Announcement the Russians stated – they would indeed, defend their territory, as they had always done, with all means at their disposal.

Demonstrations erupted in cities all over the world. Some condemned the Chinese. Some supported them. Governments prevailed upon the Chinese to withdraw their statement.

The Chinese were adamant. The southern peoples must migrate – or die. Something had to be done – sooner or later, and the Chinese had decided. They would go ahead.

---

In his command centre, 80 kilometres from the Russian/ Chinese border, General Nikolai Zhukov sat in a comfortable chair and pondered. He had been as stunned as anyone when news of the Chinese Pronouncement came through. Although, twelve months ago he had been promoted Supreme Commander – Russian Far East Forces, he had considered this a comfortable, if boring, appointment. Nothing ever happened in the far east.

Now, suddenly, the fate of Russia – and, maybe, China too, was in his hands. He had been instructed, directly – by the Minister of Defence – to defend Russian Territory with all forces at his command and, if he could not stop the Chinese advance with conventional forces, to detonate at least one battlefield nuclear weapon in front of the advancing Chinese troops – as a warning of what they could expect if they continued. This would be a manoeuvre akin to the old fashioned ploy – in naval warfare – of firing a warning shot across an enemy ship's bows.

In Zhukov's head, the warning bells had rung. He knew he was being set up as a scapegoat. If this nuclear ploy went wrong – and there was a full scale nuclear war and Russia was devastated, he, Nikolai Zhukov, would be forever remembered as the man who ruined the Motherland.

He thought, long and hard about how he could handle this.

Finally he decided to set up two – low yield – battlefield nuclear bombs on towers in cleared areas 20 kilometres from the border. This would be safer. He didn't trust the Russian missiles, nor their operators, nor even the working of the bombs. In this way he could be fairly sure at least one of the bombs would go off and exactly where it would explode.

The biggest danger was that the Chinese Commander would assume the bomb was actually dropped on his advancing troops, order retaliation and drop Chinese nuclear weapons directly on Zhukov's troops and military installations. If that happened, total nuclear war between China and Russia would be almost inevitable.

After thinking for some time he made a decision, called a trusted Aide – Leon Zherzinsky, explained the situation to him and gave his instructions. Zherzinsky would dress in the uniform of an army corporal, secretly cross the border before the deadline date and surrender to the Chinese as a renegade Russian with valuable information. He was to warn the Chinese about the two nuclear bombs, tell them exactly where they were and that one bomb would be detonated as a warning only. When Zherzinsky was sure the Chinese had got the message he would fiddle with his watch and a signal would be sent, telling Zhukov the Chinese had been informed. Just in case the watch should be confiscated there was a similar radio device in the heel of one of his boots.

Having made his plans, Zhukov went to his forward, massively reinforced and defended bunker, to await events.

---

In the following days, Yuri and Boris saw the Russian reinforcements pour in. Tanks, guns, missiles, troops, vehicles of all descriptions.

On the Chinese side – vast concentrations of troops and similar equipment were massed. There seemed little doubt from these preparations the Chinese were deadly serious but, as Zhukov reminded himself – it could still be a bluff.

About twenty kilometres from the border, on the Russian side, on the top of a barren hill, Engineers were erecting a tall slender, cable braced, tower about three hundred metres high and a similar one on top of another hill 5 kilometres away.

Yuri mentioned this to Boris who had already made friends with a number of the new arrivals. After two days Boris spoke to Yuri.

"Yuri. Those towers. There's a rumour going around that scares me out of my mind."

"What do you mean, Boris? What's so scary?"

"The rumour is that they are going to put a small tactical nuclear bomb, on top of each tower and, if the Chinese do break through and advance – they will detonate the bombs as a warning that we are prepared to use nuclear weapons if they advance further."

"My God! Boris. If that's true they could start a full scale nuclear war. And the Chinese are known to have more nuclear weapons and missiles than we do. Lets pray to God they don't start using those things"

In the next few hours Yuri thought about what he had heard and made a few enquiries of his own. The more he heard the more uneasy he became. Finally he spoke again to Boris.

"I've talked around and heard the same rumour – about the A bombs. Boris! I think we need to tip off the Chinese – that the bombs are just a warning – otherwise they may assume they are against their leading troops and push the button for full scale nuclear war."
Boris frowned and shook his head.

"For God's sake Yuri. Be very careful what you say. You will end up in front of a firing squad."

Yuri nodded. "Perhaps you're right. But I hope they know what they are doing. It's very scary."

---

At 8am, on 5<sup>th</sup> June, exactly as specified, Chinese guns and missiles opened fire. Massed tanks and supporting infantry – in camouflage and gas resistant battle gear, surged forward. Behind their defences the Russians held their fire for a short while as the Chinese came on.

In their bunker, Boris and Yuri crouched behind their anti-tank gun, their hearts pounding.

It all seemed unreal. It couldn't really be happening. But there was no mistaking the silhouettes of the first Chinese tanks as they came over the ridge on to the plain. The tanks were the latest models. They had a squat low turret, towards the front, with a long slender carbon fibre/graphene gun barrel projecting forward. This was a hyper high velocity gun, firing small diameter tungsten projectiles at immense speed. Behind the gun turret was a truncated pyramidal dome and further back, towards the rear of the vehicle, a large box-like structure with cellular markings on the top and sides – like a large honeycomb.

The semi-pyramid was, in fact, a very powerful, miniature, phased array radar and the box structure housed scores of small-ultra fast response-defence missiles.

---

Nikolai Zhukov cursed as a surge of vomit came into his throat. He swallowed, took a gulp of coffee and popped an antacid tablet in his mouth. "Maybe he was getting too old for this kind of thing."

He was in his command bunker, forty kilometres from the front, watching his screens. Surveillance drones, circling over the battle area, transmitted real time pictures and information constantly.

As he saw the massed Chinese tanks and infantry surging forward and saw the rain of missiles and artillery shells pulverising his forward positions he knew the Chinese were deadly serious.

"Doesn't look as if they are bluffing, does it Boris?" he said to his Adjutant.

"No Sir. It certainly does not."

Reluctantly he gave the order for the Russian defences to open fire. Instantly a swarm of Russian missiles rose from the surrounding woods. More missiles came from mobile launchers. Armed drones appeared from the hills. His artillery – antiquated weapons by modern standards – opened up and sent a rain of shells upon the attackers.

Scores of Chinese drones immediately appeared – to counter the Russians. Hundreds of missiles rose from the Chinese hills. The oncoming Chinese tanks, spread out across the plain at hundred metre intervals, disappeared under a gigantic umbrella of explosions and flame.

As the first missiles and shells descended on the tanks, their defence systems kicked in. Their radar scanned a complete dome of sky – from ground to ground – all around the tank. Missiles and incoming shells were located and tracked – at ultra high speed. Only missiles and shells that would actually impact the tank, if not stopped, were targeted. Defence missiles were programmed and released – in a minute fraction of a second. They blazed from their containers at immense accelerations and homed in on incoming missiles and shells, exploding them while they were still 20/100 metres away. To the onlooker, the Chinese tanks disappeared in a gigantic cocoon of exploding shells and missiles. And then they came through. 90% of them were unharmed. They appeared, racing forward, from the great pall of smoke and long thin spears of flame stabbed from their slender guns. A number of Russian tanks exploded and then the remaining ones too began to fire their long guns and missiles.

In the bunker Yuri and Boris saw the tanks come out of the smoke.

"Looks like this is it Yuri." And then their training kicked in. "Target. Eleven-o-clock. 2,000 metres" said Boris.

Yuri pressed a small joy stick and the gun swung left. He pressed a button and the sighting system located and locked on to the target. A laser flashed momentarily and the range registered. The gun fired and the Chinese tank exploded. The ultra high velocity shot from the anti tank gun was simply too fast for even the most modern defence system to handle.

"Target. Two-o-clock. 2,000 metres." The gun swung right. The laser flicked. The Chinese tank burst into flame, rockets spraying out in all directions as its defence missiles were detonated.

Three seconds later – the bunker exploded.

---

Back in his command centre, General Zhukov watched his screens; the pictures relayed from the reconnaissance drones cruising overhead. For some reason the Chinese had not blown them from the sky. He watched the advancing tanks – saw the masses of reserves, pouring in from behind. There was no stopping them now, he realised. His forces were hopelessly outnumbered.

He hesitated – but knew what he had to do. With his heart sinking he finally made his decision – punched in the code, placed his left hand on the monitor and pressed one of the two red buttons to detonate one of the nuclear bombs.

In the leading tank a Chinese commander saw a blink of blinding light. And then his anti laser goggles went black. The goggles normally had clear lenses but they were designed to protect against laser weapons (used to blind enemy personnel) or even the flash of a nuclear detonation. A detector monitored light levels and, if the light exceeded a certain level, it triggered the lenses which instantly (in less than a hundred thousandth of a second) turned black. As soon as the light levels were down again the lenses returned to normal.

The lenses cleared and he stared at a massive rising nuclear fireball, a few kilometres in front of him. The fireball began to cool as it rose and developed into a great, mushroom topped roiling column. Scarcely had he taken in the incredible scene when the goggles again went black. After, a short while they cleared once more. Where there had been one nuclear column there were now two side by side.

His communicator bleeped. He looked at the message screen.

STOP! EXACTLY WHERE YOU ARE!
PROCEED NO FURTHER.
AWAIT FURTHER ORDERS.
X5734

A few kilometres away General Zhukov stood outside his bunker looking at the two nuclear columns. He knew he had only detonated one. Both columns were made by similar battlefield nuclear weapons of about the same yield.

The Chinese had replied to his warning shot. They must have planned their own demonstration and had the missile all ready to fire – and targeted exactly on his detonation site.

The message was very clear. The Chinese were prepared to match the Russians in any nuclear exchange.

Thoughtfully he walked back and entered his bunker. He looked at his screens and knew the Chinese had hacked into his supposedly secure system. On his screen was a little figure waving a white flag. Below was a message.

WE ARE STOPPING!  WE WILL ADVANCE NO FURTHER.
WE MUST TALK.
ZAO.

He knew ZAO was the Chinese Supreme Army Commander.

He pushed the button to call an Aide. As the man came in he spoke briefly.

"Daneel – Signal all Russian Forces. CEASE FIRE IMMEDIATELY. TAKE NO ACTION WHATSOEVER UNTIL FURTHER ORDERS."

––––––––––––––

Almost every TV  on the planet carried pictures of the fighting and the nuclear detonations. The entire World was stunned.

––––––––––––––

After 24 hours the Chinese issued another Communiqué. This stated they would not be stopped and, in 10 days, would resume their advance North using whatever force was necessary. All their primary nuclear weapons were loaded, fuelled and targeted. If necessary they would obliterate every major Russian city. They accepted that the Russians could and probably would, wipe out Chinese cities in retaliation but, nevertheless, they would still go ahead as they believed the action they were taking was necessary for the overall benefit of humanity.

It was necessary for the Russians to recognise the rightness of the Chinese actions, agree to the original Chinese Proposals and prevent a full scale Nuclear War.

Everywhere on Earth there was chaos.

In every major city there were mass demonstrations. People were filmed – screaming for Peace. But more and more people were siding with the Chinese. After 5 days it became obvious that the bulk of the world's population believed the Chinese were right.

The sheer honesty of the Chinese position was impressive. By clearly and bluntly stating what they intended to do and quoting the exact time for renewal of operations, they were laying themselves wide open to massive pre-emptive strikes, both on the battlefield, and on their cities and missile installations. However, their judgement and nerve paid off. As the days went by it became more and more obvious the world backed the Chinese and, if Russia attacked China in a pre-emptive strike, then Russia would be a pariah State – forever condemned.

_____

Mikhail Tupolev took his place at the end of the table and looked at the other members of Russia's Supreme Council. He was no longer the ebullient jovial extrovert he had been. Now his face was drawn and gaunt from worry and lack of sleep.

"Well! Gentlemen. It looks as though the Chinese were not bluffing. As you know, they countered our warning nuclear explosion with one of their own, sending us a clear message. Then they stopped their troops and issued another Communiqué stating they would recommence full scale warfare in ten days time and, if we tried to stop them with nuclear weapons they would respond by going to full scale nuclear war and devastate every city in Russia with a population of 50,000 or more. I do not think they are bluffing. What do we do now?"

The Minister of Defence spoke first.

"Mr President! We do still have the capability to wipe out every major city in China. We still have enough megaton weapons – and the means to deliver – to do it."

Tupolev raised his hand. "I have decided to bring in General Rokossovsky to update us on the current state of our nuclear forces."

He pressed a button.

"Send General Rokossovsky in please."

The massive door at the end of the room opened and Rokossovsky walked in. He was a very stocky, bullet headed man, with quite a reputation for bullying.

"He doesn't look in a bullying mood now" thought Tupolev. He was, in fact, white and sweating. "Can you tell us, General Rokossovsky, exactly what the state of our nuclear forces is at the present time? Can we match the Chinese in intercontinental weapons?

Do we have a credible deterrent force, sufficient to deter even the Chinese, despite their avowed determination, from going all the way to full scale nuclear war?"

"Mr President and members of the Committee" said Rokossovsky. "You must remember the initial Statement of Intent, by the Chinese, took us, and the World, by surprise. No one ever dreamed of such a move.

Prior to their announcement, although the world was in a difficult Economic and Political situation, there seemed no possibility of a major nuclear war. No one – apart from the Chinese – that is – contemplated such a thing. The maintenance of nuclear weapons and the large rockets to deliver them is a very expensive and technical operation."

"Are you telling us" said Tupolev "That our nuclear forces are not fully functional?"

Rokossovsky shuffled uncomfortably. "It takes time, Mr President, to get missiles in tip top working condition. Rocket motors, high speed fuel pumps, precision guidance equipment must all be checked and, where necessary, replaced."

"Is it also true" said Spassky, "that the actual nuclear bombs – the plutonium cores and the fusion weapon fuel assemblies also need prolonged and elaborate refurbishment to get them in proper working order."

"That is true" said Rokossovsky, sweating even more. "The Polonium 210 – used in the initiators of the plutonium bombs – used in both fission and fusion bombs – has a half life of only 147 days – which means – for maximum efficiency the bombs need refurbishing every 6 months or so and the Tritium – used to boost the yield of the H Bombs also deteriorates and needs to be purified at intervals. It would appear the Chinese may have instigated a secret refurbishment program – both for the rockets and also the nuclear weapons, six months ago. Hints of this were picked up by our Security Services but, since there was no evidence the Chinese were bringing their conventional forces up to readiness, the reports were dismissed."

"I thought <u>we</u> were supposed to be the world's chess players" said Tupolev angrily.

"What you are really telling us" said Spassky "Is that if we have a full scale nuclear war we shall be lucky if one in ten of our rockets and hydrogen bombs actually work properly."

Rokossovsky was silent.

"Thank you! General Rokossovsky" said Tupolev. "That will be all."

Rokossovsky walked slowly out of the door, knowing that his career was ended. He also knew that, a few years ago he could have faced a firing squad.

When Rokossovsky had gone, Spassky spoke. "Well! Gentlemen, there you have it. It would seem the Chinese are not bluffing – or why would they go to all this trouble to secretly get all their missiles and fusion bombs in tip top working condition? So – if we go for full scale nuclear war they will be able to deliver at least ten times as many, fully functional megaton weapons on our cities as we will be able to do on theirs. We may still be able to flatten most Chinese cities – nuclear weapons being what they are – but there certainly wouldn't be much left of Russia. China would be devastated, certainly, but, after the Nuclear Holocaust – which might incidentally finally wreck the World's weather and contaminate half the globe – there will still be far more Chinese survivors than Russian. And the people in South East Asia, India and so on will still want to move North. Satellite Intelligence shows the Chinese are now openly fuelling and arming their largest Intercontinental Missiles for immediate launch. If we go for a pre-emptive strike they will still get enough weapons launched to more than finish us.

Gentlemen, much as I hate to say this, it looks to me that the only sane thing to do now is to agree to their demands. They have a powerful argument. The World is behind them. If we choose to fight , no matter how much we devastate China – we cannot win. Russia will be utterly devastated. We shall lose Siberia anyway. People from the rest of the southern countries will move in. We shall have no forces left to resist them. If we concede, we shall lose face, but at least we shall still be alive and have a Mother Russia. The way I see it – whatever we do we lose. Let us take the lesser of two evils!"

There were angry faces. Vicious muttering. One even shouted "Treason!" But there were a number of grave, silent faces, and after all, they were all intelligent men. After an hour's further discussion Mikhail Tupolev put it to the vote. The vote was 7:5 in favour of conceding to the Chinese and stopping the war.

Mikhail Tupolev went back to his dacha, picked up his little girl and held her to him. At least – now she would have a future. However hard he tried – he could not stop the tears running down his face.

One day before the deadline Russia capitulated. They issued a statement saying that in order to prevent further bloodshed, and in the general interests of Humanity and recognition of the desperate state of the Southern Asian nations, they had decided to accept the Chinese proposals and would co-operate with an International Committee to be set up to organise the transfer of immigrants into the Northern Lands.

The Crisis was over.

———————————

Sergei Ulanov sat at the little table in his log cabin and took another sip of vodka.

"What the hell!"

This had been their land! Their Siberia! He had lived here all his life. He loved the forest; the smell of the pines; the sparkle of the river; the freedom of the wilderness. And now! The place was swarming with Chinese. They were massacring the trees, building log cabins everywhere; ripping the roots from the ground; ploughing the tundra; even building fences.

He hated it! He hated it!

"How could the Government have allowed it? How could they have caved in?"

The Russians had always defended their territory – if necessary to the last drop of blood.

He took another, longer, swig of vodka.

"Curse the Chinese!"

They said there would be more Chinese. More and more! Some said they were taking over the whole of Siberia – from the Urals to the Pacific. They talked about compensation. What compensation? What could compensate for the loss of his lifestyle, his freedom to wander wherever he wanted; to live as he wished.

A lot of his friends from the village had gone. Moved west – to the big cities near the Urals. But he didn't fancy living in a city – even with his compatriots.

He took another swig. "Damn the Chinese!"

He picked up his rifle, walked unsteadily to the door. Maybe there would still be a few ducks on the river.

Just walking past, on the dirt track that led to the village, a small, wiry Chinaman walked by, looked at him and smiled. A big cheery smile.

Sergei looked at him. Rage surged through his body. The gun kicked in his hands. The Chinaman folded and fell.

Blearily Sergei looked at the fallen body, the rage subsiding and being replaced by a twinge of fear. He turned, went back into the hut, dropped the rifle on the table and collapsed into the cot bed near the wall.

A while later – there was a savage banging on the door. Sergei heaved himself off the bed, staggered to the door and opened it. He was instantly grabbed by a burly Chinaman.

"You! Come with us!"

Through a misty Vodka haze Sergei looked up.

A few feet away, five more Chinamen stood there – armed to the teeth. And they were not smiling.

# 2128 – DISCOVERY OF HIVa

Jake Simpson stepped off the plane at Montreal and wearily trundled his hand luggage along the corridor. Finally he arrived at the baggage collection carousel and joined a waiting throng. As he waited he reflected that, in 2128, air travel had not really changed much in 100 years.

The planes still had a cylindrical fuselage and conventional wings and tail. The wings were maybe longer and more slender than they used to be (ultra high efficiency wings they called them) with two large underslung Turbo Fan engines. And, in actual fact, they travelled more slowly than 100 years ago. Cruising speed was more like 500 mph than the old 550/ 600. More economical on fuel they said.

Suddenly he spotted his travelling case coming towards him, snapped out of his reverie, grabbed his case and headed for a transporter to take him home. Nice to be back ……………

Three days later, at 7.30 in the morning, he awoke, as usual, sat up in bed and cursed. His head ached slightly and he had a runny nose. "Blast!" One of the hazards of air travel was still catching a lousy cold. There were always a few people on board coughing and sneezing. The problem had never been cracked. "Oh! Well! It would only be a nuisance for a few days" ………………

Three weeks later he sat at his desk in the Lab, looking at the diagnostic equipment/computer and the rows of samples that he had to check out. Part of his job was routine diagnosis of biopsy samples for the Health Service and part was Research. He far preferred the Research.

A computer beeped. He pushed a button and the face of his old friend, Mike Cerdan, came on the screen.

"Hello Jake! I take it you had a good trip to Rome to the World Medical Conference. Did you take time off to spend a few hours touring or lying on a beach? I just thought I would contact you to warn that they have just announced an outbreak of Chicungunya fever in that area. Perhaps a good idea to check yourself out and see if you need a jab. Be in touch!"

The picture faded.

Jake paused, remembering the trip. Maybe he ought to check – but it had been three weeks! Surely, if he had caught fever, he would have symptoms by now – but he felt fine. He went and got himself a cup of coffee, slowly sipped at it and began to sort the samples before him. After a while he paused. "What the Hell! It would only take a few minutes." So he went along to the Self Diagnosis machine, in a corner of the room, punched in a code, inserted a finger and pushed a button. A red light came on, there was a slight prick on the finger. After a couple of seconds the light turned to amber. A few seconds more – then to green. He withdrew the finger, which now had a small flesh coloured patch of plastic near the tip. This, he knew, was a small sterile patch covering the perforation where the blood sample had been taken. He looked at his watch. Back in a couple of hours to check results. He strolled back to his desk and got on with his work.

Three hours later he stretched, then glanced at his watch. "Time flies!" He strolled over to the Self Diagnosis machine and punched in his code. He pressed a button and watched as the display came on the screen. On one indication a small light flashed. Alongside it was a code letter. "Hmm! Maybe it was a good thing he checked. Looks as if he might have this Chicungunya thing." He punched the code letter in and pushed a button. A display came up. He stared. His eyes widened. "No Way! That just was not possible. It simply was not!" For the letters flashing on screen spelled out H.I.V. – Human Immunodeficiency Virus. He stared – and then he snorted. "That was quite impossible. Quite impossible! The damn machine must be up the creek. Must be!" There was no other explanation. He went and got himself another coffee. And a biscuit. Munched and sipped his coffee and began to calm down.

After a while he decided he had better re-check. So he walked over to the Self Diagnosis machine and prepared to punch in his code again. "No! If the machine was up the creek – why use it again?" They had another Self Diagnosis machine in Lab 3. So he took the transit corridor to Lab 3, walked in, went to the machine and went through the routine. Punch in the code, put in a finger and so on. Then he retraced back to his own Lab and sat at his desk, thoughtfully.

He worked on his samples but it was difficult to concentrate. There was a nasty little twinge in his stomach – which he realised was the first edge of fear. "Damn the machine! Damn the machine! But it simply must be faulty!"

The two hours seemed to take forever. Then, over to Lab 3 and their machine. When he got there and punched in the code the machine flashed a message. 'Processing Incomplete!'. It took another ten minutes before it came up green and he finally punched the display button. The screen cleared and the display began to appear.

An icy fist gripped his stomach and fear surged through him. The little red flashing light was there and the code letter beside it. He knew what the code letter meant but punched it in anyway. The display came up. HIV – Human Immunodeficiency Virus.

"My God! How can that be possible?"

Jake wandered back to his lab and sat there for a long time – stunned. Eventually he took a deep breath, walked over to a computer and dialled up his friend Mike. After a few seconds, Mike's cheery face came up.

"Hello! Didn't expect to hear from you so soon. Everything OK?"

"Mike – you know you suggested I check myself out for Chicungunya! Well! I did! And the damnedest thing. The machine says I have HIV!"

There was a long pause. Mike's face slowly changed. He almost laughed then became serious. At the other end he could see Jake's face on his screen. And Jake was not laughing.

"Come on! That doesn't make sense! No Way! The Machine is whacky! That can't be right – can it?"

"Mike – I double checked. I went over to No 3 Lab and used their machine. The result is the same."

"That's weird!" Mike laughed nervously. He paused. "You can't have been 'playing around' can you? At your age!"

"Mike – You know me! I'm a middle aged happily married man with two kids. I haven't 'played around' as you put it, since I was a student. And I haven't fooled around with drugs or anything. I am just completely baffled – And scared!"

Mike was quiet for a moment.

"Why don't you just sit on this – over the weekend. Don't mention it to anyone else. Delete the data on the machines and we'll get our heads together on Monday. OK!"

Jake thought about it for a moment.

"OK! I think that's sensible! I'll contact you again on Monday."

Over the weekend Jake's wife and children noticed he was quiet. A bit withdrawn. Introvert. Obviously a lot of pressure at work. It had happened before. Leave him alone.

On Monday Jake was back at work. He cleared his desk, energised the computers. Instantly a light flashed. A message from Mike. Jake pushed a button.

"Contact me – NOW!"

Jake punched the buttons. Mike's face came up and Jake felt a wave of anxiety. Mike's face, normally sunny and jovial, was now serious and drawn.

"You're not going to believe this!"

"What?"

"After you contacted me I thought about it and, this morning, came into the lab early. I can't tell you why. Just on a whim – I went and checked myself on the Self Diagnosis machines. I punched myself into three different machines – all within 10 minutes. I checked them out two hours later. Jake! They say I have HIV!"

There was a long silence.

"Jake! How the hell is this possible! What do we do now?"

Jake slowly ran his hand through his hair. There was a long pause.

"Mike! I think we should set up a secure line to Professor Turnbull in London, Europe. He is the World Authority on Virus Diseases. Lets report to him. See what he makes of it."

Ten hours later, they set up a joint secure line to Professor Turnbull – much faster than they expected. The Secure Communication line light flashed. Professor Turnbull's face came on screen. He was a little wizened man with a shock of grey, unruly hair, but there was a sharpness in his eyes which hinted at a massive intellect.

"Good Morning Gentlemen! You wish to talk to me?"

"Professor Turnbull! What we have to say may sound strange – even bizarre, but we assure you – it is the truth."

"We would like to have your comments and perhaps suggestions. We are completely baffled. Perhaps you can help us."

Jake recounted his story – simply and without embellishments. Mike did the same.

"Gentlemen! I am afraid I have to tell you. I already know! Two weeks ago people over here reported the same thing to me. We have investigated and taken samples of the HIV virus and analysed them at the genetic level. What we have here is something some of us have feared for years. It is a mutant variant – a hybrid you could say. A cross between HIV1 and the common cold."

Jake sat silently, staring at Mike and the Professor on their screens. Quietly he said "Dear God!"

"Gentlemen! This must be kept Top Secret! We have done some quiet checking. We have checked human blood samples from all over the World. We estimate that more than ten per cent of the human race is already infected. We calculate that, within months, the figure will be 50% and within 12 months, 90 plus percent of the entire human race will have HIV. We simply do not know how to react to this. Even now we are struggling to assess what the consequences are likely to be. But it is bound to be devastating. Whilst we get an idea as to how dangerous this is, and what, if anything, we can do about it, we must stop this information becoming public. I don't need to spell out, to men of your intelligence, the ramifications. We have some ongoing Research, at the present time, with regard to the virulence, transmissibility and action of the new HIV which, incidentally, we have named Alpha HIV and which we denote as HIVa. I will contact you in three to four days time to keep you informed. Out!"

The Professor's face blinked then disappeared.

Four days later, Jake sat at his desk and watched the computers light up. First – Mike came on, then the Professor. Professor Turnbull did not beat about the bush.

"Gentlemen! I am afraid I have some very bad news. HIVa is worse than we feared. It is as catching as the common cold. Very easily transmissible. It is both Infectious and Contagious. The virus can survive, outside the human body for days, at least. Its rate of propagation inside the body i.e. the rate at which it reproduces itself – is at least as great as the old HIV1 which, as I have no doubt you know, was of the order $10^9$ to $10^{10}$ virions per day. Whilst only time will tell, genetic analysis indicates the virus will act to destroy the immune system as fast as, or, maybe, considerably faster, than the old HIV1. HIV1 was, of course, the most virulent of the two previous HIV variants known. Persons with HIVa will become infectious themselves within a week of their catching the infection, though they will show no symptoms other than the initial minor flu like symptoms of the first 3 to 4 days. After that the person is walking around, apparently normal but infectious for the next 6 months, at least, without symptoms.

The old HIV1 was relatively, slow acting, despite its reproduction rate, and it was common for there to be a seven to ten year time lag between initial infection and the onset of serious malaise and death. Genetic analysis indicates that HIVa is likely to be considerably faster acting, perhaps bringing malaise and death within as little as one to two years. I think, maybe, I shouldn't repeat this, but some of our staff have suggested that, having analysed the genetic variations of HIVa compared to HIV1, they are of the opinion HIVa may have been deliberately created by a psychotic Rogue Scientist with Genetic Engineering expertise or, possibly, a scientific Religious Maniac who thought he was fulfilling the will of God. I, personally, think HIVa has been produced totally accidentally. After all – it was always on the cards. It was always known that HIV1 was extremely prone to mutation and genetic variation. This was recorded way back in the 20$^{th}$ Century. At that time millions of people were carrying HIV1 for years – and regularly catching colds and flu. It could be argued that it is a miracle HIVa did not occur years ago.

Anyway! Gentlemen! It has occurred now. We must do our best to think what we can do, what the implications are and how best we can prepare for the future. The first thing to consider is how the public will react and how we can present things to minimise panic. I fear we don't have much time. Somebody, besides ourselves, is going to discover the truth and let the information out to the media. When that happens – God Help us All! Any suggestions – for Research – for Action to be taken – anything that may be useful in any way – will be greatly appreciated. Please keep in touch. OUT!" and the Professor's picture faded.

Jake and Mike looked at each other – totally stunned – unable to take in the immensity of what they had been told.

"What do you make of that?" said Jake eventually.
A pause.

"Apocalypse!" whispered Mike. "Apocalypse!"

For two days, Jake walked around in a daze. His mind seemed to refuse to accept the situation. He went through his normal work routines like an automaton.
"This simply could not be true – could it?"

However, when he woke up in the morning the nightmare was still there.  He did not mention it to anybody.  He looked at Beth and the kids, fooling around.

"How the hell could he tell them?  Good God!"

On the third day after the talk with Professor Turnbull the computer beeped.  It was Mike.  There was a message.

"Jake!  Meet me – this afternoon.  Come round to my place. We must talk!  Mike!"

When he arrived Mike ushered him into a small lounge.  There were no computers, no TVs, no phones, nothing electronic, Jake noted.

"We can talk in here.  The kids are at College.  Jenny is out." He paused.  "Let's have a coffee."

They sipped in silence for a moment then Mike said

"I have been thinking about this situation for the last two days.  It's hard to get your head around it but we must face it.  If Turnbull is right – and I'm sure he must be – then there is going to be an unprecedented world-wide disaster.  The more I think about it – the worse it looks.  If HIVa will produce AIDS within one to two years of infection, there simply won't be enough time to produce the anti-HIVa drugs in sufficient quantities needed to stop people getting sick.  All I can conclude is that there is likely to be total collapse of Civilisation. Total!  When everybody gets sick the entire infrastructure will collapse.  No transport.  No Water.  No Electricity.  No Sewage Treatment.  No Food.  With the World Population at Fifteen Billion, everything is stretched to the limit anyway.  It's bound to go."

Jake looked up wearily.

"Well!  What can we do?  If Turnbull is right – there is nothing we can do.  Nothing!  It's too late!"

"For God's sake!" snapped Mike.  "We can do something. We can try to survive."

"How can we?  We have HIVa.  I know Beth and the kids will have it – they will have caught it from me.  So how can we survive?  I haven't said a word.  If I ask them to take a test they will know something is up and Beth will find out."

Mike lowered his cup.

"Well!  I think we should try to survive.  Remember – in the history of the World – there has never been a 100% lethal contagion. Never!  There is always a percentage survive.  At least – let's improve our chances.  We need to get away from civilisation if we can.  The

Cities will become death traps. You still have that float plane of yours don't you? We need to get out to somewhere isolated – there are still a few remote areas left. Most people live in cities. We need to create some sort of hidden habitation – a sort of redoubt. Hidden in the forest. By a lake or river – with fish, fresh water, timber for burning, animals for trapping. Maybe we can improve our chances. You and I are in a special position – in the medical services. Maybe – before word gets out – we can get supplies of anti HIV drugs. Maybe – enough to last us ten years or more. We could stockpile food, equipment, weapons, ammo. We could collect information – in the form of old fashioned books. How to create fire with just sticks and stones, survival information. I'm not willing to just give up and die. Are you!?"

Jake looked at his friend.

"You're right! You're damned right! Let's give it a try!"

"We shall have to move! We may not have much time!"

Around the World – in quite a number of places – other people were having very similar thoughts.

––––––––––––––––––

Jake and Mike met again, two days later, to discuss tactics but, in the intervening two days, Jake had been having misgivings and brought it up straight away.

"Mike. Do you think we are right – to keep it secret? Is this HIVa really unstoppable? Shouldn't we blow the whistle? Let people know. Galvanise the Authorities. Perhaps they can do something. Stop it in its tracks – somehow."

"I don't think so. Jake!" said Mike thoughtfully.

"Remember Turnbull! By its very nature, this new HIVa, in modern times, is unstoppable. Wherever it started – just a few plane loads of people, travelling all over the world – like yourself – and it was unstoppable.

I read about the Black Death – in the Middle Ages. It is believed to have started in China and, initially, spread relatively slowly. In modern times we would have rapidly traced the vector and soon stopped the disease in its tracks. In those days, they knew nothing about bacteria and vectors – that is – carriers. Initially the plague bacillus had limited infectivity. Its natural host was the black rat, which it did not affect too seriously, which meant an infected rat could live and run around for quite a long time before it died. The plague bacillus could not pass easily from rat to man. However, the black rat had fleas – as most animals do – and the rat flea picked up the plague bacillus when it had a blood meal. Many fleas are fussy and will only feed off their normal host, but some are not so selective – especially if their host is dead and they are hungry. The black rat flea would then bite humans and that is how the plague bacillus was transmitted. Infected black rats commonly got into ships and were carried all over the world, taking the plague with them.

Gradually the plague spread, infecting thousands of people. And then – and this is where the similarity to the new HIVa comes in – in some human being the plague bacillus mutated. It picked up genes – maybe from the common cold – like the new HIVa – and suddenly became easily transmissible. It became able to survive outside its host, for long periods of time. It could contaminate surfaces. It could be spread by simple coughs and sneezes – like the common cold.

They called the new variant – Pneumonic Plague – meaning – from the lungs. At that point – the Black Death became totally unstoppable and rapidly ravaged the entire world population.

You can rest assured Jake – the new HIVa was totally unstoppable after the first few plane loads were infected. It is much more insidious than the Black Death. Plague victims became ill in a few days. With HIV you may not show any symptoms for six months or more and yet you are infecting everybody around you."

"OK!" said Jake, with a sigh. "I take your point!"

So – they made their plans. Chose their plot, deep in the Canadian wilderness, by a small lake (but big enough for the float plane to land and take off) connected to one of the myriad small rivers. The river and the lake still had plenty of fish and there were quite a number of small animals in the forest.

As Mike had predicted – they didn't have long to wait before the news came out. Only two days, in fact, before it hit the headlines – which was not so surprising really. After all – there were lots of self diagnosis machines – all over the world. What was surprising was – there were no great screaming headlines. No shattering announcements on TV. It was all very low key.

On one of the newspapers front pages (there were still one or two newspapers – to cater for those few people who preferred to read paper rather than scroll computers) there was an article – not even the main article. The headline was – NEW VARIANT HIV DISCOVERED. NO CAUSE FOR ALARM – SAYS MINISTER. The article went on to say the new variant of HIV (Human Immunodeficiency Virus) was believed to be a hybrid between HIV and the common cold. However drugs existed which could easily control HIV and anyone who caught it would simply take a couple of tablets once a week and they would be symptom free and non infectious. The article went on in a similar vein and, basically, gave the impression HIVa was simply not worth worrying about.

At their next meeting Jake handed Mike a copy and said –

"What do you think of that? And the TV is just as low key."

"It's the Government" said Mike. "They are afraid of panic if the truth comes out. They have leaned on the Media People and forced them to keep it low key. Quite right too!"

After a moment, Jake muttered.

"It's a good thing for us. Gives us a chance to get organised and set up. Think of what will happen when everybody gets the same ideas!"

"Did you tell Beth?" said Mike.

"Yes! I had to. She knew something was wrong – from the way I was behaving."

"How did she take it?"

"She didn't believe me. She was convinced I must have something wrong. So I showed her Turnbull's message. I recorded it. I know I shouldn't but I did."

Mike smiled a wan smile.

"So did I. Did she believe you then?"

"Yes."

"So did Jenny."

---

Two days later Jake and Mike were called to a conference – along with a dozen or so other employees of the company.

Denise Lafayette, the CEO of Montreal Pharmaceuticals Corp stepped forward. 'Denny' Lafayette was a 'tough cookie' – a no nonsense, down to Earth, administrator. She ruled Montreal Pharmaceuticals with an iron hand but, if circumstances justified it, could show remarkable consideration and compassion.

Now her face was grim. She did not beat about the bush.

"Ladies and Gentlemen. You all have computers and communicators. You all have brains so I am assuming you all know about Alpha HIV. The information I have received suggests Alpha HIV is at least as bad and probably worse than you have heard. It is probable HIVa will overwhelm the immune system and create debilitating and ultimately lethal AIDS within 12 to 18 months of the initial infection. We have also been shocked to find that HIVa does not respond to any of the existing drugs which were used to control the original HIV.

This means we have to start, from scratch, to produce effective anti HIVa drugs. Since 95% of us are already infected with HIVa it means we must study the virus, solve the problems and produce effective anti HIVa drugs within 12 months because, once you develop AIDS symptoms you won't be able to work on anything. As you must be aware, we are facing the greatest biological disaster the world has ever seen.

We are, as you know, a relatively small Pharmaceutical outfit, mainly doing work for the health service.

We have been approached by Weinstock Pharmaceuticals. They say they need every Bio-Chemist and Geneticist they can get.

I am, therefore, asking for volunteers to go work in their Research Labs. They have a substantial Research Facility here, in Montreal, as you know. Their facilities and equipment are of course, far more extensive than ours.

They are setting up a shift work system so the equipment can be operated 24/7. Sleeping accommodation is being set up at the facility.

Basically, volunteers are being asked to totally dedicate their lives to the defeat of HIVa. If you volunteer you will be asked to sleep, eat and work at Weinstocks – basically – work until you are ready to drop – then eat and sleep. Contact with families will only be by communicator. Bear in mind – every single day, or even hour lost is likely to cost thousands of lives.

I have, myself, volunteered to do basic research.

I suggest you all go home, discuss it with your families, decide if you will volunteer and let me know, tomorrow morning, your decision. Thank You!"

After she had gone Jake looked at Mike.

"Where does that leave us now?

Mike smiled, ruefully. "I think" he said "Duty Calls"

Jake went home and explained the situation to Beth. They sat silently for a while. Finally she took his hand and said "I understand. You have to go to Weinstocks. You can't let them down."

Jake smiled wanly. "I couldn't live with myself if I did. You know – I almost fancied living out in the wilds with you and the kids."

"I know! But think of this! If you or your colleagues make a breakthrough on HIVa you could save our lives too, as well as thousands of others."

———————————————

In the morning Jake and Mike contacted 'Denny' Lafayette. So did the others. No body refused.

# 2129 - USA

It was 2129; a year after HIVa had appeared and infected 95% of the human race. Already, some people were becoming sick with secondary infections. Helen Weinstock, the CEO, of Weinstock Pharmaceuticals, looked around the long table at the various Government officials and military personnel.

"Are you telling us" said Norman Myers, the Secretary of State, harshly, "that it is not possible for you and the other pharmaceutical manufacturers to produce enough anti-HIVa drugs for all the people of the USA?"

"I'm afraid – that is the reality of the situation. Sir! In order to protect a person fully from the effects of HIVa it is necessary for that person to take a dose of medication at least once a week. To protect 700 million people would require the production of over 36 billion doses per year. It has taken us 6 months to perfect and test an effective medication for HIVa before we could even start quantity production. The old HIV drugs were not adequate. To do this I have had staff working around the clock. That we are now in mass production, so soon, is in itself, remarkable. It is quite normal for the creation, development and testing of drugs, to Government Standards, to take 5 to 10 years from inception to mass use. It has simply not been possible, and is not possible, in the next 12 months, to set up mass production facilities capable of producing 700 million doses per week. Effective drugs are extremely complicated molecular constructs requiring many stages of manufacture. Making drugs is not like stamping out millions of little metal components for the armaments industry."

"Well!" said Myers, grimly, "Perhaps you'd tell us how many doses the industry <u>can</u> make."

"In the next six months I would estimate the industry can produce two billion doses, which is enough to protect seventy eight million people, rising to eight, possibly ten billion doses in the following 12 months. Ten billion doses would protect 190 million people."

"My God!" said General, George Widdeson, sitting alongside the Secretary of State, "What you are saying is, in the next six months, we can only protect one person in ten and, 12 months later, only one in four."

"Yes! General! I'm afraid I am!"

"How the hell are we going to handle this?" said Myers.

"If that is the situation "said General Widdeson, "We must set up a system of priorities. We must maintain Law and Order. We must keep administration going. Make sure power supplies are secured. Rail and road transportation, food distribution. If we are not very careful the whole set-up could collapse."

"It could collapse anyway" said Myers. "How do you think the poor devils that don't get any medication will react?"
General Widdeson rose to his feet.

"The planners, in the Pentagon, have already been working on various scenarios, in the last twelve months, of course. But I don't know if they have tackled a situation quite this bad. With your permission, Mr Secretary! I'd like to leave now and go and bring them up to speed."

"Yes! George! I fully understand."
Turning to Helen Weinstock

"And you! Ms Weinstock. I can only ask that you and all the other people in your industry, do their best."

"You may rest assured on that. Sir!"

# MAY 2130 – USA – ATTACK ON DRUG FACTORY

Marvin Jackson sought out his friend, Miguel Ramos, in his small house on the outskirts of Los Angeles. They sat down, cracked a can of beer apiece, and sat morosely. The old banter and jokes were gone. Miguel's wife was away, visiting his sick sister. Both Miguel's mother and father were ill too. It was probably only a question of time before Miguel and his wife also became ill. They had all tested positive for HIVa as had Marvin's family. Everybody had the damned HIV. Things had been bad enough already. What with the heat, the water shortages, the power failures, the ever rising cost of food and the Government cutting the level of State Benefits. Miguel hadn't had a steady job for years.

Until recently, Marvin had worked as a fork-lift driver at the big pharmaceutical manufacturing outfit in Los Angeles. But he had raised his fist to a domineering foreman and had been fired. Although he had been looking for another job for the last six months he had failed. And now this hellish HIV. Marvin's mother had become ill in the last month. He had gone to the Medics and begged for anti-HIVa drugs. The doctor had been very apologetic. There simply weren't enough supplies yet available. Only key personnel – the police, the army, the administrators, transport personnel, medical staff and so on qualified at present. Shortly, things would improve. They hoped to have supplies for everybody in the next six months. So sorry – but – that was the way it was.

Marvin had gone home and brooded. Gradually his despair had turned to rage and, finally, hatred.

After a few cans of beer he spoke to Miguel.

"Those bastards know what they are doing."

"What do you mean" said Miguel, with a frown.

"They hate our guts. This is a golden chance to get rid of us. To protect themselves and let us rot and die with AIDS. They'll never produce enough drugs to protect all of us. They'll limit production – until we are all gone."

"Come on Marvin! Don't you think you are taking it a bit far? Surely they wouldn't do that?"

But, over the next few days, Miguel couldn't help but think about it. And, when his wife began to fall ill, and he went to the Doctor – and got the same story – he began to wonder.

When Marvin came round again, Miguel told him about Maria and the Doctor. Same story!

"But, even if you are right Marvin! There's nothing we can do about it."

Marvin took a couple of pulls from his beer can. Looked his friend steadily in the eye.

"I've been thinking about it. They live and we die. Why don't we fight back? What have we got to lose – Nothing! Why don't we wreck their drug production set up? Without drugs they have the same survival chances as us. Let's level the playing field!"

"For God's sake! Marvin! Think what you are saying! And they say they will have enough for everyone in six months."

"Of course they say that. But you would be a fool to believe it. In six months they will say there have been difficulties – production problems. They'll keep fobbing us off until we are all gone. I know how the bastards work."

Although Miguel was, basically, a good natured, decent man – gradually, over the next weeks, as his wife grew worse, despair, resentment and bitterness overcame him.

"Was it possible" he wondered "that Marvin was right." The next time they met, he took Marvin by the arm.

"This idea of yours Marvin? How would you go about it?" Marvin had had time to think it out – in detail. He knew the layout of the factory; where the key installations were; how security was organised; Everything. So he spelled out his ideas to Miguel – in detail. Miguel listened. Thought about it a long time and – finally – agreed.

---

The tank truck, with a full load of 10,000 gallons of gasoline aboard, pulled into the way station and the driver climbed wearily out of his cab to go to the cafeteria for a quick meal. He walked through the door, went to the counter and ordered burger and fries. A young man of about twenty five followed him to the counter and made a similar order. Shortly after, the smiling young man approached and asked if he could share the table. The truck driver agreed. The young man chatted for a while as he ate, then asked if he was the driver of the big tanker, out in the yard. He then politely asked for a lift towards Los Angeles as his pickup had broken down. He had a place just a few miles down the road, had a spare truck and would come back in the morning to sort the old truck out. It all sounded very feasible.

After a few qualms the truck driver agreed. A few miles down the road and the affable young man produced a pistol and ordered the driver to divert on to a narrow track. The driver was warned that any attempt to communicate or operate a warning device and he was dead.

Marvin and Miguel had searched the surrounding countryside and found an abandoned farmstead. One of many that had been left when climate change and drought had made farming in the area impossible. There was a large empty barn with enormous double doors. Ideal for hiding a large vehicle such as the tanker truck.

A few days later and another tanker truck pulled in to a different way station. This time the fuel was diesel.

Marvin and Miguel spent the next two days modifying the trucks, fitting heavy steel plates around the driver's position, including a plate that could be pulled up in front of the driver, with a narrow slot, for visibility, in front of the driver's face. On the dusty land, at the back of the barn, was a low mound – where the bodies of the two truck drivers had been hastily buried. Marvin had been reluctant to kill the two drivers but could not see any other way.

Two days later the security guard, in his cubicle, at the entrance to the giant Weinstock Pharmaceuticals complex, saw two large tanker trucks travelling on the main road that ran parallel to the main building. They made no attempt to slow down and turn on to the approach road to the main entrance but carried on at normal speed. Two hundred yards further on and the lead truck slowed, turned left, off the road and headed straight for the perimeter fence. The other truck followed.

The massive truck tore through the fence and accelerated towards the wall which was the side of the main production building. In actual fact Marvin's precautions with the steel plates had been unnecessary. He was right, that the complex had added security. There was a squad of highly trained, fully armed soldiers in a room just behind the main entrance, needing only the push of a button by the security guard to bring them into action.  But nobody had foreseen the possibility of someone slamming through the side wall of the building – exactly where the most vital production equipment lay.

Marvin kept his foot down.  He ducked, just before the truck impacted the wall.  There was an explosion of bricks everywhere and then he was through, smashing and shattering through machines and equipment and on, for 100 metres into the area with the great fermentation vats and separators.  Finally the truck ground to a halt.

Miguel had followed in the diesel truck and was close behind.  The diesel truck had swerved, after smashing through the remains of the wall, slightly to one side and had hit a steel stanchion, rupturing a corner of the tank.  Diesel fuel poured and spread everywhere.

After staring, open mouthed, the guard at the main gate recovered his wits and slammed down on his panic button.  Klaxons blared.  The sergeant in charge of the security squad came on.

"Two trucks!  Smashed through the wall of the main production building – half way down Bay 3."
Seconds later – six men, fully armed and ready, were sprinting for the main building.

For a few seconds Marvin was stunned.  Despite the mass of the truck there had been some violent jolts.  Nevertheless the tank full of gasoline was still intact.  He pushed the protective steel plate away, kicked the door open somehow and stepped down on to the floor of the building, his automatic rifle in his hand.  He looked back and saw Miguel, who had gotten out of his cab before him, start to spray the computers and control equipment with bullets.  Almost immediately he saw Miguel stagger and go down.  He turned and saw a group of men racing towards him; two of them firing from the hip.  He triggered his own rifle and fired a long burst towards them, seeing two go down.  Two bullets slammed into his lower body and he felt a wave of weakness wash over him.  Suddenly, he knew what he must do and forced himself to stay upright and turn.  Another bullet hammered into him and then he triggered the rifle.  A stream of bullets ripped into the gasoline tank of the truck and fuel began to spill out. He kept his finger on the trigger until the magazine was empty.  As he began to sink to the floor, the gasoline had not fired.  Ironically it was a spark from a ricocheted bullet, fired by the guards, that actually set it off.  The last thing Marvin saw was the first flames lapping up the side of the gasoline tank.  Then – a flash of light as a bullet hit him in the head – and Nothing.

Seconds later, the gasoline fireballed.  Shortly after that, the diesel caught, and maintained a steady massive blaze.

———————————————

A few hours later Helen Weinstock picked up the secure phone and spoke to the Secretary of State.

"Myers!"

"Mr Secretary!  Helen Weinstock!  I am afraid I have some bad news.  This afternoon, terrorists attacked our main production facility.  They circumvented the security squad and smashed their way into the main production area through a side wall, using two large gasoline tanker trucks.  The facility is almost totally destroyed.  We have lost forty percent of the USA's total capability for producing anti HIVa drugs.  It will take us at least nine months to get back into production."

# JUNE 2130 – RIOTS IN SOUTH USA

Trooper Alan Jones looked up from his screen.
"Sarge! There's reports coming in from Baton Rouge. Massive rioting and looting again. I thought we had it sorted yesterday but they are back. And in force! Take a look!"
Sergeant Gomez sighed, looked at the screen, picked up his communicator and punched the buttons.

"Sir! We have big trouble again in Baton Rouge. We have reports the rioters are organised – and armed."
Gomez listened briefly, then turned to Jones.

"Tell the others! Fall in! Full gear! Thirty Minutes! We are to join a contingent of 200 marines to go down and sort it out."

An hour later, Gomez and his men, riot shields to the fore, advanced in a ragged line along the central thoroughfare towards several large supermarket buildings, one of which was ablaze. Behind them were several massive personnel carriers, packed with marines. Surprisingly, there did not seem to be much visible activity. The massive rioting and looting seemed to have died down. Gomez felt a twinge of disquiet. By now the stones and petrol bombs should be flying. They advanced another 150 yards and, suddenly, all hell was let loose. A hail of bullets assailed them from all sides. Gomez gasped as a bullet slammed into his protective vest, knocking the wind out of him. He staggered, straightened up and saw that several of his men were down, despite their protective gear. In his peripheral vision he saw a streak of fire. Then one of the personnel carriers, just disgorging a group of marines, exploded in a burst of flame.

James Wallis, Captain of Marines, frantically tapped his communicator.

"Colonel! Sir! We are under heavy fire."
"No Sir. Not the usual. I mean heavy fire from rifles and automatic weapons."
"We have just lost a personnel carrier. A number of my men are down."
"I am requesting permission for my men to go 'weapons free'. Colonel."
"This is not a riot. Colonel! This is war."
"With all due respect. Sir! You cannot expect my men to take this and not fire back. Shooting over their heads has no effect."

Captain Wallis listened in despair. The Colonel was shouting now. "Captain Wallis! I order you! Under no circumstances can your men deliberately shoot American citizens. Warning shots only! The American Forces have never, ever, opened fire directly on American citizens – and they are not going to do it now! Do you understand? Retire and return to base! Out!"

---

Three days later, Norman Myers, Secretary of State, was talking to the President in the Oval Office in the White House.

"That is the situation Mr President."

"Baton Rouge, Mobile, Montgomery and a number of other cities in the South East USA are now totally out of control. I have given instructions to State Troopers and Army personnel that they are to quietly and as unobtrusively as possible, abandon those States and move North. If these insurgents (what else can I call them) get seriously organised and move North, we shall have to reconsider the situation. However, I do not think that will happen. Quite bluntly I propose to leave them where they are and let nature take its course."

"For God's sake! Norman! Don't ever say that outside of this room."

"Don't worry Mr President. I won't."

# JUNE 2130 –USA

US President James Elroy Ferguson sat behind his desk in the Oval Office in the White House listening to his Secretary of State – Norman Myers.

"Mr President. I have to tell you that the situation at the present time is extremely grave. As you know, the HIVa drug production facility at Weinstock Pharmaceuticals in California was attacked and seriously damaged a month ago reducing America's capacity to produce anti HIVa drugs by 40%.

The situation was bad enough already, but now we will only be able to produce around six billion doses in the next 12 months. Six billion doses is only enough to protect 110 to 120 million people – roughly one in five of the total US population.

Previously we had expected to be able to protect a hundred and ninety million and it was our intention to distribute the Anti HIVa drugs to key personnel throughout the States and hope to maintain Law and Order and Essential Services.

Following the attack on Weinstock, and, the following week, the extremely violent riots at Baton Rouge, the Pentagon have re-assessed the situation and have come up with new proposals.

They checked the backgrounds of the two men involved in the attack on Weinstock – expecting them to be known dissidents or belonging to some terrorist cell. What they found was that the two men were, before the attack, perfectly normal decent, law abiding citizens. Both, however, had relatives who had recently developed AIDS. They had applied to the medics for drugs but were turned down because these drugs, being in such short supply, could be issued to key personnel only.

It is believed the frustration, and the resentment engendered, caused these two men to behave in the way they did in a misguided attempt to 'level the playing field' or, to put it another way, "If we can't have these drugs, neither shall you."

This reaction, Mr President, creates an entirely new psychological situation throughout the United States and, indeed, the whole world.

Imagine, if you will, you are faced with a long row of ordinary people, dependent on you for a life or death decision. You go down the line saying You!, You!, You! and You will die. You can

117

live, and so on and only every fifth person is given the life-saving drugs.

Is it likely, do you think, that anybody denied the drugs could accept that without feeling resentment and anger? The people at the Pentagon feel that resentment will lead, in many people, to a violent response – such as occurred at Weinstocks. They have concluded, Mr President, that the policy of distributing anti HIVa drugs only to key personnel – just one in five of the population – throughout the States – simply will not work. There will be endless rioting, violence and sabotage. Maintenance of Law and Order will become quite impossible.

What the Pentagon people are proposing, Mr President, is very drastic. They are proposing we abandon 80% of the entire USA to HIVa.

We give 100% HIVa drug coverage to a selected 20% area which means, within that area, everybody will be protected and there will be no reason for rioting and sabotage and it is likely that everything – transport, services, food supplies etc will remain functioning roughly as normal – meaning we should be able to maintain a core of Civilisation in the 20% enclave so that, when the disaster is over, the rest of the USA can gradually be brought back to normal."

"My God! Norman!" said the President. "Stop right there! You are talking about us abandoning hundreds of millions of people to almost certain death. I'm told only 5% of people are naturally immune to HIVa. The whole infrastructure will collapse. Even the immune people will probably starve to death."

"That, I am afraid, is the reality we have to face." Said Myers.

"My God! My God!" said Ferguson, holding his head in his hands, "I shall go down in history as the man who presided over the total ruination of the United States. We can't allow this to happen."

Myers looked, blank faced, at the President. "Just what we need" he thought. A gutless President, feeling sorry for himself." Somehow he allowed no trace of his disgust to show. Then, for a whole minute, the President sat there silent. Nobody moved. Nobody spoke. Then they could see the President get a grip of himself. He straightened up. His face changed. He took a deep breath.

"OK!" he said. "Let's talk this through. What about the Mexico/US Border Controls?"

"We abandon those."

"But then millions more people will flood in from Mexico."

"No! Mr President. 95% will soon be too sick to migrate anywhere. And if they come into the USA it will be just as bad as Mexico."

"I guess you're right. Tell me – where is the enclave – the 20% proposed to be?"

Myers began to relax "Thank God the President's moment of weakness had passed." he thought. "We are all human. Shock can do things to people." He reflected that even the callous, brutal, Joe Stalin – the 'Man of Steel', in a fit of despair – in World War Two – when Hitler bulldozed his way into Russia in 1941, hid himself away in his Dacha for several days – convinced that Hitler was unstoppable and invincible – before he pulled himself together and realised it was his duty, as figurehead, to stand fast and rally the Russian people.

"The Pentagon suggests we abandon all areas south and west of a line from Norfolk to Cincinnati. Cincinnati to Chicago. We instruct Weinstocks to transfer and rebuild their Pharmaceutical Plant in Baltimore. We co-operate with the Canadians who, incidentally, have a subsidiary of Weinstocks in Montreal which is already producing anti HIVa medication.

We protect the enclave, keep things under control, increase production of anti HIVa drugs as quickly as possible then, as soon as we are able, move back into the abandoned areas and help them recover.

Fortunately the Canadians will be able to produce enough HIVa drugs for themselves in a few months and will then continue to expand production and make the extra output available to us.

As long as we keep control and have no more disasters like Weinstocks in San Francisco, we estimate we can double and, maybe, triple production of HIVa drugs in the next 18 months. The surplus can be made available to the survivors and then we can start the process of rehabilitation and regeneration.

The Pentagon estimates, using this strategy, the USA will lose around 60% to 65% of its original population.

If we do not adopt the enclave policy and distribute the HIVa drugs throughout the USA – key personnel only – as originally envisaged – then we shall almost certainly lose control.  There will be total chaos and anarchy throughout the entire USA, resulting, in the next few years, of the loss of as many as 90% to 95% of the entire population.

Repugnant as it may be, the protected enclave proposal offers the best chance of saving the maximum number of people."

"I suppose" said the President "If we can't save them all – which we can't – then, logically, we must adopt the policy that gives us the best chance of saving the maximum number."

"Yes!  Mr President.  It's a tough call – but – there it is!"

"How do we go about establishing and enforcing this enclave?"

"Although openness is usually the watchword, the Pentagon recommends that we keep the policy secret as long as possible.  We empty and transfer weapon stores from the south to the enclave.  We transfer military personnel and set up a policing system along the border.  Transfer all military equipment – guns, tanks, planes, etc into the enclave as quietly as possible.

We can even transfer a lot of the equipment from the Mexico/USA border barrier – sensors, robot sentries, etc to the enclave border.  The sentries are tracked vehicles, which can operate, if necessary, on rough ground as well as roads and can be programmed to patrol areas bounded by markers – radio beacons – or by sat/nav systems.  Satellite systems will probably continue to operate efficiently for at least 5 years or so even if ground control systems are lost, worldwide.

The perimeter of the enclave – Norfolk/Chicago etc will be less than half the distance on the Mexican border.  There will be more than sufficient robot sentries to do the job should we decide to go that route.

The Pentagon recommends we install the robot sentry system along the Enclave border in any case – but not activate it unless it becomes absolutely unavoidable.  We shall have to declare a State of Emergency and Martial Law before we can proceed with such plans in secrecy.

The Pentagon people estimate we can have a skeleton border control system – Norfolk/Chicago in place in 3 to 4 months and, if we push hard, a fully operation system in place in six months.  We must work fast, Mr President.  HIVa will not wait.  Vast numbers of people are falling sick already. We must restrict use of HIVa drugs to the enclave area immediately if we are to have a reasonable chance of maintaining control."

---

In the event, it was touch and go. The military was sent in to help Weinstocks transfer what was left of their production facilities and help build a new, greatly enlarged, facility in Baltimore. It was a race against time. HIVa was even more potent than had been expected and many infected people fell sick with AIDS only 12 months after initial infection. Eighteen months after infection, 30% of people showed symptoms and, two years after infection, more than 70% were sick or had died. The staff at Weinstock Pharmaceuticals, both in the States and in Canada worked heroically and the US Military went into a state of overdrive not seen since the Manhattan Project in World War Two.

As predicted, the area outside the Enclave collapsed into total chaos and anarchy – as it did in most of the rest of the world. Hundreds of millions in America died – both from AIDS and from simple starvation as agriculture, transport and infrastructure failed. Control in the US Enclave area and in Eastern Canada was maintained. Law and Order and Civilised behaviour retained.

In 2132, the drug supply problem had been solved. It was, of course, too late to save hundreds of millions of people. The total number of survivors in North America and Canada was around 220 million. In Mid 2132, The Enclave and Canada were despatching convoys of lorries south, carrying food, drugs and other medical supplies, first into areas of the old USA and then on into Mexico and further south. Civilisation was gradually restored.

---

# 2130 – AFRICA

In Africa, in the early 22$^{nd}$ Century, the Genetic Engineers had done their job. They had created new crops – that produced twice the yield of the old. They had created new crop plants that would grow and survive where no others grew before. Also heat tolerant, drought tolerant even salt contamination resistant crops.

The Doctors had worked and slaved. They had drastically reduced infant mortality. They had almost eliminated Malaria, Blackwater fever, Dengue, Tuberculosis and a host of other maladies. They had eliminated Guinea Worm, reduced Bilharzia, Schistosomiasis and other parasitic diseases. The expectation of life of Africans had soared. What they had not done unfortunately, to any degree, was to convince the Africans to reduce their birth rate.

So now, in 2130, Africa was bursting at the seams, with 3.9 billion people within its boundaries. Africa had modernised, industrialised and exploited its natural resources. As the population had increased, scores of great cities had developed, many with over 20 million inhabitants.

However, global warming had inexorably advanced. Temperatures in the tropical zones were insufferably high, all the way to the Mediterranean in the north. Only in some of the highlands in the south and the southern tip of Africa could the climate be called liveable.

Most of the inhabitants in the cities depended for their comfort and survival on a vast expenditure of energy on air conditioning. In 2100, thirty five percent of African electrical energy came from solar power. Ten percent from massive hydro electric plants built to tap energy from central Africa's giant rivers. But over fifty percent of energy had come from fossil fuel powered electrical generating stations, burning Africa's stores of oil, gas and coal. However, by 2130, the oil and gas had gone. Some power stations were still run on gas, generated by 'underground gasification of coal' but the power supply situation was on a knife edge. With output only just meeting demand even though vast additional solar power farms had been created in the last 30 years.

Global warming had also caused secondary effects. Weather patterns had changed. The Hadley and Ferrel Cells were shifting, altering rainfall patterns all over Africa. Some of the tropic regions

122

suffered torrential rain, over and above previous experience. Other areas – prolonged droughts. Much agriculture depended on irrigation, often by water pumped from deep underground aquifers. But the aquifers were drying up – the demand on them was too great.

By 2130, food production in Africa was critical.

In the previous 100 years, Africa's immense natural riches – its vast mineral resources – had been exploited; some would say squandered. Its great deposits of copper, chrome, bauxite, iron ore and all the various minerals with which Africa had been blessed, had been stripped and sold abroad. This had financed the building of the cities, the power stations, the solar panel installations, the borehole pumps, the irrigation systems, the desalination plants and built the infrastructure that supported the cities. It also financed the massive purchases of food from abroad which supported the burgeoning population.

By the year 2130, the minerals were running out. The mines were exhausted. The oil and gas was gone. Africa could no longer afford to buy food abroad; and home food supplies were failing. So, in 2130, Africa was in a desperate situation. Heat, drought, food shortages and over population. Many had foreseen what was coming and sought to emigrate. But Europe had closed its doors. There was nowhere to go.

The appearance of HIVa was a total calamity. It didn't just tip the balance. It caused the entire organisation of Africa to collapse like a gigantic house of cards.

In 2128, HIVa first appeared. By the time it was discovered as a new strain of HIV, 25% of all Africans were already infected. In six months the figure was over 90% and, 12 months later, in 2130, people were falling sick and starting to die.

Because of the time lost in detecting HIVa as a new strain; the time required to study it, find out the old HIV drugs were ineffective, the time required to develop new vaccines and get them in production and, finally, the fact there were no large pharmaceutical companies in Africa capable of doing the research and producing the drugs, Africa had no defence against HIVa.

As people started to fall ill, the medical services coped at first. Then, as the numbers of sick people escalated, the hospitals and even the mortuaries were overwhelmed by a tidal wave of illness and death. The medical staff themselves – the doctors, the nurses, the porters, the cleaners began to fall sick, collapse and die from a variety of illnesses associated with HIVa. Drug resistant tuberculosis raged through the wards. MRSA, Clostridium Difficile and Dysentery were everywhere.

Rapidly the entire medical and health organisation began to buckle under the strain. Funeral services could hardly cope and still offer civilised burials to the bereaved.

Considering Africa as a whole, the funeral and burial services normally handled about a million deaths a week, over the whole continent. In the first month that the pestilence took hold the death rate increased to 4 million a week at which point burial services were struggling to cope. After the second month the figures had escalated to 13 million a week and the army was called in. A month later the figure climbed to 25 million a week and it became quite impossible to cope. Law and order began to falter. As more and more people in the Police and Military Services fell sick it became increasingly difficult and, finally impossible to maintain order.

In the cities, mobs of feral youths rampaged through the streets, looting and destroying. In the countryside and the wilds, as sickness and disease spread, old tribal rivalries and antagonisms reappeared and flared into violence.

When faced with disaster, human beings tend to look for a scapegoat – someone to blame. Rapidly old tribal and ethnic hatreds flamed into new life. Governments, generally, did their best. They strove to maintain control but the death rate continued to escalate until, at the height of the disaster, people were dying at a rate of more than a hundred million a week, week after week, for four long months before the numbers began to reduce.

No assistance or help of any kind was given or offered from abroad, in all this time, because, all over the world, every nation on Earth was desperately trying to cope with their own problems and, in the main, failing. Civilisation in Africa totally collapsed and chaos and anarchy prevailed over the entire continent.

There were no longer enough people to cultivate the land, collect the harvest, run the transport, operate and maintain the electrical generators and power systems. Finance collapsed. Money became worthless. Millions of bodies simply lay where they fell.

The Police and Military organisations disintegrated and dissolved after more than 30% of their numbers were sick and dying themselves.

It became a desperate, impossible, struggle for survival. Every person for themselves. Swarms of rioting youths and scavengers were everywhere. They raided police and army weapon and ammunition stores. Often ex police and ex army members joined in the weapons looting. Cities were ransacked, burned and abandoned. Tribal violence blazed. Youths embarked on a mad orgy of vandalism and senseless violence. Even children, armed to the teeth with stolen weapons, ran amok.

Never, in the history of the World, had there been such an all encompassing human disaster. For two years starvation, pestilence and violence ravaged Africa. Its people were reduced to small tribes and nomadic bands; hunter gatherers in the true sense of the words. Nobody bothered to cultivate land or grow crops. If they had done so, the results of their labours would simply have been raided and stolen. Starving people turned to what remained of any edible flora and fauna anywhere, in a desperate attempt to find food. All animals large and small – elephants to mice, snakes, bats, rats; birds of all descriptions, from the largest to the smallest, fish, insects, termites, everything that was remotely edible. It did not matter the rarity, the protection the preservation orders, the restricted areas, the National Parks. All were swept away in the struggle for human survival.

After two years it is estimated that no more than 200 million people still survived in the whole of Africa. Most of these were in the southern cooler areas but a remarkable number survived in the central rain-forest, subsisting on fish, birds, insects and all the various wild animals of the forest.

---

Joseph Adambula stared across the hut at his two wives and five children. (There had been seven, but he had lost two in the last fortnight). All were emaciated (Joseph included). His last stores of food had been raided and looted five weeks ago and they had been lucky to escape with their lives. Now there was nothing. The smallest child pulled at a pendulous milkless breast and mewled.

Joseph knew he must do something. But what? He reached for his rifle and scrabbled around for the last few cartridges he had hidden away. There was nothing out there he knew. Everything had already been shot and eaten. But – "He must try! He must try!"

He dragged himself to his feet, slung his rifle and stumbled out of the door. The heat was stifling but he had to at least make the effort. He headed for the edge of the forest, half a mile away. Maybe there was a monkey or something that had, somehow, survived. Thankfully he moved into the light shade under the first trees and then, gradually, into the more dense undergrowth.

There was an eerie silence. No birds calling. No monkey chatter. Nothing!

For half an hour he wandered. Nothing!

He was overcome by a sense of weariness. An aching lethargy. He turned to go home.

Then, miraculously, there was a rustle in the underbrush. He froze, scarcely daring to breathe, in case he should scare off whatever animal it was before he had the chance to shoot.

And then it appeared. A massive black head and shoulders and the face, staring straight at him. A gorilla!

How could there be a gorilla here? The nearest gorillas were fifty miles away. If there were any left, that is. There had only been a handful five years ago. A gorilla! But he couldn't shoot a gorilla could he? They were protected. There were massive penalties simply for interfering with them let alone killing them.

Then he thought of his starving wives and children, back in the hut. His finger tightened on the trigger and the rifle roared.

He stepped forward, looked at the trickling blood for a moment, then, taking his knife, he hacked off both legs at the hips. He slung the two massive legs over his shoulders and headed back to the hut. He would give one leg to his friend. The other would feed his family for a few days. At least they would not starve just yet.

A little while after he had gone, there was a slight movement in a group of ferns and, moments later, a baby gorilla crept forward and snuggled to its mother's head. It looked to the lifeless body – and where the mother's legs had been. And whimpered.

––––––––––––––

Civilised government was re-established in 2133, and the African National Government joined the World Association of

Nations and, finally became a member of the World Government in 2134.

# 2130 – INDIA, PAKISTAN AND BANGLADESH

When HIVa arrived in 2128 the entire Indian sub-continent was already in a critical state. The population had ballooned, over the previous century to a colossal 3.8 billion people.

Global Warming had raised the temperature to levels, in the summer, which were on the upper limit of survivability. Food supplies were absolutely critical – many were already starving.

Although, in 2086, the Chinese action had theoretically made Siberia available for migration, in practice very few people indeed, from India, could ever get there. The Himalayan mountain range and the Tibetan plateau meant they certainly couldn't walk there.

Maybe 10 million migrated from North Pakistan to the west Siberian plain but, after all, this was just a drop in the ocean.

The bulk of Indian and Bangladeshi people had no way whatsoever of getting there.

Many intelligent Indians, with financial means, had long since fled – to the USA, Canada, Europe and, indeed, all over the world – they could see what was coming 50 or a 100 years before.

So – when HIVa came and began to create AIDS, the organisation and infrastructure of the entire Indian Sub Continent rapidly collapsed – almost as fast as Africa and with the same appalling consequences.

The scenes of death and destruction were without parallel in human history. How can one describe a holocaust at these levels – where, at the peak, a hundred million human beings died in one week. The funeral pyres raged, from end to end of the sub continent – but it was not enough. The bulldozers roared and churned – from dawn to dusk and, indeed, through the night – but it was not enough.

Millions simply lay and rotted – where they fell. The only thing that thrived in all this chaos was flies. Billions upon billions in black clouds. They filled the air like a black miasmic fog, with an endless buzzing – like tinnitus in everyone's ears. And the smell was indescribable. No one – in history – had ever imagined such scenes.

There could be no escape from this horror. No respite. No succour. No helping hand. Death was literally everywhere. How anyone at all survived is nothing less than a miracle.

By autumn 2132, less than 200 million people, in total, survived in Pakistan, India and Bangladesh.

―――――――――――

At Patna, in Bihar State, in Northern India, Indira Gupta wept over her dying husband's body. She keened quietly, numbed by this final tragedy. She had lost her parents, lost her siblings, lost her children and now – this. She was one of those rare people – totally immune to HIVa – but it didn't really help her. She was still alive – but for how long. All around was death and decay. There was no food. The water was undrinkable. The heat unbearable.

Today the temperature was 46°C (115°F) but two weeks ago it had reached an insufferable 50°C (122°F). Swarms of people had flocked to the rivers and streams to try to obtain some relief. People had fought savagely for access to water.

The mighty river Ganges, a kilometre away, stank. Its surface was dark and oily and, here and there, floated patches of ashes and half unburned, rotting, remains of human corpses, dumped in the river from the funeral pyres.

She had never, ever, seen anything like it. The pyres, burning along the river bank, were enormous. A hundred metres long and a hundred metres wide. Each pyre, built up in rows 100 metres long by 4 metres wide with a 1 metre gap between the rows. Each row had a metre of wood and burnables at the base and two metres of bodies above. Each row had at least 2,500 corpses. The total colossal pyre being at least 50,000 bodies. They lit the rows, one after the other, working from up wind until, finally, there was a sea of flame and a gigantic pall of smoke, spreading across the sky.

These pyres were not the only ones. There were many others, spread across the entire continent of India. No one knew how many deaths there had been. They were running short of fuel now. Yet there were millions upon millions of bodies still for disposal. What it would be like in a month's time was impossible to imagine.

All over India things had gradually been getting worse, for the previous sixty years; even more so since the Chinese had had the nerve to challenge the Russians. Quite a number of people had left India since then – but it is difficult to drastically reduce a population of over 3 billion and it takes time. Millions had gone – to Alaska,

Canada, Siberia and Europe but India was still hopelessly overcrowded.

The droughts were more frequent and the summer temperatures insufferably high. Crops were failing. It had been difficult enough to survive before this last dreadful impact of Alpha HIV had descended on them. Now Indian Civilisation was on the brink of collapse. Pakistan was no better and Bangladesh even worse.

Indira looked down at her emaciated husband. He twitched, gasped slightly and subsided. She paused for a moment – and knew.

She lifted her face to the blackened skies and screamed.

# 2130 – CHINA AND SOUTH EAST ASIA

In 2128, the population of China had increased to 2 billion and there were a further 1 billion in the rest of South East Asia.

The Chinese had, of course, experimented with a 'one child' population control policy, way back at the end of the 20th Century, and the beginning of the 21st Century, but had quickly run into the geriatric problem allied to a shortage of young labour so, in 2015, the policy was abandoned. Nevertheless, the Chinese people did not go back to a policy of unrestrained procreation and, although the population again began to increase, it did so more slowly.

The Chinese saw what was coming, more than 40 years earlier, and did their best to do something about it – by confronting the Russians and demanding that Siberia be made available for immigration and development. However, they soon found out it is not possible to transfer billions of people from one part of the planet to another – with all the necessities and infrastructure – in a short timescale.

Despite all their efforts only 120 million Chinese and roughly 50 million others had been relocated to Siberia when HIVa arrived in 2128.

The Chinese did have pharmaceutical production facilities and did manage to produce enough drugs to medicate one in six of their people by the time HIVa created AIDS. The Chinese and other Asians already in Siberia still caught HIVa and AIDS, the same as everybody else. The people in Siberia simply had slightly less risk of starving to death. So the people of China and South East Asia were still murderously slaughtered by HIVa and AIDS. The Chinese handled it stoically and well – almost as well as the Japanese but, at the end of 2132, there were 250 million Chinese survivors, (including those in Siberia) plus 100 million other South East Asians.

# 2130 – RUSSIA

When HIVa appeared in 2128, Russia was already in a mess.

After the Sino/Russian war of 2086 when the Russians had conceded Siberia – from the Urals to the Pacific and made it available for settlement by China and other southern nations, the bulk of the Russian people – 400 million of them – were to the West of the Urals.

Some were still in Siberia – there was no reason they shouldn't be – the Agreement had only made the land free for immigration – but most of the already sparse Russian population of that area had moved West, preferring to live with their own Russian speaking comrades, as Chinese and South East Asiatics flooded into Siberia.

The food problem was particularly difficult. A hundred years before, much of Russian grain supplies came from the Ukraine. After the very dangerous USA/Russia nuclear confrontation of 2025, there had been an uneasy peace in the area. Russia kept Crimea and the Donetsk areas but did not seek to annex any more Ukraine territory.

Russia supplied Ukraine with oil and gas for which Ukraine traded grain and this arrangement persisted uneasily for many years.

However, climate change continued to develop and gradually Ukraine became more and more affected by drought. By 2100, Ukraine no longer had a grain surplus to trade and Russia was in serious trouble. They worked to offset this by growing large quantities of frost resistant potatoes in the Northern lands, including the Kola peninsular, and managed to get by.

By 2128, when HIVa appeared, food supplies were on a knife edge, as they were in all the West Asian and Middle East areas.

As HIVa rapidly converted to AIDS in 2130 and millions became sick, the precarious food balance collapsed.

Russia had no Anti HIVa drugs and anarchy and chaos spread rapidly.

With no emergency food supplies available from anywhere on Earth, hundreds of millions died in the next 12 months from AIDS and starvation.

By Autumn 2132, no more than 35 million Russians survived.

---

# 2130 – JAPAN

When HIVa first came to Japan there were 140 million people living in the Islands. This wasn't many more than it had been a hundred years before.

For hundreds of years, back into the Middle Ages, Japan had kept aloof from other nations and outside influences. They had developed their own strict codes of conduct. All was tightly controlled and organised. The peasants working in the fields, the warrior elite under their Samurai code, the warlords and barons running the country under the divine and unquestionable rule of the Emperor.

This continued to the late 18$^{th}$ Century, when Japan decided to modernise and threw open its doors to western influence. A massive focus on military powers and dominance followed which finally culminated in the shattering defeat of Japan in World War Two.

It has been said that the only reason the Japanese people stopped fighting and the war did not end in an almighty final blood bath was because, for the first time in history, the Emperor spoke directly to his people and ordered them to desist.

Fortunately, at this crucial time, the Allies saw the wisdom of allowing the Japanese to keep their Emperor and, after the war, Japan recovered, prospered and became a great economic world power.

After that, in the late 20$^{th}$ Century, they then began a long slow decline. Their Economy stagnated, they became less dynamic, the birth rate dropped and the total population of Japan began to fall rather than rise.

Japan had been unlucky in that, while she had a talented people and a fertile land, they had little or no natural resources. For their industry they had to import all their coal, oil, iron ore, copper, chrome, natural gas, etc.

One thing they did do was embrace Nuclear Power and built about 50 modern, high pressure, water moderated and cooled, uranium fuelled, electrical generating stations to produce a good percentage of their base electrical power load and reduce their conventional fuel bills. This all worked very well for a number of years until, in 2011, there was a massive 8.7 earthquake off the Japanese coast which triggered a colossal tsunami.

One of Japan's major nuclear power stations, with three independent reactors, was at Fukushima on the North East coast.

The power station was, of course, connected to the electrical grid and, in addition to supplying electricity to the grid, could also, in an emergency, take power from it for cooling purposes.

One of the great curses of nuclear power is that, once you have started and run the reactor, you cannot simply switch it off. You can shut the reactor down, reduce the power output, by which we mean reduce the reactor heat output to a minimum but you cannot switch it off to zero and walk away. There is always an amount of residual heat being produced, even with the reactor shut down. And the longer the reactor is run the greater this amount of residual heat the reactor will produce when it is eventually shut down.

This heat must be removed – usually with high powered pumps – or the reactor will gradually overheat.

A tall concrete retaining wall had been built all round the power station installation at Fukushima. A wise precaution bearing in mind Japan has always been notoriously prone to earthquakes and tsunamis.

However, when the massive earthquake and tsunami of 2011 occurred, the tsunami was very large. It surged over the wall, swamped the grid electrical connections, blew the circuit breakers and cut off the mains power supply.

Just in case there were ever any mains outages, a back-up system of diesel powered generators had been installed. These would keep the coolant pumps running while the reactors were shut down.

Unfortunately, the tsunami kept coming and swamped the diesel air intakes. The diesels died. That left only one last line of defence. A massive electrical battery system, many times bigger than a house, capable of running the pumps continuously for 24 hours or more until – that is – the battery ran flat.

Television crews had cameras trained on the power station, from a safe distance away – about 2 miles.

People began to speculate. What happens when the battery runs flat? – if, by that time, they haven't resurrected the diesels or reconnected to the grid.

Time went by and there was no word of the diesels or the grid. The tsunami had wrecked everything in that area.

After 24 hours – further speculation.  Will the reactors meltdown – or blow up – or overheat – in some less spectacular way.

After nearly 48 hours the questions were answered.  The cameras were still on the power station when they registered a massive shockwave – clearly visible at two miles range.  And then – the whole top of the reactor blew – enormous chunks could be seen ascending hundreds of feet into the sky and then falling back.  Spectacular – even at that range.

No 1 Reactor had blown sky high.  A few hours later – No 2 followed suit and a few hours after that – No 3.

The Japanese were faced with a colossal nuclear disaster.  It was only by a miracle Tokyo itself wasn't massively contaminated.  The wind happened to be blowing in a fortuitous direction.

The whole world was appalled.

Faced with this stunning demonstration of what could happen, Germany decided to abolish nuclear power stations completely – once and for all.  Everybody else put their current nuclear power projects on hold.

As a precaution the Japanese shut down all their other nuclear power stations indefinitely.  This inevitably, led to massive power shortages and a scramble to build gas fired stations to compensate – with a resulting massive economic drain on the Japanese economy.

For the rest of the 21$^{st}$ Century, Japan could be said to have stagnated.  There was little change in the early 22$^{nd}$ Century, and by 2128, when HIVa appeared, Japan was a stable country, with a balanced population of 140 million and a relatively high percentage of geriatrics.

Life was, however, becoming more difficult.  Raw materials, which Japan had always had to import, were becoming more and more expensive.  Food supplies were becoming more and more precarious.  The Japanese predilection for sea-food had, in the previous century, greatly contributed to the stripping and impoverishment of the seas all over the world.  Now, the sea-food simply was no longer available in the quantities they needed.  Whilst they weren't exactly starving, food supplies to Japan were tight and becoming tighter.

HIVa, therefore, when it came, fell on a Japan already under considerable stress.  Japan did have its own pharmaceutical industries but the speed with which HIVa rapidly produced AIDS, allied to the fact it did not respond to old HIV drugs meant, as everywhere else on earth, they were struggling to cope. There was no way enough anti-HIVa drugs could be produced in time.

It was obvious Japan would suffer enormous human losses. Probably 70%/80% or more.

In this desperate situation, once again, the Emperor spoke directly to his people.

"People of Japan! Once again we are assailed by an enormous threat. This time it is a terrible and menacing pestilence that hangs over us.

Our Scientists, Biologists and Chemists are frantically working to produce medication and vaccines to defeat the disease but they have reported to me, and I have to tell you now, that such is the speed at which the disease develops, that it will be impossible to protect more than one in five of us before the disease strikes.

An enormous calamity is therefore upon us.

If it were possible, I would willingly give my life to save my people. I give my word that everything that can be done, will be done. We must gird ourselves to weather this terrible storm. Japan and the people of Japan – will survive."

———————

As the AIDS epidemic developed, the Japanese went about their business, stoically, methodically, quietly.

They dug enormous pits, they built massive funeral pyres.

As people died they were prepared, by their surviving relatives, for collection and cremation.

No one rioted, no one rebelled, no one refused to work. Everyone did their best even until death. An incredible demonstration of Stoicism, Fatalism and Self Control.

By late 2030, only twenty million Japanese survived.

———————

# 2130 – EGYPT

By 2128, the population of Egypt had reached 225 million, a staggering figure for such a country. To feed so many people they had irrigated vast areas of the desert, pumping water from the Nile and also from enormous aquifers which existed under the Sahara Desert.

Not a drop of water, from the Nile, now entered the Mediterranean and the aquifers were massively depleted.

There had been a vast amount of water in the aquifers; water that had accumulated thousands of years before, when North Africa was a wetter, more fertile, area. A clue to the extent of the aquifers could be gained from the fact that, back in the 20th Century, Oases were dotted all over the Sahara, where ground level dipped below the water table level.

In 2128, the Oases had long since dried up and they were now pumping water from hundreds of feet down – a very expensive business. Fortunately for the Egyptians they had plenty of solar power and vast arrays of solar panels dotted the desert. They also had several large reverse-osmosis de-salination plants taking water from the Mediterranean. These plants were very energy intensive and expensive to run and, at one time, a complete nuclear power station was dedicated to run them. However, with great improvements in the efficiency of solar panels (solar energy/electricity conversion) the nuclear power station was closed down.

The primary problem was the climate. Egypt had always been a hot country in the summer, often reaching 40°C back in the 20th Century. In 2128, the temperature in summer soared to 47°C and sometimes higher. This was countered by massive use of air-conditioning units which were everywhere. In the hottest weather up to 40% of all electrical power was used for air conditioning.

When HIVa struck, Egypt was one of the countries that had no anti HIVa drugs to combat it. In late 2129, as millions of people became sick with AIDS (the actual disease symptoms caused by HIVa) and could no longer work, the entire control and infrastructure set up came under increasing pressure and June, 2130 totally collapsed.

The transport system failed first, leading to extreme local food shortages. This led to rioting and violence on the streets. The remaining members of the Police and Armed Forces (who had themselves, at this point, lost 30% of their force to AIDS) tried valiantly to get food supplies moved and to control mob violence. However, with the colossal, mounting problem of handling sick people and burying the dead, combined with increasing incidence of power outages, mainly due to loss of maintenance staff, the Police and Armed Services could not cope and the Nation fell into anarchy.

Food stores and fuel depots were raided. Armed gangs were everywhere. Much of the vandalism simply made things worse. Electrical transmission systems, transformer systems, solar installations and much other vital infrastructure was mindlessly wrecked. With power gone, all the myriad air conditioning systems ceased to work. The deep submersible pumps, pulling water from the aquifers, failed. The reverse-osmosis pumps ceased to operate. The irrigation pumps, taking water from the Nile shut down. Sewage systems failed. Domestic water supplies failed. Suddenly Egypt was in a most desperate situation.

No aid could come from elsewhere – from other countries in Africa or overseas because they too had their HIVa problems.

With power failed and air conditioning units silent the summer heat was suffocating. Day after day the temperature topped 49°C. As food supplies dwindled, people began to starve. Murderous street gangs appeared, looting and wrecking everywhere. With clean water supplies gone and sewage systems failed, disease exploded. The death rate soared, corpses were everywhere. What was left of the Army and Police forces desperately tried to collect and dispose of the bodies, bulldozing scores of thousands into immense pits dug in the desert. But it was a hopeless undertaking. Burial parties were overwhelmed. People were dying much faster than they could be buried. Rapidly things became impossible. The burial parties gave up. People became only interested in their own survival.

Immense black clouds of flies were everywhere and overall hung the heavy stench of death. All animals – camels, goats, donkeys, cats, dogs were slaughtered for food and rapidly disappeared. Egypt descended into a maelstrom of death and destruction. The other nations of the North African coast – Libya, Tunisia, Algeria, Morocco fared no better. All were in a turmoil of death and devastation.

# 2130 – EUROPE

In 2125, Europe was a loose Confederation of States – more like the old Common Market. The dream of a United States of Europe – fashionable in the early 21$^{st}$ Century – had been abandoned.

First the European currency the 'Euro' had failed. Greece had been the first nation to find it couldn't live within the constraints of the 'Euro'. In 2017, they defaulted on their Euro debts and pulled out, going back to their old currency – the drachma – which promptly collapsed in value.

They were soon followed by Italy and Spain who, while they didn't default outright, had to be massively re-financed and supported, following civil unrest and rioting caused by fiscal restraint and austerity – itself a side effect of trying to abide by the tight rules of the Euro currency.

The 'bail outs' were financed by ECB (European Central Bank) money printing on a gargantuan scale which was anathema to the prudent Germans.

Then Britain, after successive Governments, for years, had evaded giving the British public what it wanted – a Referendum on EEU membership, voted decisively, to pull out of Europe.

Finally, in a move that finished the United States of Europe dream for ever – Germany, fed up with endlessly financing and supporting profligate European Countries – and getting castigated, not thanked for their pains, threw in the towel and announced they were pulling out.

The Euro and the whole European Economic system fell into disarray. To try to rescue something from the shambles, the nations of Europe cobbled up an Economic Alliance. A Commonwealth of European States, each with its own currency, but bound together by the mutual benefit that accrued from trade agreements and other economic ties.

This state of affairs persisted in uneasy balance to 2130, when Europe, in common with the rest of the world, was devastated by HIVa. Europe was, of course, overcrowded, with a population of 900 million. (It would have been much higher but for the Draconian introduction of the Mediterranean Immigration Barrier in 2077 – which was originally intended to be temporary but quickly became permanent.

Because Europe was still a conglomeration of separate states – with substantial psychological differences in its peoples – when, in 2130, a similar situation arose to that in the USA – with only limited supplies of HIVa drugs being available, to combat AIDS, then there could be no possibility of copying the USA. The HIVa drugs were rationed out, nation by nation, on a pro-rata basis and, distributed, within those nations, to just one in five of their citizens – that is – to key personnel only. The result, throughout Europe – was exactly what the Pentagon had predicted would happen in the USA if that procedure was adopted.

Rioting, violence, anarchy, sabotage on a grand scale. The psychological differences between the people of the European Nations simply made the situation much worse. What happened in Europe was what happened in Africa – perhaps on a slightly less violent scale.

At first, people strove mightily to cope with the flood of sick and dying people as AIDS took hold but, before long, the flood became too immense to handle. Rioting and sabotage, by people denied anti HIVa drugs, who knew that without them they were doomed, became widespread, eventually causing total collapse of services and infrastructure. From that point total chaos and anarchy reigned.

It has been said that as many people starved to death as died of AIDS.

By late 2132, the total population of Europe, including Great Britain and Ireland, had been reduced to no more than 200 million. The UK and Ireland, being isolated from mainland Europe, maintained control better and for longer as HIVa exploded into AIDS but, eventually, the death toll, on a percentage basis, was almost as bad as the European mainland.

At this point Scandinavia stepped in with aid in the form of Anti-HIVa drugs, food, electrical generators, crop seeds and supplies. If it hadn't been for them the death toll in Europe would have been substantially higher.

# 2130 – LONDON – ENGLAND

Harry Cohen looked out across what, a few years ago, had been a beautiful garden. Now it was a weed strewn waste, with nettles and docks a metre high. This was a big house, at Maidenhead, on the western outskirts of London where quite a number of the 'better off' and wealthy lived. A 'well to do' area some people said.

Harry and his family had lived a good life. They had travelled the world, had a fancy boat on the river, entertained friends and had all the trappings that money could buy. Now that was all changed.

Two years ago had come Alpha HIV. His daughter Ellie had come back from a trip with 'the sniffles' she said. Ten days later, when they had got themselves checked out – they had all come up positive. They all had HIVa.

Fortunately Harry had contacts. He soon obtained supplies of the anti HIVa drugs and the family was OK. But all was not OK in the outside world. Gradually people began to sicken and die and, the world began to fall apart. The Asian servants fell ill. The gardener fell ill. Harry began to realise just how desperate things were getting and wished he had taken his family elsewhere, while there was still time. But where?

According to reports, the entire world was in a mess. Many places far worse than England. So – they had hunkered down. He made sure they had plenty of food, much of it canned and preserved. It would last for years. They had an emergency generator and plenty of diesel. He had had the foresight to double up on the big fuel tank capacity. They had mountains of logs in the garden and log burning stoves in the living area and the kitchen just in case. They had high fences, security systems and high security, double lock, doors. He had also bought extra ammo for his Purdey shot guns; the ones he used to go on grouse shooting expeditions with his friends in Scotland. A few grouse moors still existed.

However, things had not got better – they had steadily and inexorably worsened. More and more people became sick. Services began to fail. They had to use the emergency generator more and more often until it was on all the time. They couldn't get replacement diesel fuel. Supplies had dried up.

Fortunately they were all right for water. Years ago he had had a borehole drilled – they used a lot of sprinklers on the garden and lawns in the summer. But when the sewage system failed and the drains blocked up, he had to ask his son Joseph to go and dig a large deep hole in the garden and erect a tent.

Joseph was a hefty strapping lad of 23 who could look after himself, but when scavengers started appearing in groups of four and five it was better to keep a low profile. The anti HIVa drugs kept HIVa at bay and the family healthy.

Then, unbelievably, Joseph went down with agonising pains in his stomach. Harry knew it was serious when Joseph collapsed, writhing, on the floor. He prodded Joseph on the lower right hand side of his stomach – as he had once seen a doctor friend do. Joseph gasped and cried out. Even Harry could diagnose appendicitis when he saw it.

They tried to contact local hospitals. After hours of trying they managed to make contact. The news was appalling. Hospitals were hopelessly overloaded. Half the staff were away – they, too, were sick. "Operation!?" Sorry – there was no chance. The hospital reserve diesel generators were out of fuel anyway. There had been no operations performed to speak of – in the last week."

Harry watched his son die. Appendicitis! The simplest of operations would have saved his life.

Eventually they contacted the Undertaker to arrange Joseph's funeral. "Sorry – there are no more formal funerals at the present time. By Order. There are so many deaths at the present time that all formal funerals are suspended. He will have to be buried in a mass grave – along with many others – out near Windsor."

"What about the Funeral Service?"

"No! I'm afraid there will be no Service – we don't have time. I'm sorry! A van will be along to collect your son tomorrow afternoon. Give me your address again, please! Goodbye!"
Harry was stunned. This was unbelievable.

Four months later Harry, Gerda (his wife) and his daughter Ellie sat huddled by the wood burning stove in the kitchen. They waited for a pan of water to boil so they could make some soup (from some of their stock of dried soups) and coffee.

It was necessary to boil the borehole water before you could drink it. They had had the foresight to fill two baths with water before they ran out of diesel for the generator. No electricity meant the borehole pump would not work. When the borehole water ran out they would have to go to rain water.

Harry was apathetic now. He had no idea if things would ever improve. They just seemed to be steadily getting worse. Several times, in the last two months, he had had to use a shotgun blast to scare off scavengers. They had cut a large hole in the perimeter fence.

They had just finished their soup and were about to brew the coffee when there came a thunderous crash at the back door. Harry leapt for the Purdey and stuffed several cartridges in his pocket. The hellish banging continued but stopped before he could get through the large house to the back door. As he reached the utility room he could see the back door was smashed in – probably with an axe.

As he entered the room somebody leaped at him from the side, slashing at the gun with a large stave. The stave almost knocked the gun from his hands but he clung on, swung to face the intruder – and fired.

The man went down – his face a shattered mess of flesh and bone. Two more men instantly leapt into the room and came for him. Firing from the hip, he blasted one in the midriff and the man tottered to the side. The third had a hammer in his hand. Too late, Harry turned to try to fend off the hammer. The last he saw was the image of the man's upraised arm and the hammer descending. And then – a flash of light and – Nothing!

Later, a few hundred yards away, another scavenger looked back and saw the flames roaring from the roof – and the pall of smoke across the sky. Quietly he muttered to himself.
"Looks like another poor devil got the chop."

# 2130 – SAO PAULO – BRAZIL

By 2120, many of the major cities of the Earth had grown to immense conglomerations. Personal transport had long since been banned from all large cities – to reduce congestion, minimise $CO^2$ emissions and, above all, to reduce air pollution. Transport was by underground railway systems and by highly efficient, streamlined tram/train/cab systems above ground – all electrically powered. Modern skyscraper buildings had proliferated. These were miniature cities in themselves. Almost totally self contained communities.

Each massive building incorporated offices, working spaces, high speed lifts, living quarters (ranging from small bachelor pads to complex suites). There were restaurants, snack bars, coffee bars, entertainment centres of all kinds, from bowling alleys, dance halls, disco bars, night clubs to virtual reality booths (where, at the touch of a button, you could make believe you were anywhere on Earth, doing almost anything you had a mind to do).

In the lower levels and basement there were shopping centres, beauty parlours, hairdressing salons, medical and dental facilities, pharmacies and so on.

Some people had been known to live happily, in their self contained skyscraper community, for over 20 years without ever leaving the block. Many people worked in their apartments but others simply took a lift and were in their offices within a minute or so. Working time was down to 32 hours a week or even less.

The skyscrapers themselves were, mainly, straight forward, rectangular structures, with the same cross section at the top as at the base. This simplified construction and gave maximum utilisation for minimum ground space. Embellishments cost a lot of money and took up a lot of space. The rectangular block design was simply the most efficient.

The forerunners of these buildings were the original 'twin tower' trade centre buildings in New York – so horrifically destroyed by terrorists' attacks in the year 2001.

Each tower block incorporated a very effective fire control system. The top of the building incorporated a massive water tank, holding 200,000 gallons of water. This supplied water to an automatic sprinkler system on all floors.

144

In case of fire, detectors pinpointed the location of the fire, switched on the local sprinklers and sounded an alarm in the block fire control squad HQ. It all worked extremely well.

Many of the largest cities had 30 million inhabitants or more. A typical city had a core area incorporating fifty to a hundred or more of the largest skyscrapers. These were surrounded by an area of smaller, but still large multi-storey buildings. Then there was the very sprawling spread of smaller individual houses and apartments and, finally, at the outer perimeter, the detached houses, with gardens, of the more wealthy members of the community.

Unfortunately, even in 2120, in some of the large cities of South America, Africa, India and South East Asia, there were also the vast shanty towns of the less fortunate, on the periphery.

While things were working normally, everything was fine. However, a thriving, functioning city is totally dependent on supplies of food, clean water and essential materials coming in, efficiently, everyday. Also the sewage and disposal systems must work and, finally, there must be an unbroken and continuous source of electrical power.

A city of 20 million people will consume at least 16,000 tons of food a day, some 40,000 tons of clean drinking water (3 million tons if you take showers, etc into account) and at least 50,000 tons of sewage a day must be processed and disposed of and another 20,000 tons of miscellaneous trash and rubbish.

Since the modern city of 2120 relied, for its power, almost entirely on electricity, it can be seen that a reliable, adequate, electrical power supply is absolutely essential. Should the electricity supply fail then emergency supplies of food and water could be shipped in using liquid fuel powered trucks. Sewage disposal is a different matter. Emergency, liquid fuel powered generators could be used to power some lift operations to get food and water delivered to upper floors of skyscrapers and tall buildings.

Therefore, it can be seen that, when the effects of HIVa caused a breakdown of infrastructure and services, living in a city rapidly became a nightmare. In fact, cities without power became total death traps.

Millions of people found themselves virtually marooned in skyscrapers without food or water or sanitary facilities. They could escape by walking down interminable stairs, taking hours to do so, but, if they did – where could they go?

People can survive for a remarkably long time – weeks or even months – without food but they cannot last long without water. Only a few days. So, when the taps ran dry, what was there to do? The answer, as a few people quickly realised, was the massive fire fighting water tank at the top of the building.

So the sprinkler supply pipes were tapped – some by the simple but crude expedient of using a hacksaw or bullet to pierce the pipe. 200,000 gallons may sound a lot but, when there are 30 to 40 thousand people in the one building it doesn't last long, especially if there are bullet holes continuously leaking.

There was also the fact that the water in the fire fighting tanks was not sterile and a few people took to lighting fires (from smashed desks and furniture) to boil and sterilise the water.

Suffice to say that, during the Crash, there were a great number of horrendous fires, some, it was said, caused not by accident but by maniacs and psychopaths. The draining and emptying of the fire control tanks was something the building designers had never imagined. The tanks were always kept full – topped up after the slightest incident. With no working sprinkler system, fires rapidly got out of control.

It had been found, over a number of years, that the cheapest and most efficient way to build a functional skyscraper, to take 30,000 to 40,000 people was to build it with a structural steel skeleton. Some people still preferred to build entirely in reinforced concrete but it was more expensive and the building time was longer. Therefore, in 2120, most skyscrapers were built with a structural steel framework.

The problem with steel is that it cannot stand too much heat. As any old fashioned blacksmith knew – heat it up to red heat – even dull red – and it is soft and can easily be deformed and beaten into shape. The temperature at which most of its strength is lost is even lower. So – a massive steel column, normally capable of carrying thousands of tons, will buckle and collapse if it is heated to a high enough temperature.

This happened in the historic attack, in 2001, on the twin towers of the World Trade Centre in New York when terrorists deliberately flew two large passenger planes, each carrying over 50 tons of kerosene type aviation fuel, into the towers. These towers also incorporated the massive water tank/sprinkler system described earlier but the enormous amount of sustained heat generated by the large quantity of kerosene, which saturated the floors and even poured down the stairs, was more than the system could handle. The sprinklers ran out of water before the fires ran out of fuel and, from that moment, the towers were doomed.

The remarkable thing about the twin towers was not so much that they collapsed from the heat weakening the steel columns, but that they stood up for so long, enabling many people to escape.

In 2130, after the first stages of the Crash, most skyscrapers had no water in their fire control tanks. In these conditions, a relatively small fire could escalate into a tower destroying inferno.

---

It was February, 2130, and Pedro Da Silva looked at his wife Isabel in despair. They were in a small apartment on the 28th floor of a tower block in Sao Paulo in Brazil.

A few days ago the power had gone off and they were stranded.

"Not quite as bad as those higher up" he had told himself. (The tower had 120 liveable floors). "At least we can walk down if we have to."

But Isabel was too weak to make it down all those stairs and, even if they did, where could they go? This had been their home for ten years. They had no children – Isabel had a problem. Pedro had originally wanted children – at least two – he thought, but now – in this situation – maybe being childless was a good thing.

He jerked himself back to reality and realised Isabel was desperately thirsty. They had some tinned food in a cupboard, fortunately, because the food in the fridge was useless. Even here, on the 28th floor, the temperature was nearly 40°C now that the air conditioning was out. But they had had only a few bottles of water and soft drinks and now that was all gone. The taps, of course, were dry. However, he could get a pan of water if he went down a couple of floors. A friend of his had put a bullet through a supply pipe of the sprinkler system and then filled his bath. He had tried to plug the hole afterwards but the pressure was too great and he was only partially successful. There was water trickling down the stairway.

Isabel moaned. Pedro went into the kitchen, grabbed a saucepan and wearily headed for the stairs.

The water in the bath was stale and a bit discoloured. After all, you didn't need perfectly clean fresh water to fight fires.

He only took half a pan. They didn't know how long the bath of water had to last. They could only pray and hope. Maybe the power would come back on – later today – or tomorrow.

Pedro paused, back in his flat. He had been told this water caused dysentery. Isabel was sick enough as it was. What could he do? Boiling, would sterilise it but the electric cooker was out.

"Damn it! What could he do?" A burst of helpless rage surged through him. To hell with it! He would smash up some furniture – it wasn't theirs anyway – and make a little fire, in a corner of the kitchen and boil the water. Then he realised he couldn't even light a fire anyway. He had no means of starting it. You didn't normally need matches – half way up a skyscraper.

Then he had an idea. Somewhere there was an old magnifying glass – one his father had used before he died and which he had kept as a memento. He rummaged around and finally found it, cleaned it and walked to the window where he pulled back the blinds. The sun was shining in at an angle but he placed the glass in the light and focussed the light to a spot on the back of his hand – and snatched it away. He found a thin sheet of paper, focussed the spot on it and watched it slowly char. The spot dazzled his eyes but he concentrated, held the spot carefully in place. The paper blackened, then a little flicker of a spark occurred, then a small flame. Pedro dropped the paper and trod on it, then went to choose the most suitable furniture to break up. Half an hour later he had a little fire going on the floor of the kitchen area. He knew he shouldn't be doing this but he had to help Isabel. He rigged a little metal framework, from coat hangers, over the fire and put the pan to boil. It needed a bit more wood from the broken chair to do the trick but, at last, it boiled. He let it simmer for a while – just to make sure. It seemed to take forever to cool but, just as the light was going, he took some of the water to Isabel. She looked at him with grateful eyes, drank a quarter of the water and murmured her thanks. Pedro drank part of the water himself, carefully placed the remainder on one side for tomorrow. He cracked a tin of beans, ate half himself and gave the rest to Isabel then settled down, in a chair to sleep.

Pedro had stomped out the remains of the fire after he had boiled the water. He couldn't spare any water to damp it down – but it was out anyway. He slumped into the chair, desperately tired and was soon fast asleep.

Pedro awoke, gasping, late in the night. The room was full of smoke. His head was swimming but he forced himself out of the chair and over to Isabel on the bed. She was very quiet and, when he tried to rouse her, did not respond. He tried to lift her, intending to carry her out of the room and to the stairs. Before he could really get her in his arms the smoke seemed to intensify and the room swung around him. He collapsed, still holding Isabel, coughed twice and lapsed into unconsciousness.

An hour later, the whole floor was a raging inferno and the people in the floor below, screaming in terror. The people on the floor above were silent.

An hour later, as dawn broke, three floors were a sheet of flame.

As the sun just began to rise over the horizon, one side of the structure began to sag. Slowly, majestically, the enormous building began to topple. Half a million tons of steel and concrete and over twenty five thousand people. As it toppled it began to build up speed. At 45° there was massive momentum as the top half of the building slammed into the lower half of the next block. The second tower seemed to take it, shuddering as the first tower disintegrated and slid down it to the ground. Then the second tower hung there for a moment, slowly buckled at the base and then collapsed on top of the remains of the first tower. A colossal eruption of dust blotted out the entire scene – a gigantic memorial cloud for 55,000 people.

# 2131 – LOS ANGELES – USA

Patrick Doherty was in Glendale – slightly to the North of Los Angeles. He crept out of his hidey-hole, at the back of a burned out ruined building, that had once been a supermarket.

Patrick was a scavenger. A loner. It was the only way he knew to survive.

He checked the 9mm automatic was loaded and tucked it into his waist band. He also had a little .22 pistol in one sock and a vicious little knife, with a four inch blade, in the other.

Times had become really desperate now. Things had been pretty bad already but, after the Alpha HIV had come, everything had fallen apart. Food supplies had failed, water had failed everything had failed.

Fortunately, Patrick had once been in the Army. 'Special Forces' – as a matter of fact. He had learned unarmed combat. How to live off the land. How to survive in extreme circumstances. He was good with weapons. A crack shot with a rifle. Very fast and, most important, accurate with a pistol.

A lot of scavengers armed themselves with rapid firing machine pistols. Deadly when they worked – but they rapidly ran out of ammunition.

He preferred the 9mm. While others were blasting away he would fire one shot – but it was accurate. So far – he had stayed alive.

He had kept his head down – during the riots. Tucked himself away, while they looted the shops and burned the buildings. He had found himself a nice little hidey-hole, well hidden and well stocked with food and bottled water.

He was not averse to a little looting himself. When the food in the down town stores had run out, the mobs had burned the stores and turned on each other. There had been a blood bath. Safe in his little hide-away he had listened to the fire-fights. Gradually they had reduced and he wondered how many had survived. Only the cleverest – and the most ruthless.

When his food and water had finally run out, Patrick had been forced to come out and resume scavenging.

By now – all the apartments and all the private houses had been raided – for whatever food and supplies they contained.

Many home-owners had defended their property with bullets. Fighting to the last round to ward off the swarms of scavengers. But starving people are desperate – just as desperate as the defenders. They did not just go away.

Armed bands of marauders learned to co-operate. Timing their attacks and smashing their way into houses, at several different locations at the same time. They learned to do reconnaissance and work out a co-ordinated plan of attack. After a successful attack – the place was torched.

Patrick survived. He did his own reconnaissance; his own raids. He developed his camouflage – as a hopeless derelict who had somehow survived. He would approach other scavengers, sitting by their fires, eating food they had looted from somewhere – some private apartment – leaving death and destruction in their wake. He would totter up to them, lull them into relaxing their guard. Then out would come the 9mm. Three or four rapid accurate shots. Or, sometimes, lightning fast moves with the knife.

Now – his stomach was growling. He hadn't had food for days. He must eat.

Slowly, cautiously, he came out. There was nobody around. He adopted his shuffle and wandered off into a maze of ruined buildings.

For hours he wandered. Nothing. No animals. No birds No people. And then – he picked up the scent of wood smoke. Faint but unmistakeable.

He checked the direction of the breeze – tracked to the left. When the smell disappeared he backtracked to the right. Picked up the smell again. Gradually he tracked the source of the smell down. Eventually he saw it.

There were two men – huddled by what looked like a small water tank – probably a header tank from a domestic water supply – raised up on bricks and with a small fire underneath. There was a wooden desk to one side – that they were breaking up for fuel.

Patrick slowly approached – in his drunken vagrant style. The men were eating – noisily with their fingers – small pieces of meat. Several more pieces were on a piece of wood nearby – cooling.

"Could ye spare a bit – for an old man" said Patrick.
The one man produced a large, dangerous looking knife.

"Shove off! You old bastard!" he said. "We have nothing to spare."

"OK! OK! Keep cool! I'm going."

Patrick turned, as if to go. The man relaxed and put the knife away. In that moment Patrick moved. The 9mm kicked twice.

Patrick tucked the gun back into his waist band and approached the fire. He grabbed one of the bits of meat from off the wood. It was quite hot but not too hot to eat. Delicious! Whatever it was, it was delicious. He ate the rest of the meat off the makeshift platter.

When it was all gone he turned his attention to the simmering tank. A small piece of meat rose to the surface then disappeared. So – there was some left.

He looked for something to fish out the pieces from the boiling water. Any extra meat was very welcome. It would do for tomorrow and even, maybe, the next day.

Patrick came back to the simmering tank, just in time to see a piece of meat disappear below the surface. He noticed that, on this piece, there had appeared to be some discolouration – a blemish on the white flesh. But that didn't matter. If there was a bit that was bad he could cut it out.

In the next five minutes he rescued several pieces. Then another piece floated to the surface.

Patrick stared – then his stomach heaved. Suddenly he knew what the discolouration was. It was a tattoo.

# MARCH – 2135 – THE 'AMUNDSEN' VISITS SOUTH AMERICA

Lars Andersen picked his way through the ruins of what had been one of the world's great cities.

He had been surprised, at what they had put him through, after he had volunteered to go out on this mission – to explore and make contact with survivors in South America. Physical tests and psychological tests – especially psychological tests.

After he had passed they had warned him that what he would see would probably surpass his worst nightmares.

Norway and Scandinavia had been remarkably lucky. They had a relatively low population and, before the Crash, agriculture had greatly increased, particularly in the Northern areas, what with Global Warming and the introduction of frost resistant crops. In addition, the Arctic Ocean was one of the few ocean areas to still have fish in any quantity. Now that the Arctic Ocean was entirely clear of ice for several months every summer, their ships could fish all the way to the North Pole and beyond.

Finally, and very importantly, Norway had been very fortunate, in the early 21$^{st}$ Century, in having substantial quantities of oil and gas deposits in its territorial waters of the North Sea.

The Norwegians, being a canny people, had not squandered the sudden influx of wealth from the International sale of these resources – as many other nations did. They had enough sense to realise that oil and gas wealth would not last, and so they carefully husbanded the windfall and placed it in a separate investment fund. Separate, that is, from the normal Government income resulting from income taxes and taxes on commercial activities.

Bearing in mind that there would come a day when the oil income would dry up, they diversified and invested the wealth in building other, more permanent industries. One of these happened to be pharmaceuticals. Therefore, when the plague of HIVa appeared, Norway happened to have one of the best and most advanced drug producing pharmaceutical establishments in the World. They were quick off the mark and, although completely new drugs had to be developed, were one of the first Nations to produce an effective anti-HIVa drug. Although, in the short time available – before HIVa

153

exploded into AIDS, they were unable to produce the vast quantities required, they were nevertheless, able to produce enough to protect the whole of Scandinavia. Scandinavia, therefore, was one of the few areas on the planet that managed to maintain law and order, keep its facilities and infrastructure intact and working and also, to feed its people.

Lars had been only 20 years old at the time and, only later, did he realise how extremely fortunate he had been.

Britain, Ireland and Europe had also produced quantities of HIVa drugs, but nowhere near enough for the whole population. As a result Britain had lost more than 70% of the population of 105 million and, for a time, teetered on the brink of total collapse.

Europe was worse. 80% of the population was lost and the area was in a state of near chaos for two years.

Scandinavia, first, looked after its own, then concentrated on helping its neighbours – Europe, Britain and Ireland recover.

They supplied anti HIVa drugs, food, other medical supplies, equipment and agricultural supplies – seed grain, seed potatoes and so on. Then, as Europe began to recover, they turned their attention elsewhere and began to send survey ships, around the world, to make contact with surviving groups and, later, to send supplies.

They knew, from radio messages, that there were large groups of survivors and enclaves in various parts of the world and were anxious to do their best to help. However, Scandinavia was a low population area with limited resources, which is why they concentrated on helping Europe first.

Now, three years after the Crash, a number of ships had been despatched, all over the World; to make contact and see the situation in the enclaves first hand, and decide which ones should be the first to receive assistance. It had also been decided there should be a permanent record created, of the devastation of the cities and infrastructure, to prove to future generations how terrible the Crash had been and to convince people it must never be allowed to happen again.

Accordingly, in addition to the exploration teams, the ships would carry trained camera crews, and they would visit various cities although they already knew they had been abandoned.

Lars, was on the first ship, from Scandinavia, the 'Amundsen' to visit South America after the Crash.

So now, here he was, walking through the ruins of the city that had been Rio-de-Janeiro. At first he and his colleagues, having anchored the ship in the bay, had only explored the ruins in groups, armed to the teeth and in 'flak' jackets. (He had once asked where the word 'flak' had come from but nobody knew).

They need not have bothered. The ruins were, indeed, totally deserted. After two days they had seen no sign of a live human being whatsoever.

To walk through the ruins and explore the remains of buildings and apartments was sheer horror. Now he knew why they had carried out the psychological tests and checked his family's history for mental stability.

Human bones and skeletons were everywhere. In many apartments, skeletons were littered around – many with bullet holes in the skulls. In others it could be seen, some of the bones had been smashed with machetes and, in some, the skeletons were lying as if the family had simply laid down and gone to sleep. Some with obvious parents and children still cuddling in bed.

Many of the apartments had been burned and Lars had learned not to go in these.

They found the favelas – the shanty towns built on the outskirts of Rio had all been burned to the ground. Despite the fact that the city had greatly expanded in the hundred years before the Crash and the efforts of many Governments to get rid of them, the favelas had always come back, like some unstoppable parasitic growth. Now they were gone.

From the unbelievable numbers of skeletons and bones Lars had realised that, in the later phases of the Crash, all services had collapsed and organised burials discontinued. The city must have become one gigantic charnel house.

He could not imagine what it must have been like, with all the bodies, and the heat. No wonder the survivors had totally abandoned the city.

It made him think of the ruins of the ancient city of Angkor-Wat – found in the jungles of Cambodia in the 20$^{th}$ Century. What had once been a great city, had been found mainly intact – as though the inhabitants had, one day, simply walked away.

After two days of exploring Rio, Lars and his companions had found no sign of living persons so they ditched their flak jackets and often explored solo, carrying a back pack with food supplies and a plentiful quantity of water. The heat was oppressive even in the early morning and evening. Mid-day was almost unbearable.

Lars glanced upwards, to the great statue of Christ, arms outstretched, as if blessing the blackened and mouldering ruins of the city. The statue was undamaged. Lars and a friend had picked their way to the base station of the cable car system, a few days ago and found it wrecked, with one of the cars riddled with bullet holes – evidence of a vicious fire fight between gangs – desperate for survival.

Lars decided they were definitely not going to find anybody here and he wanted a break from the sickening horror and devastation. They would now move further South – Montevideo or Buenos Aires. Maybe there would be people there where, perhaps, it would be a little cooler.

He had picked his way along a rubble strewn street to a little plaza where he paused and looked along other streets. They were all the same – ruined and deserted. He turned, to start to make his way back, and in that instant, something caught his eye. He felt sure, something had moved.

For half a minute he stood there, scanning the rubble. He was just about to turn away when he saw it again. Incredulously he saw it was the head of a dog. A mongrel dog, peering at him from behind the rubble. Then – the face was gone. For a moment he wondered if he had imagined it. How could a dog – a live dog – possibly have survived in this wilderness? Through this holocaust? Impossible! And then it came again, in a slightly different place. He stared at it until he was quite sure.

"Hello! Buster!" he said – and the dog was gone.

Lars waited quietly, not moving, for about two minutes. Then he saw it, over to the left, peering at him around the end of a low wall. This time he said nothing, moved very, very slowly, and reached for the pack on his back. The dog was gone. Lars pulled the pack forward, rummaged inside and found what he wanted – a processed meat sandwich. He extracted the slice of meat, held it between his fingers and slowly extended his arm. He stood like that for a long minute and then the dog's face appeared again. It stared at him and it stared at the meat but it did not come out.

Lars was baffled and wondered what to do next? And then he realised. The dog must be very intelligent. To have survived in this hell hole was almost unbelievable. He must have been tempted before – by people with guns. Had probably seen other dogs slaughtered. Maybe even – eaten.

Lars pondered! Just how intelligent was he? Then he had an idea.

He began to take off his gear and then his clothes – everything – until he stood stark naked. He stepped forward, away from the clothes, spread his arms, fingers outstretched and turned slowly around, maintaining the posture, then stopped and stood there.

The dog's face appeared and stared at him, unmoving for what seemed an age. Lars' arms were beginning to ache. And then the dog came out, very, very slowly, and stood there, looking at him, close to the wall, ready to bolt at the slightest movement. The dog was very thin, he saw. Not quite emaciated but not far off. He must be starving – and yet he resisted the lure of the meat. Without moving he spoke in a very low voice.

"Its OK. Buster! OK! I won't harm you!"

The dog stood there. Its tail wagged slightly. Slowly Lars lowered his arms, keeping his fingers open and his arms away from his body. Slowly, cautiously, it came towards him. There was something of the Alsatian there and possibly a Collie, Lars saw.

He remembered when he was a child and his parents had given him a dog. A beautiful little golden Cocker Spaniel puppy. He had been enchanted. They had come to him on his birthday, just as he had woken up, in his bed, still in his pyjamas, and placed the pup near his pillow. He had got out of bed, lay down on the carpet and the pup had been all over him, radiating friendliness, warmth and happiness. There had been an instant bond and the dog had been his close companion for many years.

Slowly Lars stretched out his hand, palm down, towards the dog and slowly, hesitantly, it came to him. Finally it stood there, inches from his fingers. It craned its head forward, licked his hand. He gently reached forward, slowly rubbed the top of its head, ruffled his ears. The tail was wagging now. Lars slowly stepped back, put on his clothes and gear very steadily, very deliberately. The dog stood there. He took the piece of meat from his pack and offered it. Very gently it took it from his fingers – then wolfed it down. He found another sandwich and the second piece of meat went the same way.

Lars laughed, reached out with both hands, ruffled his face, pulled his ears gently. The dog went mad. His tail wagged furiously. He was beside himself with joy, turning round and round, on the spot, making little noises of happiness and pleasure.

Things had come right! He had finally found a human that behaved as he instinctively knew a human should. This is how it ought to be – with man and dog happy in each others company – as it had been for thousands of years. Dogs had learned to trust man – and love him with total loyalty and utter, unswerving devotion.

The dog had come home. So far as he was concerned – all was now right with the world.

---

Two days later they left Rio and tracked in a South Westerly direction along the coast. Again they anchored and sent a search party, inland a few miles, to the city of Sao Paulo which, before the Crash had become a far larger city than Rio.

If anything Sao Paulo was worse than Rio. As they approached the city everything seemed to be coated in a layer of grey dust. In between the standing skyscrapers were great piles of rubble. Lars knew, from pictures he had been shown, that Sao Paulo had been a city of skyscrapers. It still was, but there were large gaps and he gradually realised the gaps were where tower blocks had been and where now were just huge piles of rubble. At first he thought there must have been a massive earthquake – to do such damage but, on closer inspection, every rubble pile showed signs of burning. Many of the standing skyscrapers showed no sign of damage whatsoever. They had simply been abandoned.

The rest of the city was the same as Rio. Skeletons and bones everywhere. Sickened and appalled they returned to the ship, raised the anchor and sailed south, down to the mouth of the river Plate and the cities of Montevideo and Buenos Aires.

They found those cities just the same. Abandoned cities of death. Although they were further south – even the heat seemed just as oppressive. After two days exploring Montevideo and two in Buenos Aires they sailed south again.

A few days later they were dropping anchor in the bay near Bahia Blanca when a deckhand shouted.

"Skipper! Skipper! There's a boat coming out to us!"

Just to be on the safe side, everybody grabbed weapons and stood ready but it was soon obvious no hostility was intended. A small group came aboard, led by a tall imposing man of obvious aristocratic Spanish descent. Lars, who had learned Spanish especially for this trip, stepped forward and welcomed them.

"We too are very glad to see you! I am Carlos Francisco Garcia and these are my friends. As you know, from our radio messages, we have a large enclave on shore – probably 100,000. Thousands more survivors are coming in everyday, from the north. At the moment we are working very hard setting up cultivated areas – using irrigation from the rivers. We are mainly living on fish from rivers and sea and also every type of edible shellfish we can gather around the coast. Cultivation is our top priority – and some form of shelter. We are expecting several million survivors to come down from the north in the next twelve months. Any help you could give us would be greatly appreciated."

Lars explained that the ship was purely exploratory but they might be able to arrange for a shipload of supplies to be sent in the next few months.

Carlos went on to explain how the enclave worked.

"On the Estancias we were badly hit by the HIVa – with no vaccines or medication – losing many of our relatives and workers. There was no problem, of course, with food and water supplies. Our primary problem was marauding bands of scavengers, coming south from the big cities. Fortunately, several friends, from other Estancias and I had foreseen that one day, some sort of collapse could happen and we had built underground bunkers and redoubts and made sure we had plenty of supplies, guns and ammunition. We fought off a number of scavenger bands – they were usually poorly organised and soon left us to look for easier targets. Then we began to get bands of genuine refugees, not intent on violence but only wanting food and help. We organised these into working parties. Groups building shelters, others fishing, others scouring the shore for shellfish, others preparing land for cultivation. Gradually we developed an enclave of thousands, working together for mutual help and survival. Newcomers were told what we were trying to do. Told they must work hard and stick to the rules if they wanted to stay. If not, they could go on their way. Above all – violence would not be tolerated. Most people had seen enough violence and opted to stay. We are struggling and life is very tough but, as I said, we are now about 100,000 and think, if we can get agriculture going again, we shall be OK."

Lars looked at the tall Spaniard with new respect. He could only guess at the courage, the effort of will, the determination that had enabled this man and his friends to create such an enclave.

"Senor Garcia! This is why we are here. To help such groups as yourselves. We will do everything we can to help you – but it will take a little time to get supplies here."

"I understand! Anything you can do. Anything at all – will be appreciated."

Two days later the Amundsen sailed North.

# 2141 – WORLD GOVERNMENT INTRODUCED

In 2141 – Six years after the end of the Great Crash, a World Government was introduced. For several years, before the new government system was created, there had been many debates and discussions as to what form of Government it should be. Everybody agreed on one thing. The Great Crash, or anything like it, must never, ever, be allowed to occur again. It was time for a World Government. What they could not agree on was how it should be formed and how it should operate. Some of the greatest minds on the planet focussed on the problem and spent some time in careful consideration. What they finally proposed was unprecedented and remarkable.

They spent considerable time thinking about the problems that would face the new Government. The new World Order would be different from anything that had gone before.

Firstly, all the Nations and Races of the World must be welded together and administered in as fair and reasonable a manner as possible. No group must have any grounds for claiming that it was having unfair treatment. There must be World Wide control of Population and, since the world population was still too high at 2.0 billion, universal birth control laws would have to be applied.

Since scientists had calculated that a human population of no more than 500/600 million should be the target – if the human race was to continue to exist comfortably and sustainably into the far future – then a Universal 'One Child' policy would have to be introduced, for a period of up to 120 years. When the population was reduced to 500/600 million then the policy could be relaxed and a target, of 2.2 children per family, to maintain a steady world population, could be adopted. (2.2 rather than 2.0 is regarded as closest to a true balance figure).

A strong and effective Government would certainly be needed to enforce that. Then there was the uncomfortable fact that the world could never go back to the old 'Free Enterprise' system – with its cut throat competition and 'Laissez Faire' attitude that had led to so much exploitation and waste of natural resources. The Earth was far too impoverished for that. Like it or not (and many did not), all commercial and industrial activity must be tightly controlled. As one

161

of the world's leading intellectuals said – "Not back to the ghastly old communist system – surely!" But, as was eventually realised and accepted, - if the human economic system had to be balanced and restricted indefinitely – and never, ever, permitted to go for economic expansion and growth beyond a certain level, then – it was the only way. For the system to work, the entire human psychology of living must change. Whilst it was agreed, in the early stages, as the world was adjusting to the new, permanent population level of 500/600 million, there would be a state of flux; a period of adjustment.

When the final level was reached, people should be allowed to achieve the highest possible standard of living and personal satisfaction concomitant with a sustainable and satisfactory planet. After that, no further additional exploitation of natural resources could be allowed. People would have to learn to live happily under those restrictions indefinitely – into the far, far, future.

"What type of Government would be capable of handling that?" said many sceptics.

"It is simply impossible" said others.

So – the great minds of the Earth pondered the problem. They carefully considered all the types of government that had been previously adopted (with any degree of success), going back a couple of thousand years. The Monarchy had its virtues – and also its snags. At one time a king had absolute power – at least until the Church arose.

When a nation had, as they sometimes did, a benign king – a king who was intelligent, capable and responsible – who considered it his prime duty to administer the kingdom well and look after his subjects – then the nation usually prospered. Unfortunately, all too often, the nation ended up with a power mad megalomaniac who exploited his subjects rather than looked after them. Sometimes, because of the rules of succession, they had a raving madman as king.

Dictatorships could also be efficient – but Dictators had almost always clawed their way to the top. They were usually obsessed with power, and rarely cared anything for the people.

Democracy was held forth as a better way to govern. But was it really? Whilst it could be said that democracy gave the people a say in choosing the Government, in reality it had some considerable snags. Politicians were often extrovert, smooth talking hypocrites and liars; more interested in their own prestige, aggrandisement and glory than in the welfare of the people, although some progress was made, mainly because of the necessity to get people to vote for them.

The massive downside of the Party system was that politicians spent far more time arguing and scoring points off the opposition party, or parties, than in considering what was best for the country. Sometimes they knew perfectly well what should be done, but did not do it – for fear it would lose votes. Sometimes, if they thought they might lose the next election, they even, deliberately, took the wrong action – to leave the opposition a mess to inherit if they should win instead. Democratic governments and politicians were always wide open to the pressures and wiles of vested interests, graft, corruption, bribery (in all sorts of subtle forms) and were forever plotting and planning how to win the next election. Democracy, somehow, worked, but it had a great many defects.

A new system of World Government was finally proposed, approved and adopted in the year 2141.

In the new World Government there were no Government buildings. There was no President or Prime Minister. No arguing. No debates. No Party Politics. No Lobbying. No Bribery. No Vested Interests.

The Government consisted of ten thousand individuals, men and women, all over the globe, going about their daily lives. Every nation had its quota of World Government Members – in direct proportion to the number of people in the nation. Every member was proposed – as a person of outstanding intelligence, knowledge, wisdom and integrity – by colleagues, friends and their peers. Often they did not know they had been proposed. Once they had been proposed they were thoroughly vetted – for intelligence, background, capability, mental stability, health and psychological profile. This information was forwarded to a central super-computer which analysed the data and either chose or rejected the proposee. Often, the first the person knew about it was when they received a message stating that they had been chosen as a Member of the World Government and would serve a term of ten years.

Members could serve only between the ages of 35 and 60. To be chosen was considered both an honour and a duty. There was no remuneration or perks of any kind. If they wished, they could refuse the position but the people chosen rarely did. It was considered dishonourable to do so.

In practice it was not a particularly onerous obligation. Members of the World Government went about their daily lives in a perfectly normal manner. Only occasionally were they asked to carefully consider a Government proposal and to vote on it. After deciding, they simply used their computer, using a special pass code, and voted 'for' or 'against' or 'abstain'. The vote went to the central World Government Computer and was registered. The computer collated the votes and issued the decision. With ten thousand voting members the chances of a tie were negligible.

'Abstain' votes were usually recorded by Members who considered themselves unqualified to vote on the subject matter. A medical doctor, for instance, might consider himself unqualified to vote on a decision concerned with World Finance or the World Economy. Similarly a Banker or Financier might consider himself unqualified to vote on the universal use of some new vaccine. Every person who became a member of the World Government was required to take an Oath – promising to vote according to their conscience and for the Interests and Benefits of the Human Race as a whole.

All ten thousand members were equal in all respects. All members were continuously vetted for the ten years of membership. If a member should become mentally impaired, in any way, at any time, during the ten year period, they were 'cut out' by the computer and a new member, from the same constituency, instated. Members could also resign, at any time, if they wished. An unwilling member was not likely to function properly.

World Government was based, simply, on Nature. Every functioning World Government Member acted like a single cell in the brain of the entity that was the total human race. Ten thousand members had been chosen as a suitable number but that could be increased if it was deemed necessary. Only decisions of Global Importance were to be considered and ruled upon by the World Government. All subsidiary matters appertaining to individual states and nations, including the day to day running of those states, would be handled by National Governments and Local Councils. These were elected by the old fashioned democratic system. (People liked to think they had some say in how things were run). All National Governments and Councils could be overruled by the World Government if necessary.

# 2614 – THE 'ORION' FINDS TREASURE

In May 2130 at the beginning of the collapse, in Egypt, as the Army and Police were beginning to lose control, a small fishing boat eased out of Alexandria harbour, headed out to sea and then turned West, tracking along the African coast. For two days and two nights the boat travelled uneventfully but in the afternoon of the third day a problem arose. Another, slightly smaller, fishing boat appeared, ahead and a little to the south.

---

Achmed Salar and his two companions were out, as usual, scouring the sea for any sign of a ship, large or small. Although their boat looked like a fishing boat and Achmed and his friends looked like fishermen, the boat had two very powerful engines and, under a tarpaulin at the stern, were several automatic rifles and three RPGs (Rocket Propelled Grenades). The three men were pirates.

Slowly Achmed eased the boat North, not so much that it would be obvious they were going to intercept but to close the gap to within striking range. The vessel approaching them was small, but they had seen nothing else all day and it might be worth investigating.

Slowly the distance between the two boats narrowed; Achmed keeping his eye on the other for any sign of reaction. The skipper of the approaching boat was obviously nervous because, even while there was a good distance between them, Achmed saw he was turning North. He gunned the engines to full power, dropping all pretence and, within 20 minutes they had closed to within 150 metres.

Achmed stood up, holding a rifle, signalling the boat to stop and fired a short burst into the air. There were two men on the fishing boat and one stepped to the side, raising his hands in a gesture of surrender. The other man disappeared. Slowly, Achmed approached to 100 metres, his two companions standing in the prow with their weapons pointed.

Suddenly a hail of bullets came from the wheelhouse of the enemy boat and one of Achmed's friends toppled. The other opened fire, first cutting down the man who had stood in the open and then riddling the wheelhouse, before sinking to his knees and collapsing.

Achmed cursed, gunned the engines, and swung the boat away. As he did so he felt a hammer blow in his midriff and, looking down, saw the red patch of blood. In a rage, Achmed swung the boat anew and headed back for the enemy. He locked the steering and lurched to the stern, pulled up the tarpaulin and lifted one of the RPGs to his shoulder. A wave of nausea swept over him but he forced it aside and aimed the RPG at the enemy wheelhouse. Another bullet struck him in the chest just before he squeezed the trigger. The rocket blazed from its tube and then Achmed slowly sank to the deck. He had aimed at the wheelhouse but he was losing consciousness as he fired. The missile impacted the enemy boat just above the water line, detonated and blasted a hole in the side.

In the wheelhouse, the skipper dropped the automatic rifle and clutched at the wheel to steady himself. A bullet had come through the wood work and struck him in the thigh. Another had hit him in the stomach. He locked the wheel and then searched out the first aid kit. The bullet to his thigh had missed the artery and he strapped a pad over the wound. There was no exit wound so the bullet must still be in his leg. The stomach wound didn't look too bad but he knew he must be bleeding internally. After placing a pad over that, he went down to check the boat damage.

There was a substantial hole but most of it was above the water line. However, water was sloshing in occasionally. A wave of weakness swept over him and he knew his only chance was to get to shore and seek help. There was no way he could repair the boat in his condition. Returning to the wheelhouse he swung the boat towards the distant shore and switched the engine to full power. Three hours later he was still at the wheel but he knew he was a dying man. The shore was only a mile away now but the boat was wallowing horribly. Ten minutes later and the engine died. Ten minutes after that the boat slowly sank beneath the waves.

---

Mohammed Kassar stood on the prow of the research ship Orion and stared out over the blue Mediterranean.

It was May, 2614, and he and several other Archaeologists from the University of New Copenhagen were investigating the coast off Tunisia, primarily looking for the remains of Carthaginian and Roman galleys. It was reputed that a sea battle had occurred somewhere along this coast and so they were checking the sea bed using sonar.

After nearly 3,000 years any remains would show up as merely a ridge or deformation on the sea bed. Mohammed and his colleagues were equipped with personal diving gear that enabled them to go down and work for up to half an hour at 150 feet depth. Whenever they spotted a likely looking deformation on the sonar then one of them would go down and do a quick survey. Nineteen times out of twenty the formation would simply be a natural structure of the sea bed. Only when they found something really interesting would they set up the undersea robot explorer system.

At half past three Mohammed had a call from Sonar. He went down and had a look at the display.

"I've got an anomaly here" said Joe Gregson the sonar operator. "Don't know whether it's worth investigating. Its not large enough to be a galley but, you never know, might be the remains of an ancient commercial ship – with amphorae and all that."

Mohammed paused. He hadn't been down for three days. He felt like a dive but didn't really want to go waste his time.

He looked at the ripple on the sonar display again, mulled it over and finally said.

"Yes. OK. I'll go down."

Half an hour later he was ready. He checked everything, found it in order but noted that the gauge on his air bottle indicated he would only have enough air to stay on the bottom 12 minutes. Well! That was usually enough to check if it was a natural formation or something more interesting.

Ten minutes later he was over the side and diving steadily downwards through the clear water.

Reaching the bottom there was no sign of anything unusual and he realised he must have deviated in some way and lost the anomaly. He commenced a routine search procedure and gradually moved outwards from his initial position.

And there it was! A mound on the sea bed. He closed on it, checked his gauge and was startled to see he had only 3 minutes left. He slowly circled just above the hump. A slight projection caught his eye. He scuffed deposits from around it and cursed. It was the remains of a ship's wheel. And now he looked, there was a faint outline of the remains of a wheelhouse. Obviously this was what was left of a fairly modern fishing boat.

"Forget it!"

He straightened up, preparing to lift off and start the pull to the surface. As he straightened, his eye caught a bright metallic glint a few metres away.

He paused, looked at his gauge.

"Time up!"

On a whim, he grabbed his camera, swam over the metallic object, took a picture and headed for the surface.

Back aboard, he sorted himself out, had a coffee and, finally, checked his photo. There was definitely something metallic there. Something silvery.

"Pity it wasn't golden" he thought. He went to the computer, plugged the camera in and enhanced.

"How strange!" It seemed to be a corner of a metal box. There appeared to be some sort of whitish corrosion but there was a clear patch of silvery metal.

Mohammed called Joe over and showed him the photo.

"Your anomaly was just a fairly modern fishing boat but, just as I was leaving I spotted this and photographed it. I couldn't stay, I was running out of air."

"Hmm!" said Joe. "Perhaps some navigation equipment or a tool box or something."

"But it wasn't where the wheelhouse was. It was metres away, probably near where the prow would have been. I'm intrigued! Could you spare the time, tomorrow, for me to go down again and check it out."

Joe pondered.

"Well. OK! Don't suppose it'll matter to delay a couple of hours."

The following morning, having checked they were over the anomaly, Mohammed was over the side and on his way down, with camera and a few small tools. His air bottle was full this time.

He soon found the wreck, made his way forward, and found the metallic projection. He soon realised that it was much larger than he expected. Around it there was the rotten and encrusted remains of a wooden crate and a fragment of corroded metal strapping.

He chipped and hacked away and finally revealed what looked like a metal box. It was actually an exact cube about 35 centimetres each side. There was no sign of any hinges or catches anywhere. Finally he had it completely exposed. When he tried to turn it over he found he could rock it slightly but not move it over. After taking several photos he headed for the surface.

An hour later, everybody on the ship was speculating.

The following day, a winch was operating, with a cable and sling capable of lifting 250kg, going down to the wreck.

Mohammed was down there this time with several of his colleagues and they manhandled the cube out of the detritus and on to the sling. They were surprised to find that the cube, although apparently robust, was surprisingly light to handle in the water. A little lighter and it would have floated. 30 minutes later it was aboard the Orion.

When they had cleaned it and examined it they found that there were, indeed, no catches, hinges or any apparent way in. The cube looked like a solid block of aluminium but careful scrutiny showed it had been precisely welded, almost certainly by machine.

"Looks like we shall have to cut our way in" said Joe. "But we'll have to be very careful. We don't know what's in there."

"We have a very thin bladed, hand held, mini circular saw in the lab, that we use for cutting through ancient wood or even bone" said Mohammed. "Let's use that!"

Gently, gradually slicing deeper and deeper, they found the cube was a simple cubic box – 10mm thick. After about an hour, Mohammed had cut all the way around and gingerly lifted the top off the box, to reveal another metal box inside. This was found to be made of lead about 3mm thick. When he first cut through the lead there was a slight hiss of ingoing air, indicating the box had been hermetically sealed. Slowly he cut around the lead until, finally he could lift off the lead top.

Everybody on the ship was in the room now, crowding around.

When the lead lid came off he was faced with a mass of fibre – probably kapok. Gently, slowly he lifted the kapok out, bit by bit, until the object within was only covered with a few thin layers of silk. Mohammed took a deep breath and pulled off the silk.

"I don't believe this" he murmured. He reached into the box and gently, reverently, lifted the object. Placed it on the table. There was a general intake of breath and then a chorus of "Oh's and Wow's" throughout the room. They found themselves looking at one of the most stunningly beautiful artefacts ever created by the hand of man. The funeral mask of Tutankhamun.

# APRIL – 2647 – DAN KEALEY'S SHIP APPROACHES GREENLAND

Dan Kealey stood on a little observation platform, with the Ship's Engineer, on the fore-deck of the massive sailing ship taking him to Greenland. There was a stiff South Westerly wind blowing with fairly heavy seas. The ship was travelling North West and was heeled over to a considerable angle as well as pitching in the heavy swells. Fortunately, Daniel had a strong stomach. The rest of the immigrants (about 950) were down below, mainly in their bunks.

The ship had four towering, slender, masts, each mast carrying a single enormous, blue/black, sail. In addition to being efficient sails, the sails were also vast flexible solar panels. A large area of the upper deck was also blue/black colour. Every so often the ship turned, ropes and pulleys creaked, the great sails shifted over and the ship heeled, on a new tack. Not a single person was to be seen. Everything was entirely automatic. He had sought out the Ship's Engineer and asked him if he would mind explaining how the ship worked. To his surprise, the Engineer had been pleased. It was nice to find someone who was interested – and it made a break in routine.

"Is the ship powered only by wind and solar power?"

"Not quite. She does have a bio-fuel powered generator and a tank of fuel for emergencies but it is rarely used. The solar panels provide power for the computers and all the electric motors needed to operate the ship. There is a large, high energy–density, storage battery to provide backup power when needed and at night. Whatever the journey – the computers work out and plot the optimum route – taking into account wind direction and speed. They can control and tack the ship up wind to within a degree or two of the limit. Throughout the trip the computers update and re-compute for any changes in wind and conditions and are, of course, continuously in communication with the Global Weather Service computers. In the tropics or anywhere where the ship is becalmed the ship can switch to electric propulsion, even finally using the diesel/electric generator if there is insufficient battery power. The electric motor drive is, of course, hoisted out of the water and stored when not in use.

As you may have noticed, the ship is a different shape to the old ships, with an underwater bulbous projection at the prow and a

171

blunter forward shape. The rear end of the ship is extended and tapers down to what you could almost call a 'pointy rear end' with the boom and the electric motor drive raised out of the water.

The shape of the ship was strongly influenced by study of the shape of the Blue Whale – the biggest of all whales – weighing up to 100 tons or more and with a streamlined body. A blue whale, which unfortunately is now extinct, could cruise, almost effortlessly, for days and even weeks, at a speed of 16 kilometres an hour and could boost, if necessary, up to 50 kilometres an hour for a short time.

The real secret to the efficiency of the ship is the fact that the whole underwater surface is covered in a soft, rubbery plastic layer or skin. Way back in the 20th Century, scientists were amazed to see dolphins and porpoises swimming easily alongside ships at remarkably high speeds. They did calculations – using the drag factors and mathematics they used to design the ships of the day – and said that dolphins simply should not be able to travel at anything like the observed speeds. Their bodies could only, at the most, produce a fraction of the energy needed.

They investigated and found that the dolphins skin, and the layer beneath it , was very flexible and rubbery and, at high speeds, the skin flexed and moved in such a way as to vastly reduce the micro turbulence of the passing water that normally caused much of the drag that a solid hulled ship experienced.

Eventually the scientists managed to produce an artificial version of the dolphin skin – which is the rubbery coating used on this ship. With the push created by the sails this large ship can cruise easily at 20 to 25 kilometres an hour where, without the coating, it would only be able to do – say – 10 to 15. The ship is capable of transporting over a 1000 passengers across the Atlantic or several thousand tons of freight. Bigger versions, with six masts are used on the Pacific."

# 2647 – DAN KEALEY CHATS TO FRIENDS AND LEARNS ABOUT THE NEW CIVILISATION

It was July, 2647, and Daniel Kealey was lounging in a chair on the campus of the University of New Copenhagen chatting with his friends.

They had pulled a couple of tables together to make a single, large table.  Down the centre were various drinks, biscuits, cakes and fruit.

To Daniel's left sat Joshua M'beki, a tall elegant African and to his right was a slender, fine boned beautiful Chinese girl – Anna Chi Lin.

Immediately opposite Daniel was a tall, athletic blond Norwegian – Eric Gundarson and either side of Eric sat, on his left, Indira Beshti – an elegant dark skinned girl from Northern India and, to his right, a spick and span, smartly dressed Japanese – Shiro Hirokawa.

At the head of the table sat Pierre Cardin – a good looking, dark haired, bearded, Frenchman, full of gallic charm.

Despite their many backgrounds – from all over the world – they spoke English.  English was now the World Universal Language.  It stemmed from way back in the late 20th century when the first computers and mobile communicators were created and manufactured in America – an English speaking country.  The Industrial Revolution had also started in an English speaking country – Britain – and, for more than 100 years afterwards, nearly all the technical and scientific articles were printed in English.  Also, many of the nations of the world – at onetime part of the old British Empire – had become familiar with the language.

Some people (mainly the English themselves) had said that English was a difficult language to learn, but the truth was that it was relatively easy compared to others.  The old Chinese language – Mandarin – was fiendishly difficult by comparison and a Chinese typewriter – almost impossible.  The simple fact was – you could get by quite well, in everyday life, with just 500 words of English and everybody became familiar with the QWERTY keyboard.

However, many people, in countries all over the world, still liked to speak their own original language so it was extremely common for people to speak their native tongue as well as English.

As they sat there, drinking and chatting, an imposing looking Japanese, about 35 to 40 years old, walked up to their table.

"Good Afternoon! Professor Honda. Won't you join us?" said Eric.

"Certainly I will!" said Professor Shiro Hideki Honda. "Even better if you can spare a beer."

Daniel fetched another chair and the Professor sat down and took a sip of his beer. He asked how they were all settling in and laughed and joked with a very easy manner. After a while Daniel said.

"Professor Honda! I suppose I shouldn't impose on you now but there are so many things I would like to ask you – about Greenland – about science – about life here and so on. Please tell me if I am out of order."

Honda smiled. "Not at all! I am delighted you wish to learn. That is what I am here for. I am happy to transfer knowledge – both formally and informally. And if I can chat with my students out here, on a glorious day, and sipping a beer – so much the better."

"Here, on Greenland, as you know, we have this settlement of only 10 million people, so far, in the southern area and around the coast. This will gradually be increased to, maybe, 40 million or so in future as more ice melts and makes workable land available. With the Internationally agreed 'Universal Two Child Policy' now in force, the 10 million here will gradually increase due to ageing until they reach about 30 million. The other 10 million will be made up by immigration from over-populated areas in the rest of the world.

After the International Future of The Human Race Agreement, in 2342, when it was agreed the entire planet should belong to the human race as a whole and all old fashioned ideas of individual nations and boundaries should eventually be scrapped, Denmark agreed (as part of the International Agreement) to the shared colonisation of Greenland.

Every so often, an agreed batch of immigrants is allowed in and this will continue until the maximum permissible number of inhabitants is reached. In other words, the maximum number that can reasonably and self sustainably exist on Greenland into the indefinite future. We think that is likely to be 40 to 45 million.

Selection of immigrants is on a lottery basis. Every nation on
Earth is allotted a quota, based on the total population of that nation in
the year 2645. For instance China is allotted a quota of 2 million,
India 1.25 million, Africa 1.3 million, Europe 1.7 million and so on to
reach a grand total of 10 million immigrants to Greenland in the next
30 years.

So – if China, for instance has 20 million applicants to go to
Greenland, the 20 million will be allocated numbers and, out of that
20 million, the 2 million lucky ones will win their place in a computer
selected lottery. Only young single unattached people will be eligible.
The intent is to promote inter group mixing and produce a true multi
racial gene pool on Greenland in a few hundred years.

Another reason for the colony being formed only from young
people is to enable the group to devote most of its energies, in the first
40 years, to building the cities, dams, power stations, roads, railways
and general infrastructure, and not, initially, have the additional
burden of looking after the old and infirm. Similar colonies, (for want
of a better word) have been set up in Northern Canada, Alaska and
Siberia. The Great Crash of 2130 to 2133 demonstrated that the
sooner the human race is 'blended' into one indistinguishable group,
under a single World Government, the better."

Daniel smiled and, turning to Anna Chi Lin, said "Well! I'm
certainly happy with the system. It was a wrench, leaving my parents
in the old country – Britain – but how wonderful to be here in such a
green and pleasant land with such great friends."

For a moment they gazed across the valley, with its
flourishing green fields of crops, to the young forests along the lower
slopes of the mountains. Across the valley a clear and sparkling river
meandered and, in the far distance, a range of magnificent snow
capped mountains.

Way up the valley they could see the mighty buttress of a
dam and the squat power station buildings below.

"Professor – I must say I was surprised, when I arrived, that I
did not see arrays of wind turbines as I was so used to – back home"

"No. We are very fortunate here and most of our power is
produced by hydro-electric power stations on our many large rivers.
The perfect situation. Reliable, clean, continuous power. No

pollution of any kind and very good economics. We have very long life turbines and generators.

Thank heaven we don't have the old Nuclear Power Stations, with all the hazards and nuclear waste problems. Do you know some of them took 300 years to decommission and cost far greater sums to decommission than to build? We don't have coal fired power stations either! When the oil and gas ran out, the old countries, desperate for energy, turned to the massive reserves of coal still remaining and gasified vast quantities of the coal layers in situ in a process called Underground Gasification of Coal. The gas produced was burned in enormous power stations producing vast quantities of $CO^2$.

Efforts were made to extract the $CO^2$, before it left the power station chimneys, and this was then liquefied and pumped through miles of pipes and, finally, forced at high pressure into rock formations deep underground. Millions of tons were disposed of in this way but the cost was enormous, used up even more energy and, in the end, the amount of $CO^2$ being produced by the power stations was so great that the quantity being sequestrated made very little overall difference. So, by 2070, the system of $CO^2$ sequestration was abandoned.

We actually still do use underground Gasification of Coal, here on Greenland, but mainly for conversion into liquid fuels, rubber, plastics and chemicals. Very little for directly fuelling power stations.

Greenland, and the world, was fortunate, of course, in still having unexploited deposits of various metals and minerals after the Crash. The reason being these deposits were sealed in under a mile thick layer of ice and are only now becoming available.

We are also fortunate in having many rivers very suitable for the introduction of salmon – now a major world food source.

The city of New Copenhagen is built close to a major river which, incidentally, is a near perfect salmon river. The long building you see in the distance, alongside the river, is the salmon hatchery.

To bring salmon back, from near extinction, we had to take some of the last few wild salmon left, for spawning. The farmed salmon, so popular before the Crash, had lost their natural foraging and homing instinct.

In this hatchery alone we now hatch 500,000 eggs a year, rear the young salmon to a certain size, then introduce them to the river. The baby salmon pick up the scent of the river, which is then

programmed into their brains.  They go to sea, instinctively travel to
the feeding areas, grow to full size and come back home to their river
of origin.

When we have fully re-established the salmon run, we expect
a million salmon or more to come back up this one river alone, every
year, and we have many similar rivers.  They will then be sustainably
cropped and the rest will naturally reproduce in the river and we can
then dismantle the hatchery.

A few miles from here, we are mining a gravel deposit in the
river flood plain to provide gravel for this and other rivers.  We grade
the gravel and use it to create near perfect spawning beds further
upstream.  We have eliminated some birds such as mergansers and
cormorants to give the baby salmon the best chance of survival.  We
also limit the number of seals along the Greenland coast.  If we did
not do this, the seals, which heavily predate the returning salmon,
would multiply to enormous numbers.

There is now a World Salmon Protocol which prohibits all
fishing for salmon at sea, both in the salmon feeding areas and along
the migration routes.

Salmon will be a major sustainable source of protein for
humans all over the world in the future."

––––––––––––––––––

"Professor" said Daniel "I'm reading about the terrible
effects of Alpha HIV during the 'Great Crash'.  Where did the Alpha
HIV originally come from?"
Professor Honda spread his hands.

"Alpha HIV didn't really come from anywhere.  We think it
was generated within people.  If you are asking where it first started,
we really don't know.  The whole world was infected before anyone
knew what was going on.

Research indicates it probably started in southern Europe, but
with air transport as it was in those days it could have been anywhere.
People had been suffering from HIV (the old strain) for over 100
years.  However, by the end of the 21$^{st}$ Century HIV had been
forgotten, sidelined as relatively unimportant.

Where once, back in 1990, it had frightened the world, by
2128 it was now considered no more important than a common S.T.D.

(Sexually Transmitted Disease). It had not been eradicated but, anyone who thought they had HIV, (casual sex was still the most common form of propagation), went to a clinic, got themselves tested and, if they were infected, were simply given a pill to take, weekly, for the rest of their lives. The drug suppressed the effects of HIV and rendered them non infectious (but did not totally eliminate it), so the person could live a normal life. There were still a few million new cases a year but they were gradually reducing.

So – It was no longer considered a serious problem. In 2128, only a couple of small labs still made the medication.

Originally, human beings caught HIV from monkeys – around the years 1900 to 1920, probably from eating them – which was common at that time.

Simian Immunodeficiency Virus (SIV) had been endemic in monkeys, probably for thousands of years. Such a virus usually crosses the species barrier by picking up genes from another virus endemic to the second species."

"You mean the viruses mate – in the same way that bacteria from different species sometimes conjoin or mate to swap genes?"

"No! Viruses are different. They are a very small – basically a primitive parasitic life form. In fact, it is arguable if they are really alive at all. Unlike bacteria they cannot independently reproduce themselves. The only way they can reproduce is to break into a living cell and hi-jack the cell's genetic system to reproduce copies of themselves. A virus is basically just a packet of genes in a fairly simple container.

To reproduce – a virus has to commit suicide i.e. destroy itself. It attacks a cell by cutting a hole in the cell's outer wall, with an enzyme, then enters the cell through the hole. Once inside, its outer container disintegrates and releases its genetic material, sometimes in fragments. The genetic material then migrates and insinuates itself into the genes of the cell. The cell genes are hi-jacked and forced to use all the cell's reserves and energy into making copies of the virus.

The cell eventually dies and bursts, releasing anything from dozens to thousands of new virus particles. These then migrate and infect other cells. It almost seems a miracle that we can survive virus infections at all.

However, the body has a very powerful immune system.
Millions of immune system cells constantly patrol the body, monitor
everything and attack any foreign life form – from quite large
parasites to bacteria and viruses. With virus infections, the immune
system cells detect virus infected cells and destroy them. Destroy the
complete cell – eat them – you could say and eliminate the lot – cell
plus all the virus genes and parts and all.

HIV is unusual. It actually parasitises the immune cell itself.
Very insidious! The body is, of course, producing immune cells all
the time, but HIV gradually destroys them faster than they are
produced so the body's immune system gradually weakens.

The HIV virus doesn't attack any other type of body cell, so
there are no obvious symptoms. Symptoms only arise when the
immune system is so impoverished that it cannot cope with handling
the other diseases that constantly attack the body. Only then – maybe
12 months or more after the initial infection – does the infected person
realise anything is wrong. Meanwhile that person has become flooded
with HIV virus particles.

Fortunately, the old HIV was not infectious or contagious
and could only be transmitted person to person by intimate body
contact i.e. sexual or, rarely, wound to wound contact or by blood
transfusions or by drug addicts sharing needles. Nevertheless, despite
these limitations, as many as 40 million people, all over the world, had
been infected by the end of the 20th century.

If we consider the replication of viruses, we realise that, if a
person catches more than one virus disease at the same time – which
is quite common – then there can come about a situation where a cell
is infected by two different viruses at the same time. You can
therefore, have a situation where two viral genetic sequences, from
different viruses, are jostling to infiltrate the cells genes at the same
time.

Occasionally, therefore, the two different viral gene strands
can become disrupted, mixed and a hybrid virus produced. It is in this
way that virus diseases cross the species barrier. This process occurs
fairly frequently, all the time.

A number of human diseases are believed to have passed
from animals to humans in this way – such as HIV, Ebola, Marburg
virus, Syphilis and many others.

A classic example was the murderous 1918 influenza epidemic – which killed more people than the preceding Great War. This influenza was proved to have been an avian (bird) flu which crossed the species barrier – because of close human contact with domestic chickens.

Later the SARS virus and H5N1 flu – both very dangerous viruses – also crossed from birds to people, but these were spotted early and contained by rapid action.

It is believed HIVa was created by a person with HIV being, at the same time, infected by influenza or the common cold. Since an HIV sufferer could be flooded with replicating HIV viruses for years, then this occurrence must have been extremely common. Why the HIV/Influenza hybrid did not occur many, many years before it did has been a puzzling question. The answer is probably that HIV actually needed several genetic modifications at the same time – not just one to convert it to HIVa – and this would greatly reduce the likelihood of it happening. Nevertheless, in 2128 it finally did.

We thus ended up with HIVa – a virus as catching as the common cold but which showed no symptoms for 6 to 12 months or so and was fundamentally lethal. The final result was that, before HIVa was detected and fully recognised for what it was, over 25% of the world population was infected. At this point it was quite impossible to stop and, in a few more weeks, 95% of the entire world population was infected with HIVa.

It has been suggested, by a number of people, that the genetic modifications to the old HIV virus, necessary to create HIVa, is such that it is more likely HIVa was created by a psychotic rogue scientist than that it naturally evolved. We shall never know!

When the Scientists and Authorities around the world first learned of the situation, and realised we were on the cusp of a Global Disaster of unprecedented proportions, they acted rapidly to keep the information top secret so as not to cause planet wide panic. They secretly gave orders to the pharmaceutical companies to produce as many millions of doses of the existing HIV drugs as possible – drugs, which you may remember, did not cure but only rendered HIV dormant. Although the drug companies complied, it was found that HIVa did not respond to the old drugs as HIV did and completely new drugs had to be developed. This took time and it was found to be

impossible, in the limited time available, to produce the many billions
of doses which would be required for worldwide treatment.

Firstly, Europe and America then China and Japan which
also had the necessary pharmaceutical production facilities, ordered
full scale production. However, the time it takes to develop such
drugs and get them into full production and the speed with which
HIVa develops into full blown AIDS meant that only limited supplies
could be available before 2132. Consequently all production of anti
HIVa drugs could be made available, initially, only to key personnel
and, later, to indigenous populations. Supplies were allowed to be
exported elsewhere only when the national requirements were
fulfilled. Since this was quite impossible in 2131, it meant that Africa
and a number of other areas received no early consignments of anti
HIVa drugs whatsoever and, no doubt, helped create the situation that
Africa was the area to first suffer total economic and organisational
collapse. However, many other countries rapidly followed Africa into
collapse and chaos. Indeed, nowhere escaped totally unscathed and
HIVa went on to create the greatest disaster in the entire history of the
human race."

They sat silent for sometime then Anna spoke.

"Professor Honda! I know you have been involved in
developing some of the latest techniques of DNA manipulation and
Genetic Engineering. Can you tell us what you do and some of the
applications?"

Honda laughed.

"Good Grief! There would be enough for several full scale
lectures there but I'll try to summarise and give you an idea.

When we finally mastered and computerised Genetic
Engineering we found we had tremendous power. Power that we had
to use very, very carefully. We could delete, transpose, replace or
modify any gene, anywhere, on any chromosome of any animal.

We can simply insert a sample, containing the DNA of the
selected animal, in the analyser and, in a couple of hours, we have the
complete genetic sequence – down to the last letter – on a data base.
The G.E. computer has been programmed with the function of every
gene. We simply instruct the computer with what we wish to do and
the computer controls equipment that modifies the chromosome of the
chosen animal to give us exactly what we want, and then inserts it into

an egg cell of the animal. The egg cell is then implanted into a living specimen of the chosen animal and triggered to begin development. In due course the first modified animal is born or hatched from an egg and – away you go.

It is now perfectly easy to eradicate almost any animal we wish. The simplest way is to create a male of the species that is stronger, more sexually aggressive, more capable and longer lived than a normal male and whose progeny is always 100% of copies of himself. No females. When these are turned loose they compete with the natural males, mate with the natural females and produce many more modified males, and so on, in an exponential progression. In a remarkably few generations there are no more females and the species dies out. This method can be used to eradicate any species that uses simple male/female reproduction.

You may have noticed that, earlier, I said we could eradicate almost any animal we wish. I said that, because there are a few species of animal on which it won't work. It won't work, for instance, on animals that are hermaphrodite such as earthworms and snails. Snails have both male and female genital organs. Two snails will mate and cross fertilise each other. Both then produce eggs. There is also a species of lizard in South America that has only one sex – female. The lizards reproduce by parthenogenesis. No males needed. There are also some fish that spend half their lives female and then switch to being male. I assure you we could eradicate these if we wanted to but it would be a bit more tricky.

The simple male modification technique was used, first, to eradicate certain biting flies and mosquitoes. The disease Malaria has been almost totally eradicated by eliminating the mosquitoes that transmitted it. Malaria itself is amazingly difficult to control. It is a parasitic disease with half a dozen different stages in its life cycle. As you know, it is a devastating parasitic disease which attacks human blood cells. It has the remarkable ability to evade the immune system by regularly and continuously changing its surface proteins so it cannot be recognised and targeted by the immune system. Since Malaria itself was so difficult, it was obviously much easier to target and eradicate the vector – the mosquitoes. Other biting flies that transmitted diseases were also eliminated.

We also eradicated the cane toads that had been mistakenly introduced into Australia – and the rabbits. We eliminated the stoats, goats and deer that were causing trouble in New Zealand and the grey squirrels that had been wrongly introduced into the island of Britain.

Some people wanted to eliminate the camels that had been introduced into Australia but it was decided they weren't doing much harm and there were benefits. We have to be very careful, of course, before an eradication is authorised, especially if a local eradication, such as the goat elimination in New Zealand, is required. If we weren't very careful we could exterminate the species from the entire planet. Then we would have to go through the process of Regeneration and Re-Instatement to bring them back."

Professor Honda turned and with a humorous sparkle in his eye, said

"Incidentally you might be interested to hear this story." "One of our students, having studied Genetic Engineering, and become proficient in the programming of the computers and functioning of the equipment, decided to carry out a bit of unauthorised experimentation. To cut a long story short – he produced a Genetically Engineered tame domestic white rabbit to assist him, so he said, in the maintenance of his garden. The rabbit normally lives in an open ended hutch in one corner of the garden. Everyday, if the weather is suitable, the rabbit leaves his hutch and does a patrol of the lawn and garden. Firstly, he carefully checks the lawn, and then carries out a searching patrol of all the paths, borders, flower beds, etc until he has covered the entire garden. The merest sprig or leaf of dandelion, plantain, groundsel or any other edible weed is instantly devoured. He does not touch a single leaf or stem of any of the flowering plants and shrubs anywhere in the garden.

There is a simple single magnetised wire buried in the ground around the perimeter of the garden and the rabbit stops at this point and will never pass over the wire. He always goes to a selected corner of the garden in order to urinate or defecate.

When he is at home, the student pushes a button on his personal communicator, which sounds a certain tone, and the rabbit instantly comes to him for fuss and affection and any titbits the student may offer. In the evening the hutch sounds another tone and the rabbit goes home to bed. The student gets a lot of visitors to see his pet and often bemoans the fact that private businesses are no longer allowed. He says – with a female – he could breed copies, sell them and make a fortune.

The Principal is not amused – says it was a serious misuse of College computers and equipment. I suppose he is right. If everybody played around like that what on Earth would we end up with?"

The Professor smiled.

"On a more serious note – with the current Universal Two Child Policy extant throughout the world, it was decided Genetic Engineering should be used to ensure that every couple who wants a child should be guaranteed a child totally free of all genetic defects. The DNA of both parents is checked and, if there is a risk of transfer of a genetic defect, then eggs and sperm samples are taken from the parents. Conception takes place in vitro in the laboratory, the fertilised egg checked and any genetic defects found are corrected. The fertilised egg is then implanted into the mother's uterus. The resulting child is free of any heritable defects and so, of course, are it's progeny – it's descendants. In this way we have eliminated Down's Syndrome, Cystic Fibrosis, Autism, Epilepsy and many other genetically involved diseases. We have also drastically reduced the incidence of cancer.

We could, if we wished, modify the genome to give the child a talent for music, mathematics, art or even ball games. For instance a talent for music often runs in families. The Strauss family comes to mind. We could take a genetic sample from a talented musician, compare it with the parental genome and modify the baby's genome to suit. However, the World Council of Administrators and Scientists have decided to leave the natural variation of humanity as it is and, at this stage, only carry out genetic modification to ensure the health and wellbeing of the person and the descendants.

Accidental pregnancies are now very rare since the mandatory contraceptive implant was introduced. At eight years old, all girls are fitted with a small electronic/chemical implant which is 100% effective and lasts a lifetime. It can be switched on and off by a coded electronic impulse – which procedure is usually done at the local hospital if a child is desired and authorised. Most couples are delighted with this system as it completely eliminates the need for any mechanical contraceptives and allows a full, natural and spontaneous sex life."

"This all sounds remarkable and wonderful, Professor
Honda!" said Anna. "But – I take it – this Genetic Engineering could
be very dangerous if mis-applied."

"Oh! Yes! A very great deal of checking and cross checking
is done before any Genetic Engineering Project is finally authorised.
It would be very easy to upset the balance of nature and cause an
ecological disaster. Unintended consequences could cause a disaster
impinging directly on the human race!"
Eric chipped in. "How – exactly?"

"Well! Said Honda "I'll give you an example of how a
biological intervention could have resulted in disaster for humanity.
Yet – nobody at the time appears to have realised it. Fortunately we
got away with it. It was only much later that anyone realised how
dangerous the action had been."

"We are all ears, Professor" said Anna.

"It starts back in the nineteenth century – when settlers were
first moving into Australia from England. The indigenous animals
were marsupials – which were strange and not particularly liked by
the settlers. So they imported all sorts of native animals from their
home country, including rabbits. The idea was – that if they lived and
multiplied, the settlers could enjoy shooting and also eating them.

Enormous numbers of rabbits were regularly eaten by
Europeans at that time.

Anyway, the rabbits were successful. Too successful. In the
absence of natural predators the numbers took off. Rabbits are very
fecund. The numbers exploded into millions. By the mid $20^{th}$
Century they were becoming a plague – stripping vast areas of
Australia clean and turning what had been useful farmland into a
desert.

In the mid $20^{th}$ Century people were just beginning to think
of biological control. They did not have any Genetic Engineering
expertise, at that time, but they could and did experiment with the
introduction of natural predators – and disease. Some of the
interventions were laughable in their naïveté.

Err – If I may divert a minute. There was some island –
somewhere in the Pacific – I think – where settlers moved in – taking
goats, chickens and so on and, unfortunately, rats. The rats multiplied,
eliminated the local wild life, and started on the chickens. To

eliminate the rats the settlers decided to introduce snakes. The snakes ate all the rats – then they too started eating the chickens. So the settlers introduced mongoose – to kill the snakes. So the mongoose killed all the snakes – and then the mongoose started on the chickens. What the settlers did after that – I have no idea!"

They all laughed.

"Getting back to the rabbits. The problem was tackled by a bunch of rather more sophisticated scientists. They decided to try to eliminate the rabbits by disease.

I don't know how – but they found or created a viral disease to destroy the rabbits. It was a murderous disease called Myxomatosis. It infected only rabbits and was spread by fleas. Rabbits have their own brand of fleas and, like many fleas, they prefer to feed exclusively on their own chosen, hosts. Myxomatosis was absolutely lethal. It killed something like 95% of all rabbits infected.

Without too much serious thought they turned it loose in Australia. It spread through the rabbit population like wildfire. Rabbits died in their tens of millions. The few surviving, naturally resistant, rabbits rebred. But as soon as a group started to build, the disease came back – and decimated them again. Rabbits were rapidly reduced from a plague to a minor nuisance. So – the intervention was considered a great success.

Back in Europe people heard of this and some farmers decided – in Europe and England – that, maybe, they would be better off without rabbits too. They were too numerous – and a pest. Not as bad as Australia because there were natural predators – foxes, badgers, buzzards, stoats, etc, to keep them down – as well as an army of farmers with guns – who regularly shot loads of rabbits for the market.

You would have thought they would have left well alone but – No! Somebody brought myxomatosis back from Australia and turned it loose.

It would have been easy. Collect a few fleas from infected rabbits, put them in a small phial and smuggle them back, in your pocket, on a plane flight to Europe. The disease took off in Europe too – and the rabbits were massacred!"

Professor Honda paused.

"You know – it frightens me – just to think of it."

"Myxomatosis was not only lethal – it was a dreadful disease – most cruel. The infected rabbits developed terrible lesions – all over their

body. It attacked the head, formed lesions in the ears, turning the
rabbit stone deaf. It attacked the eyes – turning the rabbit totally
blind. And in this awful, awful state the rabbit lingered for days
before it finally died.

Now! If you stop to think about it. The Black Death –
Yersinia Pestis – was a disease of rats, spread by fleas. It made the
break to humans, - by humans being bitten by hungry fleas leaving the
dead rats. Note – Humans do not eat rats.

And in mid 20$^{th}$ Century, they deliberately introduced a lethal
disease into rabbits in Europe – spread by fleas. Not only that – the
similarity of rats with fleas and rabbits with fleas – but millions of
people in Europe regularly ate rabbits. It was a common food source.

As the myxomatosis plague spread, millions of people must
have eaten myxomatosis infected meat. Infected rabbits shot before
the symptoms appeared. Even when the disease was at its worst –
there were still rabbits in shops for sale as food.

How they got away with it – I'll never know! The whole
scenario seems – to me – to be a total recipe for disaster. And
myxomatosis was far worse than the Black Death. Yersinia only
killed 30 to 40 percent of the infected rats. Having transferred to
humans it then killed 30 to 40 percent of infected persons.
Myxomatosis killed 95% of infected rabbits. What if it had
transferred to people? The amazing thing is – during the time
myxomatosis was at its worst – and for over sixty years afterwards –
when myxomatosis was still endemic in Europe – nobody seems to
have recognised the danger."

"Wow!" said Anna. "Professor – that is mind blowing!"

"Yes!" said Professor Honda. "It is! Unfortunately – one of
the great and terrible lessons of history is – that the human race –
despite its intelligence and stunning brain power – can be incredibly
blind."

" Professor Honda!" said Indira "I have heard you were
involved in some of the recent work on cancer. Could you tell us
something about that?"

"Yes!" said Honda. "But I will be brief. After the Crash, the
ghastly disease of Cancer returned – because, worldwide, hospital
infrastructure and treatment facilities had almost totally been
destroyed. Now, however, with our advanced genetic engineering

knowledge, we have re-created the techniques which practically eradicated Cancer in the mid/late 21<sup>st</sup> Century.

In the early 21<sup>st</sup> Century, the methods used to try to control Cancer were basically crude and primitive. At that time, the methods used were surgery, chemo-therapy and radiation. It could be compared to stone-age methods of bludgeoning an animal to death. Later, more subtle and effective methods were introduced. The techniques developed later in the 21<sup>st</sup> Century involved using genetically engineered viruses.

As you know, Cancer is caused by the body's own cells changing and, basically, rebelling against the body's control systems and growing rampantly and uncontrollably, eventually causing lethal damage and death.

The change, from the original, normal, body cells, is usually caused by some form of genetic damage or modification, which can be caused by such things as radiation, chemicals, bacterial or viral infection, or even simple physical injury.

Damaged, modified cells, once they become cancerous and malignant, change in a number of ways and, remarkably, become capable of manipulating their environment, triggering the growth of local blood vessels to supply extra nutrients to the cancer and even developing the ability to reproduce by producing seed cells which are insinuated into the blood vessels and distributed throughout the body (metastasis).

It follows, therefore, that an active cancer cell has a number of differences from a normal body cell and it is these differences that we exploit. What we do is take viruses such as herpes, chicken pox, etc and genetically engineer them so that the virus seeks out and preferentially attacks the cancer cells.

We use what you could call a 'double whammy'. One of the viruses directly attacks cancer cells, replicates inside the cell and destroys it in the normal way or triggers apoptosis (causes the cancer cell to self-destruct). This gets rid of a lot of cancer cells – but not all. Then we use a second type of engineered virus. This also seeks out cancer cells but does not seek to kill it directly. It acts to modify the surface of the cancer cell so that the human body's immune system recognises it as foreign and attacks and destroys it.

The immune system is very powerful and can destroy most bacteria, viruses and parasites that attack the body. The power of the

immune system was demonstrated when doctors, way back in the $20^{th}$
Century, first started trying to transplant organs and body parts from
animals and human donors.  If the immune system recognised the
transplant as foreign, it immediately attacked and rapidly destroyed it.

Some diseases – such as Malaria – developed the ability to
keep changing their surface proteins – in effect, camouflaging their
surfaces – so they were not recognised by the immune system cells as
foreign to the body.  Cancer also uses a camouflage system and fools
the body's immune system that the cancer cells are perfectly normal
body cells and thus are not attacked.  In effect our genetically
modified virus acts to strip off the camouflage and makes the cancer
cell detectable for what it is – a malignant and invasive perversion of
normal body cells.  The immune system then detects and attacks, and
the cancer cells, remaining after the effects of the first virus, are
rapidly wiped out.  It is quite rare for a cancer to withstand the effects
of the two viruses and, if it does, we have other viruses we can use –
as backup."

"Incidentally." said Professor Honda.  "I take it you will all
be going to Professor Sulawesi's Lecture tomorrow on the Great
Crash – sometimes called the Apocalypse."

Everybody nodded.

"I would prefer not to if I could" said Anna.

"I understand that" said Honda.  "But this is a mandatory
lecture.  You are only allowed to avoid some of the most harrowing
sequences if you are medically certified as being liable to
psychological damage.  And even then you must see most of it.  You
understand the reason, don't you?  It is vital that the people of
tomorrow – and, particularly the leaders, know what hell can be
created on this Earth if we don't stick to some basic rules – chief of
which is control of population."  He rose to his feet.  "I think I will
leave you now!  I have some notes and videos to prepare.  Thank you
for the beer and I enjoyed our chat."

"Professor Honda" said Daniel.  "We were delighted to have
your company.  We shall be here again, same time next week and we
would be extremely pleased if you could possibly spare the time to
join us again.  And there will be some spare beer."

Honda laughed.

"I might just do that!" he said.

---

It was a week later, another fine day, and Dan, his friends and Professor Honda were again enjoying a beer and a chat on the campus. There was banter and joking and a little fooling around, then the conversation became serious.

"Professor Honda" said Anna "The last time we were here you fascinated us by telling us about Genetic Engineering, elimination of pest species and the story of the weed eating pet rabbit.

I know there is an International Program of Regeneration and Re-Introduction of Extinct Species in which you are involved. Would you be willing to tell us something about it?"

"Certainly!" said Honda "But first – pass me another can of beer would you?"

"By 2150, a great number of animals – birds, fish, insects and large land animals had already gone extinct. Fortunately, in 2026 a group of enlightened billionaires had seen the danger and clubbed together to finance a 'Foundation of Regeneration'. Earlier, a Foundation had been set up to save plants and, at Svalbard, on the island of Spitzbergen, in 2008 a repository had been set up (in the permafrost, maintained at a constant temperature of minus 20°C) containing tens of thousands of samples of seeds from various plants. Under these conditions the seeds are expected to remain viable for up to 20,000 years.

This 'Seed Bank' represented an emergency supply of plant genetic material for use in the future should the need arise.

The group who acted in 2026, decided to do a similar thing for animals and a repository was set up to create an animal gene bank. Tens of thousands of samples, ranging from entire small animals and insects to small samples of flesh and teeth, from large animals, were stored. Each deposit contained several samples from different animals of the same species (so as to have some degree of genetic diversity).

The repository also included samples from animals that had long since gone extinct (where this was possible) such as skin, teeth, bones etc. As a result of this wonderful foresight we are now, (in 2647) able to regenerate a vast range of animals that had gone extinct,

thus putting right a great deal of the enormous damage the human race
had inflicted on the planet.

In the next few hundred years we expect to re populate the
Earth with animals and, to a great extent, bring it back to the diversity
that existed before the Industrial Revolution. In fact, we may even do
better than that. We may even bring back species that went extinct
thousands of years ago. Examples would be the woolly mammoth,
mastodon, woolly rhinoceros and so on.

In the case of the mammoth, for instance, we would extract
DNA from samples of mammoth skin and bone – which we know
would not be perfect – and blend it with DNA from a related species
such as the Indian elephant. We can check and control the blended
DNA with computers and computer controlled equipment until we get
a viable genome. This would be inserted into an egg, extracted from
an Indian elephant and implanted into an artificial uterus, (generated
from elephant cells). (We are already doing this kind of thing in many
artificial uteri in our laboratories). The resulting foetus and animal
would not be a true mammoth but a chimera – say 50% Mammoth
and 50% Indian Elephant. When we have produced the first chimera
we would then take DNA from the chimera and again blend it with
DNA from another mammoth sample to produce another chimera –
this time the resulting animal would be say – 80% mammoth and 20%
Indian Elephant. The process could be repeated until the resulting
mammoth would be indistinguishable from the original.

Bear in mind that most human beings alive today are not
100% modern Homo Sapiens but a blend of Homo Sapiens and Homo
Neanderthalensis. As well as the mammoth we could, of course, bring
back other extinct animals such as the Sabre Toothed Tiger but I doubt
if we would wish to.

There would, of course, be considerable discussion before we
embarked on the reinstatement of any long extinct animal. At the
moment we are only working on recently extinct animals such as the
Rhinoceros, the Bengal Tiger and Bluefin Tuna."

Daniel scratched his head thoughtfully.

"Fascinating! Incidentally you mentioned using an artificial
uterus to nourish and grow the embryos. How do you do that?"

"Well, originally, we experimented with cattle. We had to
develop a transgenic cow with an impaired immune system – so that a

foetus with foreign DNA would not be rejected. But it was a lot of trouble. Then we found we could grow independent organs, including uteri, in a nutrient solution in a sterile environment. When an egg is implanted, we can induce the growth of an umbilical cord and a placenta. At this stage we swap from the original nutrient solution to a pumped blood supply. Real blood – without, of course, any immune system cells. Works very well! We could use a biological heart to do the pumping but, in actual fact, we simply use a motorised peristaltic pump to pump oxygenated blood, with the necessary nutrients, to the uterus and placenta.

The blood we use is changed periodically and replaced by new blood 'milked' from transgenic cows. The extraction is painless and the cows take no more notice than they would if they were giving udder milk. Basically we use variations of this set up for all large mammals. Insects and fish are a bit trickier. With fish we work on just a few eggs, with the aim of creating one male and one female of the species we are reinstating. Then we are away.

It is a little more difficult with birds but we can produce artificial eggs – any size we want. The shell is created from porous ceramic. The lining, albumin and yolk grown from engineered chicken cells – immune system modified, of course, and we seed the DNA impregnated egg cell on to the surface of the yolk. They even brought back the Madagascan Elephant Bird that way.

It's going to be a hell of a job bringing back the extinct Blue Whale. They are going to need a tank 25 feet long and an artificial uterus capable of carrying a 5 Ton foetus – but they think they can do it. Don't forget – when the baby animal is produced it is only part of the job. The baby has to be nurtured, reared to full size, reintroduced back into the wild – educated if necessary. Now you see why it may take hundreds of years to reintroduce our lost species. Some people have suggested we could re-introduce species that have been extinct for thousands of years. It might be possible, but if there are only DNA fragments it might be necessary to produce a hybrid – using DNA from an existing related species. (All the animals on the planet, including ourselves, are related, as a matter of fact – to a greater or lesser degree). Then, working from the hybrid, introducing more DNA from the extinct species to produce a second generation. So you could have – 1st generation – 50% of what you want. 2nd Generation

75% and so on. 95% reincarnation would probably be indistinguishable from the original.

This latter technique was brilliantly foreseen in an ancient 21$^{st}$ Century classic film called 'Jurassic Park' where scientists, working from preserved DNA fragments and DNA from modern animals, re-created Dinosaurs, including Tyrannosaurus Rex. In the film they referred to using 'fill in' DNA from frogs when, of course, the correct modern animal to use would be a chicken. Birds are, after all, descendents of the only dinosaurs to survive. They are actually dinosaurs. We simply don't recognise them as such. 'Jurassic Park was a brilliant film – but a bit unlikely. We struggle to find DNA in 40,000 year old samples. So to find DNA 65 million years old would be nothing less than a miracle. And who would want to bring T Rex back anyway? Probably the most lethal land animal that has ever lived. It would be capable of having any of the most dangerous modern predators for lunch. As you will realise – Regeneration and Reintroduction all takes time. We reckon there is enough work to keep us going for 500 years."

Incidentally, one of the extinct birds that we have re-generated is the Dodo. Originally Dodos lived on the island of Mauritius and were a large, flightless, turkey sized bird – in actual fact a close relative of pigeons. They thrived on the island, which had no natural predators and, when man first arrived, showed no fear and were quite tame and easily captured. Human beings soon found that they were extremely good to eat – especially roasted – and in a remarkably few years the poor Dodos were wiped out. Dodos have been re-generated and it is found they really are delicious. The flesh is tender with a distinctive flavour. In a few years you may find Dodos on the super-market shelves alongside chicken and turkey."

———————————

"Professor Honda" said Eric "How do you think things would have developed if there had been no HIVa?"

"Candidly! I don't think it would have been much different. Maybe the timing would have been different. Maybe they could have delayed the Crash for another 50 years or so but I still think some sort of collapse would have happened. With such a high human population, Global Warming continuing, crops failing, aquifers depleted, soil fertility failing, due to nutrient impoverishment and salt contamination, and natural resources drastically depleted, the world situation would gradually have become worse and worse.

I think, once the population passed 12 billion, without any drastic action – such as a 'one child policy' being universally imposed, some form of a Crash was inevitable. At fifteen billion it was merely a question of time. HIVa simply acted as a trigger. A catalyst – if you like! – but a rather drastic one! Although the Chinese had acted to facilitate mass migration into Siberia – it all takes time. Time to clear the forest. Get agriculture going. Build the roads, railways, houses, infrastructures. In the event – only about 150 million had actually migrated to Siberia before HIVa appeared and the Crash started. 150 million was, of course, far less then the actual population increase during that time.

In other words – despite migration to Siberia, the population situation in the southern nations during the period between the Sino/Russian war and the appearance of HIVa was getting worse not better. If another 100 years had been gained, for instance, the total number of migrants to Siberia is unlikely to have exceeded 1 billion at the very most. In any case, it would have been impossible for 15 billion people to survive, solely, in the Northern regions of the world for long – even if all the southern peoples had been able to migrate north (which would have been a virtual impossibility). One way or another the population had to be reduced – and quickly. We simply didn't have the 200 years or so it would have taken a universal one child policy to get the population down to sane levels. And the world, at that time, was not ready for – and would not have accepted – a 'one child policy'. A universal one child policy was only possible after the psychological shock of the Crash. Don't forget – A universal one child policy creates enormous economic problems for a period longer than the policy is in force. The world before the Crash could never have accepted or coped with that. Only World Government and world economic control could handle that. So – Answering your question – I think a population crash was inevitable – one way or another – whether or not there was HIVa."

---

"Professor Honda" said Anna. "What I can't understand is
why people didn't wake up to the situation and do something about it.
Surely it was obvious they were heading for disaster?"

"Yes! It does seem surprising. I think it is because most
people are primarily interested in their daily lives. Most of the time
before the Crash, for many of the people on the Earth, life was good
and getting better. In general people like to laugh and be happy. They
don't want to worry or be sad or unhappy. People prefer not to think
about unpleasant things. And the political systems, the economic
systems became a 'locked in' mindset. No one wanted to think about
or talk about impending disasters. So everyone tended to go on as
before, as though the good times would go on forever.

The late 20$^{th}$ Century, and on into the 21$^{st}$ Century, was a
time of great profligacy. Human beings ruthlessly and thoughtlessly
exploited the planets resources. Little thought was given to the long
term future. Only the immediate future mattered. Enormous amounts
of food were casually scrapped and thrown away. Animal populations
– land animals and fish stocks were devastated across the planet with
hardly a second thought, and many went extinct. The Human Race
took over and exploited the planet like a plague. Vast areas of forests
were burned and destroyed to produce arable land.

By the early 21$^{st}$ Century it was quite obvious that this
profligate human life-style could not go on. The planet was being
almost irretrievably damaged. A few dissenting voices were raised
and the first efforts to start Conservation Projects were made.

Incredibly, no nation on earth, with the sole exception of
China, was willing to discuss or admit there was a population
problem. No one wanted to even think about it. Life was too good!
So the profligacy went on and the population continued to increase.

By 2050, things were beginning to get difficult. The
population had increased to ten billion. The World Economy was still
functioning reasonably well but problems were looming. Aquifers, all
over the world, were failing. Vast quantities of water had been
pumped from underground deposits of water, called aquifers, to
irrigate crops in areas of low rainfall. Some aquifers were
replenished, annually, when the rains came and water percolated
slowly down through the earth and rock formations. But the pumping

was often greater than the replenishment. The entire city of Venice began to sink – because of the water extracted from below it.

Many enormous aquifers were formed of what was called fossil water – water that had been there for thousands or millions of years. Aquifers that had been formed eons ago when rainfall in the area was greater.

An insidious effect of irrigation was slow ruination of the land by salt contamination. To conserve water, sprinkler systems and the most efficient system – trickle feed – used only enough water to keep plants flourishing. There was no run-off. This meant that the bulk of irrigation water eventually evaporated. Since all water used for irrigation contained salt – in greater or lesser degree – then, gradually, quantities of salt were deposited as the water evaporated. After many years, the salt content of the soil built up until plants could no longer cope and crops failed. There was nothing that could be done to remove the salt – only an excess of rain could wash the salt from the soil.

Efforts were made to develop salt-tolerant crops, but as early as 2014, it was announced that an area as large as the whole of France had already been lost to cultivation by the effects of salt contamination. Much irrigation was, of course, by water pumped from rivers and many rivers were so reduced in volume that only a relative trickle reached the sea. In Russia, so much water was removed from the rivers flowing into the Aral Sea (previously one of the largest lakes on earth) that the Aral Sea almost totally dried up and visitors were confronted by the sight of the rotting remains of quite large ships, in the middle of a desert, like stranded whales on a seashore.

By 2050, with Global Warming beginning to be noticeable, the Arctic Ice Sheet was completely melted from the surface of the sea for several months in the summer. Also – vast quantities of ice had already flowed from the Greenland glaciers and melted in the sea. (Although it would still take another 1.000 years to completely clear Greenland). Both the melting of the sea ice, and flow from Greenland, meant that vast quantities of fresh water had been introduced into the Arctic Ocean. Also, rainfall had increased over the Siberian Tundra areas and major rivers, flowing North, had increased their flow, leading to an input of yet more fresh water.

What is not generally appreciated is that the Arctic Ocean is a
substantially enclosed sea, surrounded by land, with the main
connection to the rest of the world's oceans through the North
Atlantic. (Get a Globe of the Earth or a satellite picture and look
down from above the North Pole). There is a small connection to the
Pacific through the Bering Strait, but that is very narrow (70
kilometres or so) and shallow.

There exists the extremely important Ocean Current called
the Gulf Stream, flowing from the Caribbean north eastwards. Most
of the warm water carried by the current travels into the Arctic Ocean,
on or near the surface, where it mixes with the Arctic water, cools and
falls to the sea bed, where it then flows South. In fact, the Gulf
Stream is not simply part of a simple conveyor system in the Atlantic
but forms part of a Global circulation system called the Thermo-
Haline Circulation. Cutting a long story short, the fact is that, as the
Arctic Ice Cap melted and vast quantities of ice flowed into the sea
from Greenland, enormous quantities of fresh water, (which is much
lower density than normal sea water), accumulated on the surface of
the North Atlantic and Arctic Ocean. When this fresh water mixed
with the Gulf Stream it reduced the density, so the cold water falling
towards the sea bed did not fall so fast. The 'push' acting to keep the
current flowing was reduced and the Gulf Stream slowed.

The entire, World Wide, Thermo-Haline Circulation system
was affected, and this contributed to changing weather patterns all
over the World. The first thing that was noticed, in the early 21st
Century, was that the powerful winds in the upper air – the 'Jet
Stream' – a river of air that flows continuously all around the
Northern hemisphere, was changing. The Jet Stream slowed down,
and began to meander, far more than it used to do. This was very
important, because the high pressure and low pressure systems,
(cyclones and anti-cyclones), that form and create the weather we
experience every day, are basically spawned from vortices formed on
the sides of the Jet Stream. So, if the Jet Stream varies and wanders –
the weather systems also vary and wander.

In the early 21st Century it was noted, particularly in Europe
and North America, that the weather was becoming more
unpredictable. It all depended on the vagaries of the Jet Stream. This
was, of course, bad for cultivation and crop production. In Europe it

was noted – if the Jet Stream moved South there were un-seasonal frosts and cold spells – and often – torrential rain. If the Jet Stream moved North they experienced droughts and excessively hot spells. Since the entire World Thermo-Haline sea current circulation was changing, the air circulation patterns all over the world were also changing. (There is a Southern Hemisphere Jet Stream similar to that in the North).

So – as a result of Global Warming affecting sea-circulation patterns – the air circulation patterns began to change. Finally, around 2050, the Hadley Cells began to change. Hadley Cells are large North/South permanent circulation patterns. A good example is the Equatorial/Sahara Desert circulation. Basically, the hot moist air, formed over the equatorial jungle of Africa, rises and, as it cools, dumps nearly all its water, in the form of rain, back down on the jungle. Having risen, the air then moves North and, when it has cooled sufficiently, falls back to ground level, and then travels back to the Equatorial area to complete the circulation. The whole 'loop' is called a Hadley Cell. You will note that most of the water is released as rain as the warm moist air rises. It sheds a little more, over the savannah, as it travels north but, when it descends (over the Sahara Desert) the air is dry, which is why the Sahara gets practically no rain. Incidentally, 5,000 years or so ago, the Hadley Cell circulation was different and the Sahara area was a fertile land, with gazelles, lions, elephants and so on roaming.

So you see how Global Warming does not simply act to make the country you live in warmer but can drastically change weather patterns and conditions all over the world. Some people may live in a relatively cool, pleasant area – but they may find their crops fail because of drought. Others, in another area, may find their crops are devastated by excessive rain and floods. These effects started in the early 21st Century and gradually became worse as time went by.

By 2080, things were getting very difficult. The world population was nearly 12 billion. Much of the great wheat growing areas of the American mid-west were now suffering almost permanent drought as were large areas of Europe and Ukraine. However, genetic engineering had produced drought resistant versions of crop cereals and other crop modifications, such as blight and frost resistant potatoes, high yield and rust resistant varieties of rice and so on. It was still possible, therefore, to feed 12 billion people. Although a few voices were raised, pointing out the dangers, no serious decisions were made to take drastic action and the population continued to increase but more slowly."

Professor Honda glanced at his watch.

"I am afraid I must leave you now. Perhaps I'll see you again next week. Thanks for the beer."

When Professor Honda had gone, Daniel turned to Joshua M'beki.

"What did you say you were studying, Joshua?" said Daniel, thoughtfully.

"Rocketry and Deep Space Drives."

"That sounds very demanding and cerebral! Why did you choose that?"

Joshua smiled and ran his fingers through his hair.

"Oh! I have been interested in Engineering since I was a kid. When I grew older, learned more about the Stars and the Universe and, particularly, the 'Genesis Project', I determined to be part of it."

"I have heard of the Genesis Project but, I confess, I don't know much about it. Perhaps you can educate me."

Joshua paused, and then said

"I think the Genesis Project is the most imaginative, wonderful and fascinating project the human race has ever undertaken. It may take hundreds of years to crack all the problems but, now that humanity has sorted itself out and reached a stable and steady balance with the rest of the planet, we have all the time in the world.

Years ago, the Nations of the World expended vast sums of money, and enormous effort, in a fundamentally futile endeavour; producing military systems and vast quantities of weapons, which, if used, would have caused untold devastation on the planet. Now, with our New Civilisation, we don't need or want such things, so we have a far more efficient society. Stability can be, however, slightly boring. Some brave soul realised this and suggested that the human race needed something special; something magnificent and inspiring to dedicate itself to; something transcending mundane everyday life; something for the human race to devote itself to; an undertaking to be proud of.

The Genesis proposal was devised and submitted to the World Government for consideration. Many people thought it would never be passed. After all, it involved a great deal of work that would have no direct benefit to the human race. It would involve expenditures of important raw materials, valuable fuels, a release of $CO^2$ and other pollutants and massive commitment of human time, effort and energy – to create and deploy something that would not directly benefit a single person on this Earth. Nevertheless, it would be a wonderful, glorious undertaking which, if successful, might enable Earth Life to live and, maybe, flourish on other planets long after life on Earth itself had ceased. It might even mark the start of the spread of Earth Life throughout the Galaxy.

It was estimated the project would need the dedication of 1% of the World's Gross Domestic Product for, maybe, a couple of hundred years but the human race could stand that – now that international strife and the need for massive armies and weapon systems had been abolished. The Genesis Project would provide the human race with an Aspiration. A fabulous dream. A purpose – over and beyond everyday living.

Against all expectations, the World Government – Ten Thousand of the World's most intelligent and competent men and women – voted Yes! Let's do it! And so – here I am – intending to be part of it."

"I must admit, Joshua, listening to you, you really do make it sound magnificent. I wonder if you would be willing to take the time to explain to me exactly what the Genesis Program is about and what it is intended to achieve."

"Well! Dan. To understand what the Genesis Project is really about, you first need to know some of the background. Since the dawn of the space age – way back in the 20th Century, people have dreamed about the idea of man going to and colonising the stars or, to be more exact, planets around other stars. However, when the problem is analysed, scientifically, it is simply not practical or possible for human beings to go to the stars. The distances, to even the nearest stars, are simply too enormous and the problems of getting on to an extra-solar planet too great. The very nearest star, Alpha Centauri, is just over 4 light years away. When you realise that one light year is roughly six trillion (six million, million) miles, you realise the scale of the problem. Journeys to the stars – the nearest stars – will be not be in months or years but in tens of thousands of years or more. Apart from that, to establish a viable human colony

you would need a group of at least twenty people and a veritable
Noah's Ark of animals and plants together with a few thousand tons of
equipment and stores. And when you finally reached the new solar
system you would have to slow down, go into orbit around the new
planet and then, somehow, transfer all the people, animals, plants, and
equipment down to the planet's surface. Any Engineer who seriously
considers the problems soon realises that it is out of the question.
Human beings, themselves, are simply not going to the stars.

However, if we study the evolution of life on this Earth we
realise there could be another way to colonise the stars. On this Earth,
evidence indicates that life was created the hard way – from basic
simple chemical beginnings to modern highly evolved multi cellular
animals. This has taken an immense amount of time – roughly four
billion years. For the first 3.4 billion years nothing larger than single
cell life existed. It took 3.4 billion years for the first primitive life
form to evolve into the extremely complex single cell that was the
precursor of multi-cellular life. From that first, multi-cellular, living
thing, all life on Earth, big enough to see, has evolved. You and I, and
all the various other animals on land – large and small – from fleas to
elephants. Plus all the plants, plus everything in the sea. Every living
thing large enough to be seen without a microscope is related – closely
related. All use DNA as the basic information storage molecule. It
may be difficult to realise that a beetle, a shrimp, a tuna fish, a dragon
fly, a fir tree, an elephant, a dandelion, even the fungus that grows on
a piece of mouldy bread – are all our relatives. Fairly close relatives
in fact.

A little further thought and investigation shows that we are
also related to all the bacteria – both aerobic and anaerobic – on the
planet. In other words – all life on Earth is related – all generated
from one initial amazing spark of life. When we think it through, we
realise that nearly six-sevenths of all the time that life has been on the
Earth was required to evolve and perfect all the intricate details of the
functioning of an individual, microscopic cell. And only when that
was achieved could evolution take the final step to multi-cellular life.
Once we realise this fully, and get if firmly in our heads, we realise
there might be a magical way we really could colonise the stars. It
might just – only just – be possible."

"What if – instead of trying to send human beings to the stars – which is quite impossible – we send a small container with – say – a kilogram of Earth Bacteria. A kilogram, because bacteria are so small, would be trillions upon trillions of bacteria. There could be hundreds, nay, thousands of different types of bacteria – aerobic and anaerobic – adapted to all sorts of conditions. There are even bacteria that can stand 500 times more nuclear radiation than a human can. We deliver this canister of Earth bacteria to a suitable planet around another star. A planet with liquid water, preferably in its early stages of development. If only a few, out of the trillions of bacteria, survive the journey and the conditions of the new planet, and multiply – the seeding would have been successful."

"If you think about it carefully – the bacteria we propose to introduce are, in reality, very advanced forms of life – the end result of over 3 billion years of evolution. If we were successful we would have thus short circuited the time required to produce advanced and possibly intelligent life on the new planet. On Earth it only took an additional 600 million years to produce us – and all the magical diversity of life that exists here. So – in a fraction of the time it took here – on our Planet Earth – you could have a new fabulous planet. Not a carbon copy of Earth. Evolution would be free to develop life forms that suited that particular planet best."

"Some people have argued that we should not interfere with the development of life, if any, on any extra solar planet. But we have good reason to believe that some of the evolutionary break-throughs that led to advanced life on Earth, were so unlikely and fortunate – and might easily never have happened at all. So you might have a perfectly suitable extra-solar planet – with the conditions for life existing for billions of years – and yet never, ever, have life evolve beyond the planet being covered in a layer of black slime. What a waste of a rare planet that would be. And it is very noticeable – for all the searching that has been carried out – we have never, ever, found a trace of a signal from intelligent life anywhere than on Earth."

"Anyway – the World Government has decided we ought to give it a try."

"That sounds fantastic. Joshua! What a wonderful project. But I can see there will be a great many problems to solve."

"There will indeed. And nobody can be sure if they will all be solved. But we already have a good idea of how the Genesis

Starship will be built and how it will work. One of the big problems is that at the end of the journey, the starship will have to slow down in order to release the capsule into the ocean of the new planet. In order to slow down, the starship will have to take with it sufficient fuel. This will drastically reduce the speed at which it will travel across space after leaving the solar system. This means the journey might take 40,000 years or more. However, this is not as big a snag as you might think. Interstellar space is at minus 270°C so, during the cruise phase, everything will be in deep freeze. On Earth, samples of bacteria and even algae, that have been frozen for half a million years, have, when thawed, been found to be viable and alive. So the length of time spent in deep freeze is not as important as you might think. It is highly likely that minus 270°C will preserve bacteria much better than any low temperature here on Earth."

"There are plenty of other Engineering problems to do with the construction of the starship, of course. Are you sure you want to hear about them?"

"Yes please Joshua! I have a free afternoon today. That's if you have the time too."

"Well! The first thing that comes to mind is propulsion, of course. Two methods are under consideration. One is simple chemical propulsion. That is small, high efficiency, low thrust rocket motors. But even the best chemical engines will only give us a relatively low terminal velocity. The great virtue is – they are simple – and, as I have said – time, for the journey, is not so important. In any case – for the first part of the journey – getting away from the sun – towards interstellar space, the engines will not be used at all. The starship would be assembled in Earth orbit. Then a very low thrust rocket pack will be attached to push the craft out of Earth orbit on to an elliptical path. Then, in a number of passes, Earth's gravity would be used to 'slingshot' the craft away from Earth and out towards Jupiter. At Jupiter, that planets massive gravity field would be used to, again, 'slingshot' the spacecraft up to a speed of over 80,000 miles an hour – which exceeds the suns escape velocity at that radius – which will take it into interstellar space. This manoeuvre, incidentally, was successfully carried out for the first time, way back in the 20th Century, with the launch of the Voyager spacecraft."

"The use of the 'slingshot' manoeuvre means that a very fragile spacecraft construction can be used, as the gravitational field of the 'slingshot' planet acts exactly equally on every molecule of the craft – so no acceleration forces will be experienced by the craft. Incidentally, as I said before, the starship would have to slow down to deliver the canister to the new planet. However, the craft would only need to carry enough fuel to slow it down to below the parent stars escape velocity. Then a reverse 'slingshot' effect can be used, even if there are no other planets around the star, to slow it down.

The other propulsion alternative is an electric drive. In this, the 'rocket' would be, in effect, a glorified particle accelerator. Basically, a stream of ionised gas is accelerated along an electrified tube and, after being electrically neutralised, is ejected at high (very high) speed. This type of rocket would be very much more efficient. In other words it would boost the starship to far higher speeds for the expenditure of the same amount of fuel. The big snag with the electric drive is that, so far, no one has been able to get a practical amount of thrust out of it. However, some scientists think that, by using multiple, extended accelerator tubes and megawatts of power, it might be possible. Experiments are being carried out.

The power source of the starship would be a compact nuclear reactor/generator. The reactor would be a near critical mass of uranium 235. In other words a controlled nuclear bomb. Unfortunately, although, in space, no shielding would be needed (the reactor would only go critical when it was way out past Jupiter) the reactor and generator is likely to be a relatively heavy piece of equipment. That is, of course, if it can be made to function efficiently at all. The rest of the starship would be fantastically fragile and light. Probably 97% of the total weight of the starship when it leaves Earth will be fuel. The fuel would be in ultra thin carbon fibre/graphene tanks (more like balloons or bags), attached to a fragile lattice work spine. The tanks would be jettisoned as they empty.

Once the design is finalised, and everybody satisfied it is a functional design then we would start to construct and despatch the starships. We would not just construct and send one or two but, maybe, 40 or 50 over the next 200 years; maybe to planets that would take 150,000 years or more to reach. In deep space there is nothing to change or corrode the starship. The only thing to worry about is cosmic rays affecting the electronics. But we can design computers

with parallel, redundant circuits; even self checking, self correcting
circuits.  So – why not trips of 150,000/200,000 years?  As long as the
starship wakes up at the end of the trip and does its job – what does
time matter.  And even 200,000 years is just a blink – in cosmic
terms."

"That sounds remarkable, Joshua!  A wonderful dream!  I
have little doubt – with your brains and enthusiasm, you will get your
Degree.  Let's hope you get to work on such a fantastic project."

---

A week later Daniel and his friends, together with Professor
Honda, were again chatting together and sipping beer.  Two of the
girls were drinking white wine – one of the first to be produced from
the new vineyards of southern Greenland.  After half an hour's casual
chat and banter between the group, Eric turned to Professor Honda
and said "Professor!  I still don't quite understand why $CO_2$ levels and
global temperatures continued to rise after they took drastic action to
curb $CO_2$ emissions in the early 21st Century.  Can you explain?"

Professor Honda took a sip of his beer.  "Yes!  I think I can.
There were a number of factors but, basically, they were too late.
Once the planet warmed above a certain level – a number of positive
feedbacks kicked in.  For instance – once the Arctic ice cap began to
reduce in area – at the midsummer minimum – the writing was on the
wall.

Ice and snow on the Earth's surface reflects 95% of the suns
radiation falling on it, back into space.  In contrast, blue water absorbs
over 90% of the radiant energy impinging upon it.

So – when thousands of square miles of ice becomes
thousands of square miles of open water – there is a massive input of
extra heat – directly into the sea.  This is independent of the
greenhouse effect.  It is an additional, related positive feedback.  The
extra warmth in the sea will directly contribute to additional sea ice
melting in the following year – and so on.

Another feedback is the effect of warming on the vast
northern Tundra areas – Alaska, Canada, Scandinavia and Siberia.
There were trillions of tons of peat, locked up in permafrost, in those
areas.  As the permafrost began to melt, enormous quantities of peat
thawed and began to decay – producing $CO_2$ and methane.  Methane,

by the way, is over 20 times more potent than $CO^2$ as a greenhouse gas. Also – just under the peat – in many tundra areas, there was a layer of methane hydrate.

Methane hydrate is a solid compound – like wax – formed by methane and water under the right conditions of cold and pressure. Quite a small increase in temperature can cause the methane hydrate to decompose and release free methane to escape into the air.

It was noted – in the very early 21st Century, that large quantities of methane were being released by the tundra. These releases of greenhouse gases are quite independent of human emissions and quite uncontrollable – another major feedback.

Tundra releases do, of course, add directly to the greenhouse gas levels measured and cancel out the beneficial effects of human $CO^2$ reductions.

In the late 20th Century, nobody expected the twin feedbacks of ice melt and Arctic $CO^2$ release, to kick in so quickly, but scientists were caught out by what you could call a quirk of nature.

They knew, from their measurements, that, by the end of the 20th Century the Earth had only warmed by an average of ¾°C so they were not unduly alarmed.

Unfortunately global warming does not occur evenly. Powerful currents in the sea and winds in the upper atmosphere change. Global warming is uneven. Some areas warm up faster – some even cool down instead of warm. What happened, unfortunately, is that the Arctic areas of the world warmed up much faster than the average. Where the Earth, on average, had warmed ¾°C, much of the Arctic Tundra areas had warmed by as much as 2°C or 3°C. Hence the sudden melting of the permafrost – another positive feedback that was quite uncontrollable once it had started.

I will mention that there were also large quantities of methane hydrate deposits under the shallow coastal waters around the Arctic Ocean and some enormous deposits under the deep ocean floor. Some scientists were afraid this, too, could be triggered if sea temperatures rose.

It was even suspected that the world's worst ever mass extinction - the great Permian Extinction – when 95% of all life on Earth died out – was due to an enormous release of methane from methane hydrate deposits, triggered by an extreme Global Warming event.

Fortunately their worst fears were not realised. In the late
21$^{st}$ Century there were substantial releases of methane from sea bed
methane hydrate deposits – mostly from the North Siberian coastal
area but also from areas off the North American coast and near Japan
but the total did not reach the cataclysmic levels some scientists
feared.

Also – in the early to mid 21$^{st}$ Century, the human population
was still exploding and there were many backward nations developing
rapidly. For their economic development they needed energy. Much
of this energy was produced by burning coal, oil and gas in power
stations. When there were International Conferences to decide
restrictive rules on $CO_2$ release – which clamped down heavily on the
developed nations, special dispensations were made for developing
nations. In effect they were allowed to do what they liked.

They were helped and encouraged to use solar panels, wind
generators and other low $CO_2$ sources of power, but much of their
power was still produced by burning coal, oil and gas. So – human
$CO_2$ emissions, in total, did not in fact, reduce.

At a later date – large quantities of $CO_2$ and methane were
released when the Chinese and other Asiatics moved into Siberia
around 2087 to 2130. The Chinese didn't waste much time, and
rapidly set about felling and clearing the enormous pine forests in the
area.

They felled the trees, constructed millions of log cabins,
ploughed up the tundra for cultivation and so on. Millions of tons of
tree branches were burned, and vast quantities of $CO_2$ and methane
were released from the ploughed up tundra.

All in all – it's a wonder greenhouse gas levels aren't higher
than they are."

"Professor Honda!" said Anna "Is it true that we, here on
Greenland, and people elsewhere in the world, are still using coal and
releasing $CO_2$ into the atmosphere?"

"Yes! Quite true. But with only 500/600 million people on
the planet – and if we are careful to use the absolute minimum that we
need – it is acceptable.

Vegetation on land and plankton in the sea has the capacity to
absorb quite an amount of $CO_2$. It has been calculated that if we keep
$CO_2$ release below certain levels it will not increase $CO_2$ levels in the

atmosphere.  At the present time $CO^2$ levels are actually beginning to come down.  It is true, of course, that any $CO^2$ we release will slow the reduction rate down but it has been decided that, on a world-wide basis – a certain level of human $CO^2$ release is acceptable.

We need gas, oil for lubricants, rubber, plastics and many different chemicals.  Although air travel is drastically reduced, we need liquid hydrocarbon fuel for those.  Liquid hydrogen is simply far too bulky to use in aircraft.

So – we still use coal.  We don't mine it, as they used to do.  We use a process called Underground Gasification of Coal.  Much simpler and easier.  No mines required.  No underground labour or robots.

When we locate one or, commonly, multiple coal seams underground – by drilling or seismic surveys – we drill down to the coal seam and curve the drill sideways, to drill a hole along and through the seam for a kilometre or so.  We have equipment now that can accurately locate and navigate the drill point with remarkable precision.  Incidentally – they were developing this technique way back in the 21$^{st}$ Century.  Having drilled an L shaped hole along the coal seam they then start drilling again from a point 2 kilometres away and drill another L shaped hole coming back to join with the first hole to create a complete U shaped drill hole.  So you end up with two vertical holes – two kilometres apart – connected to a horizontal, two kilometres long, hole through the coal bed.

We then introduce a more slender pipe, carrying pure oxygen, down to the coal level, plus a simple pyrotechnic device for ignition.  The oxygen is turned on, the pyrotechnic device fires and the coal instantly catches fire.

Initially enough oxygen is fed in to burn a small quantity of coal.  The heat is trapped and rapidly builds up to a temperature that will roast the unburnt, nearby, coal.  The oxygen supply is then reduced to a very low level – just enough to maintain the temperature.

In this way an enormous amount of coal, surrounding the borehole can be roasted.  The heat drives off the volatiles, in the form of gas, which escapes from one of the surface holes of the U shaped borehole.  This is then tapped off and taken to a refinery.  All the volatiles are driven from the coal by the roasting process, leaving a carboniferous remnant called coke, behind.

Believe it or not, we can then convert the coke into gas as
well, if we wish, by introducing a controlled amount of steam down
the borehole into the coal seam. This reacts with the red hot coke to
form a burnable gas. Everything is computer controlled and very
efficient.

A few boreholes can produce all the gas we need for years.
Ninety eight percent of the gas coming from the borehole is useable.
No more than 2% is carbon dioxide. Most of the gas is, of course,
converted into liquids, rubber, plastics and chemicals, as I said earlier,
but some gas is used as gaseous fuel.

Way back in the early 21$^{st}$ Century it was discovered that
there were large amounts of combustible gas trapped in porous rock
formations deep underground and ways were devised to exploit this.
Some of the shale formations were of enormous size – thousands of
square miles in area and hundreds of feet thick. The amount of gas in
these formations was immense. However, to extract the gas it was
necessary to use a very messy and expensive process called 'fracking'
which stands for Hydraulic Rock Fracturing.

They used to drill holes, down to and through the rock, in a
similar manner to the coal drilling I have described, and then, in a
rather complicated process, force a special fluid plus sand and a
chemical mixture, into the rock, at very high pressure, to create cracks
in the rock. This process releases gas, from the pores of the rock,
which flowed back up the borehole pipe and was then collected.
Hydraulic fracturing of the rock around the borehole could only
extend for a limited range so, to exploit a large shale formation fully,
it was necessary to drill many boreholes – maybe thousands upon
thousands – as was done in America.

The big snag with fracking was that it used very expensive
equipment and each borehole used enormous quantities of water, sand
and some very unpleasant chemicals, to fracture the rock and keep the
cracks open for the gas to flow.

Once the Underground Gasification of Coal was perfected – a
much simpler, cleaner and better way of producing gas – the
'fracking' system was abandoned.

I think I should apologise for going on at such length about
the coal process. It is probably because I was, for a time, years ago,
involved in setting up the system on Greenland. Greenland, by the

way, does not have much coal but we have managed to find a few deposits."

Daniel looked across the campus and across the valley to the rows and rows of buildings to the North. To him, at this distance, they looked like nothing less than rows and rows of enormous black teeth. All the buildings were aligned East/West with a single enormous black sloping roof facing South.

"Not exactly a copy of Oxfords dreaming spires is it?" he said.

The professor smiled.

"At this stage, everything on Greenland has to be functional. Maybe, in a couple of hundred years time, we can relax and create a few fancy buildings. As you know, we have few wind generators on Greenland. They were mainly abandoned as too expensive and inefficient. The wind is too variable and making the generators themselves consumes too much, very expensive, materials in their construction. For power we opted for hydroelectric generators for prime load. Fortunately, Greenland has an abundance of mountains, glaciers and rivers, similar to Scandinavia. Hydro power is backed up by solar power, in the summer months only, of course, and heat pumps.

All buildings are oriented East/West with one single slope (about 50°), south facing, solar panel roof. Solar panels are cheap, high efficiency, low maintenance with a self cleaning surface. Every building has its own self contained battery energy storage system. All building walls and roof incorporate a high efficiency thermal blanket. All windows are made of a multi laminate that lets in light but blocks all infra red radiation from going out. So all the buildings are very thermal/efficient.

A large heat pump installation takes heat from the river and supplies it to all buildings via a grid system. It can actually be reversed to cool buildings on hot days in the summer.

It must be quite a shock to the migrating salmon, going up the river, to encounter a sudden change in river temperature over a short distance – but they seem to cope. I suppose it can't be as bad a shock as passing from the salt sea into the fresh water river.

As you will have noticed – most of our metalwork and construction is in aluminium, not steel. In the summer the hydro-electric power stations produce far more power than we need – when we are also producing solar power – so we then use the electrical surplus to produce aluminium. We still produce small quantities of steel for specific applications but for construction we mainly use aluminium. Much cleaner and nicer than steel. In the winter – when we have no solar power, we shut down aluminium production and use nearly all the hydro power for general use.

The invention of cheap, efficient solar power panels and, finally, the creation of very cheap thin, flexible, solar panels – almost like a flexible sheet of black plastic – meant that large, multi bladed, wind generators became less and less practical and economic. However, wind generators are still used in some areas in the North to generate power in the winter months and where there is insufficient hydro-power.

Incidentally, I don't know if I mentioned – because of the probable sea level rise in the future, no new cities will be built at a height of less than 75 metres above sea level. This is a nuisance, of course, and many cities will have separate Port facilities as close to the city as possible. This is because of Global Warming, which we know is here to stay for the next 5000/10,000 years or so. The Greenland and Antarctic ice will continue to melt and the sea will continue to rise. So – Port facilities are designed as cheaply as possible and, when the water level rises too high, will either be moved or abandoned and new facilities constructed. The cities will be safe from flooding for the foreseeable future."

"Professor Honda" said Anna "I have read that the World Government has imposed a total ban on the development of super intelligent and conscious computers. Why is that?"

"Well!" said Honda "It is basically to ensure human safety and also for ethical reasons.

Some people have argued that scientists and Electronic Engineers should be allowed to continue their research and experiments and innovate freely and, indefinitely. That they should be allowed to develop super-intelligent electronic brains, conscious brains even, if that is possible.

But the question arises – do we really need such devices and, logically, there must be dangers.

If we should develop an electronic brain, far, far more intelligent than our own, could we really be sure nothing could ever go wrong and it turn against us? And, if it did – what could we do about it? We would be outthought, outmanoeuvred, out predicted at every turn. The machine would predict that we would try to sabotage it, take action against its power source – seek to destroy it – and take the necessary precautions in advance. If it was really super intelligent it would always be one step ahead. And it really might turn hostile. Who knows what would happen then?"

The Professor paused a while and then continued. "What is the purpose of building robots? It is to help human beings. To reduce the drudgery of boring work. To undertake work that is dangerous or excessively difficult for humans. To enable us – humans – to have a better life.

It would be insane to develop electronic brains – robots of any kind that could – one day – be a threat.

If we cannot – using ordinary non intelligent, non conscious super computers – but using our own brains – understand the workings of the Universe then – let us do without that knowledge. The most important thing on this Earth is the happiness, health and security of all the human beings on it.

To risk everything, so that a small group of cosmologists can, one day, say "Hurrah! our super intelligent, conscious computer has finally worked out which theory best accounts for the Nature of the Universe". Maybe a lot of us would like to know the answer to a lot of cosmological questions – but not at the ultimate risk of the future of the human race.

Humans must come first.

In 2029, in view of the rapid advances made by electronics experts in the development of neural circuits and the potential for such circuits to facilitate creation of genuine artificial intelligence and even self conscious machines, the United Nations set up an Investigative Committee to look into the benefits and potential dangers of such machines.

Their Report concluded that there could, indeed, be great dangers and, in 2032, an International Law was passed banning the construction and development of thinking and self conscious machines.

However, the wording of the ban did not totally preclude experiment and development of neural circuits and further

experiments, some legal, some clandestine, were carried on in some
Laboratories for the next 100 years.

In 2149, the World Government reconsidered the question of
the problems associated with the development of Super Electronic
Intelligence and Consciousness both from the ethical point of view –
possible distress of the conscious computers themselves and the
inherent danger. It was voted that, on both counts, the development of
super intelligent and, particularly, conscious computers should be
banned. The human race should be able to progress quite nicely
without them."

"Professor!" said Eric. "There seems to be an enormous
difference between the way people lived – before and after the Crash.
Can you comment on that?"

"Yes!" replied Honda. After the tremendous shock and
devastation of the Crash the survivors took a deep breath and,
gradually, began to construct some sort of new life and civilisation.

Everybody, over the entire planet, agreed that a similar
Population Explosion must never, ever, be allowed to happen again. It
was agreed the surviving population of around 2.0 billion was still too
high and a Worldwide One Child policy was finally adopted and
introduced in 2145. This policy to be continued for several
generations until the total population was reduced to around 500/600
million.

After that, a more flexible policy would be adopted with a
target figure of approximately two children per family – the system
then to be adjusted to allow a continuing population of 500/600
million with a peak number of no more than 700 million.

The desperate and prolonged struggle for survival had
fundamentally and permanently changed human thinking attitudes.
People now accepted, without question, the need to control
population, but they also realised the old way of life was crazy and
unsustainable. They realised, with a deep certainty, that the only
things that really mattered were for people to have a roof over their
head, a small, happy, healthy, family; food in the larder, a job and a
few fun things. They could now see that the old style of life was
inherently profligate, wasteful and unsustainable.

For example – hundreds of millions of people used to fly, in
enormous aeroplanes, thousands of miles, all over the planet, burning

enormous quantities of fuel – just to go on holiday. Just to lounge and play on some foreign beach or see the sights and landscape of a different country.

Thousands of millions of people owned private transportation vehicles, each consuming substantial quantities of liquid fuel or electrical power, merely to travel around for unnecessary personal pleasure and entertainment. These vehicles were commonly driven for a distance of 10 to 40 thousand kilometres a year by merely one person.

Many enormous ships, powered by vast quantities of liquid hydro-carbon fuel, cruised for thousands of miles, for no purpose, other than to entertain the passengers. People worked for ridiculously long hours, often commuting 100 kilometres or more, from where they lived, to their place of work, to support this lifestyle. People strove and competed viciously to create wealth, over and above their need, often just to show off to friends and neighbours. Totally false values were commonplace. For instance, when the average wage was 30,000 old dollars a year, ridiculously wealthy people would pay tens of millions of dollars for a nondescript artwork – some painting that almost anybody could have done – simply because it had some, in fashion, artist's signature on it.

People, both men and women, wore real gold jewellery, encrusted with real diamonds, costing ridiculous amounts of money – when it was possible to buy, for a few dollars, identical jewellery, made from imitation gold and precious stones, so good that only an expert could tell the difference.

People bought personal transport vehicles (in those days called cars or automobiles) with enormously powerful engines – capable of a speed of 240 kilometres an hour – even when there was a government imposed mandatory speed limit of 112 km/hr and they could never use the power. These personal vehicles were commonly scrapped and replaced after a short time – long before they were worn out – merely to be replaced by the latest – more fashionable model. Vast quantities of valuable and almost irreplaceable raw materials were consumed to produce personal trinkets, baubles and gadgets of all kinds. The world, before the Crash was obsessed with personal wealth and status symbols.

After the Crash a Census had revealed that 2.0 billion people had survived – an amazingly high number considering the

circumstances. But the planet was a ruin. Much of it was now simply
too hot to be habitable by man. Global Warming had continued after
the Crash, temperatures continuing to climb steadily. $CO^2$ levels at
the time of the Crash had topped 600ppm. The planet was now 4.3°C
warmer than it was before the Industrial Revolution.

4.3°C does not sound so much but the figure is a global
average. Nearly two thirds of the Earth's surface is covered by water
and the average depth is nearly 10,000 feet. The sea, therefore, is a
colossal heat sink and absorbs an enormous amount of heat for very
little sea temperature rise. The land is different. Land heats up much
more and much faster. It had been noted, many years ago, that land
temperatures rose far higher and faster than global average
temperatures. What a rise of 4.3°C global average temperature
actually meant was that average land temperatures on much of the
surface of the globe, rose by as much as 14.5°C above pre-industrial
levels in the Arctic areas and 8.3°C in the Tropics. Most of the land in
the tropical areas, except for that at very high altitude was
fundamentally uninhabitable by man, (and most other animals) as well
as a fair amount outside the tropics.

The areas unfit for human habitation by 2200, included 95%
of Australia, 95% of India, 80% of China, 80% of Africa, 60% of
South America, 90% of the Middle East, most of South East Asia and
Indonesia and 50% of the USA. On the plus side, of course, Alaska,
Canada, Scandinavia and, above all, Siberia had all become eminently
habitable and that was where, in the future, the bulk of the Earth's
human population would live. The ice on Greenland was melting
rapidly but, so great was the volume, it would probably take another
thousand years for it all to disappear. Nevertheless a substantial part
of Southern Greenland was now habitable.

In 2140, the World Conference settled down to discuss co-
operation and how the human race should live in the future. After
much discussion, it was decided there must be some form of World
Government. Old fashioned ideas of racial differences must be swept
aside. The Human Race was all one race and must co-operate and
work together for the common good. Conditions that led to the great
Crash must never, ever, be allowed to occur again.

The first thing that must be considered was the population. If
the world was to have a balanced system – with human beings co-

existing with the rest of the life on the planet – in healthy harmony – into the far, far future, then 2.0 billion was still too many. It was resolved that action should be taken to reduce the number, by birth control means, down to a figure of 500 million. It was resolved that a planet wide 'One Child' policy would be adopted and enforced until the population was close to 500 million. Then it would be possible to relax and adopt a 'Two Child' policy permanently and indefinitely. Later on – minor adjustments to the two child policy could be made as and when it might be necessary, to adjust the total world population and keep it around the 500 million figure. It was resolved that, as soon as the New Civilisation was scientifically and financially able, action should be commenced to reinstate as many of the original animals (land animals, fish and birds) as should be deemed suitable. This to include many animals, fish and birds driven extinct since the beginning of the Industrial Revolution and during the Crash and also, possibly, a few animals, such as the Mammoth, driven extinct by human activity previously. This action depending, of course, on whether the necessary DNA samples and data was available in the Repository.

It was also resolved that since, in future, the human race must live in a sustainable and economically balanced state, into the indefinite future, with no expansion of population, no changes in the standard of living associated with increased consumption of the Earth's Natural Resources allowed, then all Industrial and Manufacturing facilities, all Agricultural and Food Producing Industries, Fisheries (both Farmed and Wild Sea) and any activities concerned with the Consumption of Earth's Natural Resources must be under Governmental Control. Firstly by the World Government. Secondly by the Regional Governments. This would mean there would never again be any large private businesses of any kind, operating on a simple profit making basis.

Some delegates demurred and argued that this was going back to the hated Communism. But it was pointed out – the old style Capitalism was simply and utterly incompatible with a static population, static economy, a minimum use of Earth's Resources and a balance with the rest of the planet. The Age of Profligacy, the Age of Excessive Consumption, the Age of Selfishness was over. Everybody knew what that had created. Basically there had to be a new mind-set. Everybody had to think in terms of co-operation and

216

happiness in simple everyday life. There was still music, dancing, theatre, socialising. Still a thousand and one things to interest, occupy and entertain people.

Excessive consumption and selfishness was out. No more blasting around in private transport vehicles. No more flying around the world unnecessarily. No more wasteful sea cruises. No more of anything that created unnecessary consumption.

People would have to learn to be happy with simple things – and happy where they were – in the Community they were in. Happy to be alive, to be healthy, to have friends, to dance, to have sex, to enjoy food, to have a child or, when things had settled down, two children. To write, to sing, to play music, to play games, to communicate. The Old Way of Life was gone.

Forget Capitalism. Call the new system Enlightened Socialism, enlightened Communism, call it what you like, but it had to be. In future everything must be balanced and balance meant a degree of control. All peoples of the world would be given as much freedom as was possible, compatible with maintaining balance. All people would enjoy the best Standard of Living possible – compatible with balance. People would be allowed to run small businesses – Hairdressing Salons, educational facilities – music lessons – training facilities. Anything that did not involve or, in any way incur additional consumption. Any additional income – over and above the norm – would not be allowed to be used in any way that incurred additional consumption.

World Government, and the systems they introduced were successful – as you know – because they are the systems we have today in 2647. Be thankful your forbears, back in 2140, were so far sighted."

# 2648 – ECONOMICS LECTURE BY PROFESSOR J K PATEL

## ECONOMICS, BUSINESS CONTROL, WAGES, TAXES, ETC, IN 27<sup>TH</sup> CENTURY.

Professor Patel strode on to the stage.

He was a small, wiry, very active, middle aged, man whose ancestors had originally come from a little village in the foothills of the Himalayas in old Pakistan. One of his forbears had been one of the founding fathers of the University of New Copenhagen. Another had been a member of the very first World Government. He had a brilliant brain, absorbed knowledge like a sponge and, naturally, expected everyone else to be the same. So he was inclined to be impatient – and did not suffer fools gladly. At the centre of the stage he stopped at the lectern and raised his hand.

"Good Morning, Ladies and Gentlemen. This lecture is to tell you how the economic system of today works – and why the system we use in the New Civilisation has to be drastically different to that which appertained during the Old Civilisation before the Crash."

He paused. A small group of students were still fooling about, laughing and joking. With a touch of irritation he banged his gavel down on his lectern hard and pushed a button. The lights went out, a gong boomed briefly and the lights came back on.

"Now! Settle down and we will proceed.

First we will consider the way things were in the Old Civilisation, particularly during the Industrial Revolution, which completely transformed the World and made it possible for the human race to multiply, spread and dominate the entire planet as never before. Unfortunately, by its very success it sowed the seeds of its own destruction, which finally came about in the years 2130 to 2133."

Professor Patel went on to describe the beginnings of the Industrial Revolution. The triumph of science and human ingenuity. The Wars. The evolution of society and so on.

He went on. "By and large – the Free Enterprise, Capitalist system of the West was extremely successful, particularly during the early years. The important thing to note, here, is that they were operating on a pristine, relatively unexploited planet. In the 19<sup>th</sup> and
218

early 20<sup>th</sup> Century, the world's mineral resources were practically untouched. There were vast forests. Enormous areas of land, suitable for cultivation – were unexploited. The seas were full of fish. There were massive deposits of coal, oil, natural gas, metal ores and minerals. The Potential was immense.

It was in this environment the free enterprise system thrived. Creative, imaginative, individuals, with drive, started businesses and built them up to become colossal business empires. In the process they created wealth, employment, prosperity. Everybody benefited – though not equally. The top businessmen and industrialists became immensely rich, the Government received more taxes, the working men received more pay – though often they had to fight hard for it – usually through the Trade Unions.

It was a dynamic age and led to great progress but, fundamentally, it was fuelled by the natural selfish human desire for personal wealth, power, fame and glory. This is fine if it can be adequately controlled and channelled to contribute to the common good.

Europe led the way and, because of the general increase in prosperity and betterment of the standard of living, experienced the first population explosion. The rest of the world followed Europe's lead – some sooner – some later, and industrialisation swept the planet. However, despite the success of the system there were enormous snags. Unbridled Capitalism was extremely competitive, aggressive and brutal. Governments learned to control it – apply rules and regulations until remarkably civilised Free Enterprise/ Capitalist systems dominated the entire world.

However, when we analyse the system carefully, we realise it was extremely inefficient, wasteful and profligate. Consumerism was encouraged. Vast sums of money were spent on advertising by industry, extolling the virtues of the latest gadgets. Products were endlessly re-designed and modified, not so much to greatly improve the product but to make others look 'old fashioned', 'out of date', 'quaint', 'archaic' and so on. People were brainwashed into believing that they were 'behind the times', 'backward', 'old fashioned', etc if they did not have the latest cars, televisions, mobile phones, computers, etc. Every manufacturing business sought to maximise production, and enhance profits, by every possible means.

Products were manufactured, not to last, but with built in redundancy and planned obsolescence. The ideal product would last just long enough until the new model came out. Long enough to satisfy the customer but not long enough to reduce sales. Governments were forced to bring in legislation to ensure products lasted a 'reasonable' length of time and were 'fit for purpose'.

This consumerism created a massive demand for raw materials of all kinds. Colossal mines were created to excavate millions of tons of raw materials – iron ore, copper, nickel, coal, etc from the ground. Thousands upon thousands of oil wells, gas wells, water boreholes were drilled and operated. Iron ore and coal consumption figures were in billions of tons per year.

Basically, the prices of these commodities were fixed by a 'supply and demand' free enterprise system. For instance – if there was a shortage of copper, the price went up until some manufacturers could no longer afford to buy. Some businesses would go 'bust'. People would lose their jobs. Product prices went up. Then other enterprising people would search for new copper ore deposits, open new mines. The supply would increase. The price would come down. More manufacturers start up again.

Obviously, in a system like this, boom and bust was the norm – even when the world fundamentally still had plenty of raw materials available. The system was intrinsically unstable. Vested interests – the commodity suppliers – periodically sought to deliberately control or restrict supplies to push up prices and maximise profits.

A particularly pernicious example of this was restriction of crude oil supplies. Crude oil was vital as a raw material for production of fuels, lubricating oils, rubber, plastics, fertilisers for crop production, etc. Unfortunately, massive deposits of oil existed in only a few places on Earth. In the mid 20th Century, some of the countries fortunate enough to possess large deposits, clubbed together to form a cartel called OPEC (Organisation of Petroleum Exporting Countries) to restrict supplies and force up prices. In effect they held the rest of the world to ransom. Within nations, legislation was enacted to prevent this kind of activity but nothing could be done Internationally other than going to War. So OPEC flourished for over 50 years and exploited their situation, extracting billions, nay, trillions of dollars in excess profits from the rest of the world.

In many manufacturing industries it was usual to add 10% profit margin, over and above the total costs of making a product, as a normal, acceptable, profit margin. 20% or more was considered excessive. As an indication of the enormity of the OPEC exploitation, consider that, in the year 2014, the world price of oil was 110 dollars per barrel, when the actual cost to Saudi Arabia (an OPEC member) – to extract the oil from the ground and prepare it for sale was no more than 5 dollars per barrel. An absurd situation. The result of the artificially high oil price was to raise the prices of goods and services everywhere and depress world trade, creating scores of millions of unemployed people worldwide.

The 'Supply and Demand' pricing system applied to all commodities – rubber, cocoa beans, corn, meat, oil, coal, metals, everything. It can be seen, therefore, that the commodities markets were in endless flux, with prices fluctuating up and down all the time. If there was a drought, creating a grain shortage – the price went up. If there was a good harvest – the price went down. In hindsight it seems a miracle the 'free enterprise' system ever worked as well as it did.

However, the entire planet, with the exception of a few, very small, groups, developed the free enterprise, consumerist, 'free for all' mind set. It became almost like a religion.

So great was this 'mind set' that, even in the early 21$^{st}$ Century, very few people indeed raised any alarms, voiced any misgivings about how the human race was proceeding. It should have been obvious the system could not continue indefinitely. Should have been obvious there must come a day, not too far in the future, when the music would stop, when the copper, the nickel, the oil, the gas would begin to run out. When the world population would finally become too great to feed. However, during the 21$^{st}$ Century, Industrialisation continued. More and more, backward nations industrialised. Demand for raw materials and all natural resources continued to increase, as did the population and, as did the demand for energy. In these conditions it was impossible to totally control and restrict carbon dioxide and methane emissions and the atmospheric greenhouse gas levels inexorably rose.

By mid and late 21$^{st}$ Century, as natural resources became more and more, in short supply, the instability caused by 'supply and demand' price fluctuations became increasingly pronounced. The world staggered from one economic crisis to the next.

At the beginning of the 22$^{nd}$ Century, by 2128, the entire world economic situation was becoming critical. There were endless shortages of raw materials. The population was just over 15 billion. The seas were hopelessly impoverished. Food production on land was critical – they could only just feed the world's population. Global Warming was becoming very serious. Weather patterns were becoming drastically changed. Droughts had ruined the great grain producing areas of America's mid west and Asia's Ukraine. In China, India and South East Asia, crops were failing. All over the world artesian water supplies were running out. Large areas of irrigated land were becoming poisoned by salt contamination. Summer temperatures, in tropical areas, were reaching the limit of human tolerance. Billions of people wanted to migrate. Hundreds of millions were unemployed. Health services were failing. Rioting and civil strife was everywhere. Civilisation was teetering on the brink of some sort of collapse.

The appearance of HIVa was the final straw. It probably made the collapse worse than it would have been without it. Maybe, without HIVa there would have been a lesser disaster – with only a quarter or a half of the world's total population lost. This would have been disaster enough but, after that, the world may have staggered on, sticking to the same old formulae and, a half century later, another collapse – another disaster. Who knows – maybe hundreds of years of endless disaster/ recovery/ disaster until, eventually, the population was reduced to sustainable levels.

We shall never know. The effect of HIVa was to create a massive sudden collapse. A shock so great that 87% of the total human world population was lost. A shock so great that the entire world economic system was disrupted. A shock so great that the survivors of the world's nations all agreed to co-operate as never before.

It was recognised that there were two possible futures for humanity. One – was where the world went back to its old ways and where everyone struggled to survive. The other was where the peoples and nations of the world co-operated and worked together to create a New Civilisation, built on different principles and new standards.

The First Option was bleak indeed. Human beings have a tendency to fragment into factions and tribes and move towards violence and strife.

A classic example of this was the colonisation of North and South America by a group of humans who crossed the Bering Strait from Asia about 14,000 years ago.

A small group, probably no more than 30 to 50 individuals moved across the Bering Strait – probably on sea ice – and found themselves alone – with not one but two, continents available for them to colonise. In this vast space – which they had all to themselves – they moved south, exploited its vast resources and multiplied. Over time they multiplied more, spread out and occupied other areas. They then fragmented, split up into tribes and gradually occupied the whole of North and South America – from the icy shores of Canada in the North to the wilderness of Tierra Del Fuego at the southern tip of South America. Despite having this vast area in which to live – an area that could have supported a hundred times their total number if it had been managed correctly – what did they do? They proceeded to fight amongst themselves. Inter-tribal warfare became the norm. From the plains Indians in North America to the Aztecs and Olmecs in South America – they fought. Human beings have a penchant for strife and violence.

---

If no rapid action had been taken to unify and re-organise the human race quickly – after the Crash in 2130 to 2132 – the whole world could and probably would, have degenerated back to a world of endless tribal strife and conflict. And the natural world – this beautiful Earth – already impoverished and devastated by the excesses of the Old Civilisation, would have been damaged even more.

It is interesting to recall – the Native Americans – those descendants of the group that crossed the Bering Strait – despite the fact there were never many of them, compared to later human numbers – managed, nevertheless, to exterminate the Mammoths, the Mastodons, the Camels, the Horses, the American Lions and a whole lot more besides.

Fortunately – after the Crash – the surviving peoples of the World, led by a few outstanding individuals of remarkable foresight and drive, got their heads together and vowed to work together, in peace and harmony to produce a New Civilisation. The big question was – How could it be done to produce a high degree of Civilisation, with a decent standard of human living, in balance with Nature on a planet with very limited remaining resources.

The big deposits of oil and gas were gone. The massive mines for copper, nickel, chrome and many other metals and minerals were worked out. Much agricultural land was seriously impoverished and overworked.

Firstly it was decided the number of human beings on the Earth had to be reduced to sane and sensible levels. It was decided the numbers should be reduced to a total of 500 million by a birth control system. It was also decided that there had to be a totally new economic system. No mineral deposits of any kind, anywhere, could be privately owned. Nor could any land or sea areas. All must be commonly owned. All manufacturing facilities above a certain small size must be commonly owned. The old word for this was 'Nationalised' but the word nationalised implied belonging to a nation and that too, should not be. These things must belong to the entire human race.

All agriculture, forestry, mining, mineral extraction, fisheries and human habitation would be organised and controlled on a global basis. Large areas of land and sea would be set aside as nature reserves with minimum human intervention and interference. The reserved areas of sea, particularly, would act as breeding havens, reservoirs of fish stocks to replenish areas that are regularly harvested for food. Everything, to be planned on the premise that the whole planet should be in balance – with human beings simply a reasonable part of the whole planetary biomass. The Earth should be a healthy, thriving, bio-diverse entity, able to continue developing and evolving for millions of years into the future.

If the data indicated, at any time in the future, that humanity was too great a burden – overloading the natural resources, then the World Government would take action, through population control means, to redress the balance and bring the total human population down to calculated balance levels.

Economics, and all industrial production would be organised on a worldwide basis. The old 'supply and demand' system would be abolished.

This approach meant that all remaining deposits of valuable raw materials, no matter how small, could be worked. It was no longer a question of raw economics, it was a question of necessity. Poor quality land could be worked, as well as better quality. Prices of everything would be fixed, by reference to the World Government. For instance the price of wheat would be fixed and would remain fixed at that level, for 20 years or more. If there was a poor harvest and a shortage of wheat – the price did not go up – as in the old days. Instead it was rationed out, on a pro-rata basis. When there was a good year – and a glut of wheat – the price did not go down. Instead the Government would order a switch of land use for next year – and the excess put into storage.

The prices of commodities and minerals were fixed in a similar way. It was no longer a case of uneconomic mines being closed. If, for instance, there were still low grade deposits of copper ore still existing in an old mine – at levels which were once considered uneconomic to operate – then the Government would order the mine to be re-opened and operated. The price of copper would be fixed, again for long periods of time. When there was insufficient copper the price would stay the same. The supply would be rationed, again on a pro rata basis. What meagre deposits that were left on the Earth could be used.

Obviously, economics still come into the working of the system. The operation of all mines, as with cultivation of land, operation of factories, etc would all be carefully monitored and the true costs – in terms of human labour, expenditure of energy, cost of equipment and so on logged. If more than sufficient copper, for current needs, was produced then the most expensive, uneconomic mines would be shut down or mothballed but registered as available for another time, as the supply situation worsened. Badly impoverished arable land might be planted with non productive crops – to be ploughed in, to boost humus and ground fertility, or a system of crop rotation introduced with the land lying fallow every 3$^{rd}$ or 4$^{th}$ year. These were uneconomic practices that would not have been practiced in the old competitive days.

It should be mentioned that, at least with agriculture, some effort to move in this direction was made in the late 20$^{th}$/ early 21$^{st}$ Century. Some Governments stepped in, subsidised the farmers and used subsidies to pressure farmers into taking actions they would not otherwise do – such as leaving land fallow, planting specific crops, controlling milk and meat production and so on. The Government also, to a degree, controlled prices – both to the farmers and of their produce.

In the New Civilisation, Government control would extend to everything – but in a benign way. The target was to benefit the entire human race – to create as happy and as pleasant a life as possible for people, concomitant with living on a badly impoverished world and in balance with all other living things on the planet. Price controls meant that living costs did not fluctuate wildly. The costs of food, services and products did not change drastically. Shortages simply meant rationing – not price increases. A glut simply meant plenty was available – the product was not cheaper. People have said the New Civilisation was Communism. In the New Age it is best to mentally discard all the old 'isms'. Fascism, Liberalism, Socialism, Communism, Toryism, Totalitarianism. Simply think – how could the world be run, in the state that it was in – to achieve a controlled, balanced Civilisation with happy people, living in harmony – in balance with the Earth and the rest of Nature – going on into the future – for thousands of years. There have to be rules. There has to be control. Otherwise there will be chaos. A murderous free for all.

The system that has been created gives stability and security. Economic stability. Political stability. Security for everyone. Security in employment, in housing, in health, in world peace and co-operation. Everybody sees that it works. Only a few misfits want to rock the boat. There are always a few that are never satisfied.

Everybody who works is paid a reasonable wage – for the work they do. A doctor is paid more than a clerk – to compensate for the years of study at a low wage, the dedication and the effort – but only a relatively low multiple of the clerk's wage – not ridiculously high. It is all computerised. Every occupation is valued and rated. But no-one is paid insane incomes. In the old days, someone who had a natural gift – for playing football or golf or driving a racing car – was paid insane amounts – millions of dollars when the average wage was in thousands a year. We still have footballers, golfers, racing drivers, tennis players – and they play and drive – entertaining the crowds. But now they do it for the pleasure, the thrill, the fame and the glory – not for sheer cash. No one now is allowed to become multi millionaires or even billionaires as there used to be. No one now is allowed to build and own colossal mansions and personally own thousands of acres.

Everything is shared out more fairly. However – no one is encouraged to be lazy. Everyone who is capable is expected to contribute. The disabled are looked after and given a low but reasonable standard of living. Free loaders are discouraged. Anyone who is fit and capable and will not work will end up at near starvation levels.

Single young women are not allowed, as they once were, to have a number of children, simply to be provided with a home and State Benefits – mainly for the children's sake – so they could sit around and have an easy life. The mandatory contraceptive implant and birth control rules, of course, prevent that.

Now, in 2648, nearly everyone has a happy, easy-going, secure life. They can get married – or live together – and have two children. They have sufficient food, good health services, a four day, 28 hour working week, a decent house. Two months holiday a year. There are facilities everywhere for games, sports and various occupations.

People are encouraged to socialise, play music, join archery clubs, bowling clubs, dancing clubs, play football, go fishing, swimming, gliding, rowing and a thousand other things beside. They compose music, paint, make sculptures, invent, discuss, cultivate and create gardens and so on.

Some people have said that this is not a progressive society – that progress will slow down – that we will stagnate. It is true that there will not be the spectacular, frantic, rate of scientific and inventive progress there was in the 20$^{th}$ and 21$^{st}$ Century, but – does it matter? We shall still progress. It is in the nature of humans to be curious, to discover, explore and invent. Albert Einstein thought out and produced his remarkable Theory of Relativity when he was a poorly paid patent clerk in a Zurich office. We are in no mad hurry – we have all the time in the world – millions of years, if we are sensible – and carry on as we are now. Progress will continue. The Geneticists will still work to unlock the deeper secrets of the genome. The chemists will still work to improve the efficiency of our solar/ electric panels. The engineers will still work to improve our robots, our transport, our bridges – because they are interested, not because what they do will make them millionaires.

There is the question of Governmental Finance and expenditure. The financing of the health service, the public roads, the subsidising and financing of the farmers, the miners, the police and so on. Fortunately, we do not need to spend fantastic sums on weapons and armed forces as used to be the case. And it was realised the old fashioned taxation system – with its legions of Inland Revenue employees, was a colossal burden. At one time in the 21$^{st}$ Century, it was estimated the cost of collecting the taxes could be as high as 25% of the total tax take. Now, it is all computerised. There is no Inland Revenue. No tax returns No Tax evasion No Tax Avoidance.

In practice it is as though everybody has a 40% tax take deducted from their pay before they even know it. It is as though there is a 20% VAT added to goods and services but no one knows it. The computers work out what is required. The amount people are paid in credits, automatically, monthly into their electronic accounts is simply about half of what equates to the value of their gross product. It is as though the computer pays them half of what they earn and pays the other half to the Government. There is no tinkering with tax rates at the bottom end or top end of the scale. If it is decided, for instance, that someone's pay at the bottom end of the pay range, is too low then there is no tax modification. The pay is simply increased. There has never been a problem at the top end. The pay has never been too high. There are pay differentials, of course, in all kinds of employment. People are encouraged to educate themselves, to become skilled, to become experts because every form of employment has a series of grades – from the lowest grade/ lowest paid at the bottom to the highest grade/ highest paid at the top, so there is always an incentive to better oneself. The difference between lowest and highest pay in an occupation is enough to create an incentive but not at the insane levels that used to apply.

Excessive personal stress at work has been eliminated. In the old days people were under constant pressure to give maximum effort, all the time. The target – for the running of an efficient business – was maximum possible output from the minimum possible staff. This often led to a situation where a business was employing, say, 500 overloaded, overstressed employees working frantically, at the same time as there were 500 others, perfectly capable of doing the job, sitting twiddling their thumbs – unemployed just down the road.

We have abolished excess stress and abolished unnecessary unemployment. Where the pressure is great or the work particularly onerous we employ more people.

Undoubtedly it is less efficient than the old system but, since today it is no longer a commercially competitive world system, it does not matter. What does matter is that everybody that is capable does work and contributes to the overall GWP (Gross World Product). If everybody works reasonably well then everybody benefits.

Gross World Product is assessed every year and adjustments made. If the GWP goes down then everybody is slightly worse off. If it goes up they are slightly better off. There are no changes to pay and salary rates. Prices of goods and services are simply adjusted, slightly up or down. No capable person, of working age, is allowed to be unemployed for long. They are allowed to seek the employment they prefer, for as long as they like, but they must work, in some capacity in the meantime. Job applications, interviews, etc must be in their own time. After all, a four day week, 28 working hours a week and plenty of holidays, at whatever job one is forced to do, is hardly slavery, while one is searching for a preferred job.

Those who wilfully refuse to work at anything, while physically or mentally capable, will find their automatic payments into their accounts rapidly reduce, over a few months, to subsistence, near starvation, levels. For them borrowing will be prohibited.

Incidentally, borrowing is allowed, under certain circumstances. Applications must be made to the necessary Authority and the loan authorised. An example would be a loan to a young, recently married or partnered, couple who wish to furnish their new apartment or house. The house itself is community owned and is rented at the lowest possible rent. Houses are designed to have a lifetime of at least 200 years and, as the accumulated rental must only build up to a sum that is sufficient to build the next replacement house, the rental figure is extremely low.

The economic system means that monetary inflation has been abolished so there is no 'built in' inflation charge. Occupants are required to treat the property with respect and do a small amount of periodic maintenance – cleaning, painting, repairing, etc. The property is inspected every 12 months and, if there are signs of misuse or neglect, penalties are applied. A furnishing loan would be provided at almost zero interest rate, effectively from the community and repayable over a number of years by deductions from salary. If the couple should later split up the loan would be divided and repayments deducted from the separate salaries.

When a child is born, a woman is exempt from working for 5 months before the birth and 2 years afterwards, while continuing on full normal pay. When the child is 2 years old it would go into a crèche during working days and the mother expected to resume work.

There are, of course, a vast number of details of organisation other than those quoted here, but whilst it is impossible to please everyone and it is certainly true that there are a few small dissident groups, nevertheless statistics indicate, and most people believe, that the New Civilisation is a great success. A higher percentage of the human race is now happy, contented, satisfied with life, healthy and well fed than at any time before in the history of the world.

———————

With regard to the conservation of metals and raw materials. The Government can authorise the operation of mines and mineral deposits anywhere, no matter how 'low concentration' or 'worked out' the deposits are. There are continuous, ongoing salvage operations to recover sunken ships of all kinds from the sea bed. Old waste tips, on land and in the sea are 'mined' and sorted, mainly robotically, to recover the many valuable metals and raw materials discarded so casually, years ago. Everything manufactured and produced today is carefully dismantled and re-cycled when it comes to the end of its working life. Everything is designed for maximum life and easy repair and refurbishment. It is a crime to burn anything that could be recycled.

Eventually, in the far future, there will be no mines, no natural sources of the uncommon metals and minerals left at all. However – the metals and many of the minerals that were previously taken from the ground are still on the Earth. It is a question of whether they are recoverable and recyclable. We shall then have to survive on recycled materials and those we can synthesise. We shall probably replace many metals and minerals with organics. Already scientists have synthesised organic materials stronger than steel and have created organics with semi-conductor properties.

As I said earlier, all but the most basic weapon systems have been abolished. We no longer need tanks, heavy guns, intercontinental missiles, war planes, war oriented submarines, warships and so forth. The production of these systems used to constitute an enormous and ongoing drain on the National finances of nearly every nation on Earth.

One of the most important World Government Acts of all was the total abolition of nuclear weapons. It took many years to dismantle these weapons and dispose of the plutonium and uranium fissile materials in a safe manner – but it was done. Also – all the know how – the technical information and complex technology involved in making hydrogen bombs and Plutonium nuclear bombs was destroyed – the drawings, the data bases, the information was destroyed, deleted, wiped. All persons with personal knowledge were forbidden to make any notes, records or pass information to anyone else – on pain of death. Fortunately, the creation of a Hydrogen Bomb was an extremely complex, sophisticated, technologically difficult achievement. Making hydrogen bombs is now classed as a 'lost art' as is the construction of 'implosion' type Plutonium based atomic bombs. Uranium based atomic bombs are different. It is remarkably easy to make an atomic bomb using Uranium 235. Almost any clever Engineer could do it.

The key to abolishing Uranium type atomic bombs is to get rid of the U235.

Cutting a long story short – Uranium type atomic bombs can only be made using Uranium 235 – a rare isotope of Uranium and it is extremely difficult to extract it in useable quantities. Extremely specialised equipment has to be used.

To prevent the manufacture of Uranium nuclear bombs, all existing stocks of U235 were contaminated by being mixed with Uranium 238 and a law passed that no one is ever allowed again to enrich Uranium to bomb grade levels. So – the nuclear bomb problems were solved and the world is now free of the threat of nuclear weapons which hung, like a pall, over the human race for so long.

Another feature of the Old Civilisation was the enormous expenditure by manufacturers, service providers and nearly all forms of business, on advertising. Often the advertising and promotion costs of a product or service was a very substantial (up to 30% or more) portion of the total price. This was enormously inefficient but was considered an essential expenditure of any competitive business.

The customer, of course, bore this cost, usually without realising or knowing it. All advertising of this nature has been abolished, resulting in a great reduction in costs. A vast range of consumer products are still created and full details of the products are available on any portable communicator but large scale, competitive advertising is gone. Cities ablaze with enormous neon signs are a thing of the past as are the millions of lights, strung along motorways and public highways. Traffic is automatic nowadays. No lights needed, night or day. Satellite pictures, taken from orbit, back in 2015, showed vast areas of cities and thousands of miles of connecting highways, ablaze with light at night. The whole planet glowed. A colossal waste of energy and equipment. Satellite photographs taken now, at night, show only faint glimmers of light, here and there.

The New Civilisation is vastly more efficient than the old, in so many ways. It had to be, on the drastically impoverished planet that was inherited. What we have now can last, into the far, far future if we are careful and stick to the basic principles. Economy, Efficiency and Restricted Population. So now, Ladies and Gentlemen, you should have some idea of the vast differences between the Old Civilisation and the New and appreciate your great good fortune in being alive today, in the year 2648. Good Night."

# 2648 – PROFESSOR PATEL'S LECTURE ON THE NEED FOR POPULATION CONTROL

## NEED FOR POPULATION CONTROL, THE GERIATRIC PROBLEM AND CRIME CONTROL

"Good Morning Ladies and Gentlemen. This Lecture is about the need for Population Control and – specifically – the overriding need for a One Child Policy immediately after the Crash and the Geriatric Problem that arose rapidly thereafter.

As you know, approximately two billion people survived, worldwide, the great Human Civilisation Collapse and Disaster of 2130 to 2133 which we now know as the Great Crash or simply the 'Crash'. At first sight it would appear that a collapse of the human population from a peak of 15.2 billion to only 2 billion would have solved the world's population problem for a considerable time. This, however, was not so, as I intend to demonstrate.

There is no doubt in my mind, we are very fortunate indeed today to live, as we do, in a sane and civilised world – with a limited world population of only 500 million. Because we have these restricted numbers we can all live in peace and comfort, with adequate food, happy social lives, excellent health services and many other modern benefits, secure in the knowledge that our children, their children and their descendents, going forward into the far future, can look forward, endlessly, to the enlightened lives and conditions we enjoy today on a healthy, enriched and rejuvenated planet.

It could, Ladies and Gentlemen, have been very, very different. We could so easily have slipped into an endless, barbaric, age of vicious competition, strife, warfare, pestilence and famine on an impoverished over-exploited world.

Fortunately, almost by a miracle, during the Crash, small areas of the world remained under control, with infrastructure intact, and some civilised society survived to spread enlightenment and bring the whole of humanity back from the brink of chaos. We are very lucky that the creation of the New Civilisation occurred so rapidly because, as I will show, there was only a short window of opportunity to get the population under control at sane levels. Just fifty years could have made the difference between a chaotic world of endless strife, tribal wars and perpetual misery and the wonderful, world we inhabit today.

---

Imagine the conditions that existed immediately after the Crash. After the hellish conditions of the Crash, survivors, having somehow come through the most desperate situations and found themselves alive in a sea of chaos, would want, more than anything else, to get back to some semblance of normality. Above all they would want homes and children. In such a situation the drive to procreate is enhanced. As long as there is sufficient food available they will procreate – no matter how primitive and desperate the living conditions.

If we consider the situation carefully we realise that most of the survivors are likely to be young – aged between 18 and 35. Nearly all geriatrics will have disappeared as will a great many middle aged people and, unfortunately, most of the children. What you have then, is a world full of virile, extremely active and capable, young, energetic human beings. Otherwise they would not have survived. However, they will live in a drastically changed world. It will take some time before medical services are fully restored. Therefore, there will be a high infant mortality. Let us assume, therefore, that the survivors will only succeed in reproducing at an average rate of just 2 children per family who will grow up to have children of their own – merely replacement rate. What will be the result, in 60 years or so, of reproducing at that rate?

You may say, instinctively – no problem – they are merely reproducing at replacement rate. But you would be wrong. The result would rapidly be chaos.

Let us consider. The survivors are healthy. The 2 surviving children are healthy. Let us say – with only 2 billion people on the earth – there is enough food. Let us say the average expectation of life for the survivors and future generations is 80 years – a little optimistic but – bear with me. Let us divide an average expectation of life into 4 quartiles. The first 20 years we will designate as J (for Juvenile and Junior). The second quartile as A (for Adult and breeding age). The third quartile as LA (for Late Adult – non breeding but still active). The fourth quartile as G (for Geriatric – non productive and many needing care).

Going forward, into the future, in 20 year increments, it can be shown, on a very simple chart, using basic arithmetic, what is likely to happen.

I am now going to project a chart, on the screen and use a pointer to indicate, as I proceed. However, you all have a copy of these charts in your notes on your desk in front of you. I am doing it in this way as I think, following these and the straightforward arithmetic, it will stick in your minds better than fancy complicated projections on a computer screen.

I will now refer to Chart No 1.

You will see, top left, the initial figure of 2000 survivors. All figures will be in millions so 2000 denotes 2000 million survivors. The chart goes away to the right, subdivided in vertical lines pitched 20 years apart, going into the future, 120 years ahead. Let us see what happens.

Starting at the zero line – which is immediately after the Crash, we have the 2000 million survivors. (Remember – these are all young active, breeding age survivors). After 20 years they have produced their (average 2) children so, after 20 years we have the 2000 million survivors (still alive) plus 2000 million children. So, in just 20 years the world population is now 4000 million. After another 20 years we still have the survivors (ageing now) plus their children and the children have now produced their own children. (The survivors are now grandparents). In just 40 years the world population has ballooned to 6000 million people. After another 20 years the survivors are at the end of their lives now – geriatrics, but in the previous 20 years they have become great grandparents and in only 60 years the world population has reached 8000 million people. Don't forget that people are only breeding at replacement rate. The survivors are dying off now and children are only being born at replacement rate so the population will now stabilise.

Now, Ladies and Gentlemen, perhaps you grasp the problem and the danger. Our simple analysis is very crude – but effective. You will all realise, no doubt, that, in reality, the 8 billion figure would never be reached. The human world would, in its impoverished state, collapse back into chaos, disease and famine long before that.

**CHART 1**

## FUTURE WORLD POPULATION PROJECTION

- BASED ON AN AVERAGE OF 2 CHILDREN PER FAMILY—CONTINUING INDEFINITELY

YEARS AFTER THE END OF THE 'CRASH'

NUMBERS ARE IN MILLIONS

NUMBER OF SURVIVORS = 2000

ASSUMING AVERAGE EXPECTATION OF LIFE AT BIRTH = 80 YEARS

J = JUVENILE/JUNIOR (QUARTILE 1)
A = ADULT/BREEDING AGE (QUARTILE 2)
LA = LATE ADULT (QUARTILE 3)
G = GERIATRIC (QUARTILE 4)

| | 0 | 20 | 40 | 60 | 80 | 100 | |
|---|---|---|---|---|---|---|---|
| | | 2000 A | 2000 LA | 2000 G | 2000 G | 2000 G | 2000 G |
| | | 2000 J | 2000 A | 2000 LA | 2000 LA | 2000 LA | 2000 LA etc |
| | | | 2000 J | 2000 A | 2000 A | 2000 A | 2000 A etc |
| | | | | 2000 J | 2000 J | 2000 J | 2000 J etc |
| TOTAL WORLD POPULATION | 4000 | 6000 | 8000 | 8000 | 8000 | 8000 | 8000 |
| NUMBER OF GERIATRICS | | | | 2000 | 2000 | 2000 | 2000 |
| GERIATRICS-PERCENTAGE OF TOTAL POPULATION | | | | 25% | 25% | 25% | 25% |

**CHART 2**

## FUTURE WORLD POPULATION PROJECTION

WITH CONTROLLED BIRTH RATE PATTERN FOR RESIDUAL WORLD POPULATION OF 500 MILLION

YEARS AFTER THE END OF THE 'CRASH'

NUMBERS ARE IN MILLIONS

ASSUMING AVERAGE EXPECTATION OF LIFE AT BIRTH = 80 YEARS

J = JUVENILE/JUNIOR (QUARTILE 1)
A = ADULT/BREEDING AGE (QUARTILE 2)
LA = LATE ADULT (QUARTILE 3)
G = GERIATRIC (QUARTILE 4)

| | 0 | 20 | 40 | 60 | 80 | 100 | 120 | 140 | 160 | 180 | 180+ |
|---|---|---|---|---|---|---|---|---|---|---|---|
| **NUMBER OF SURVIVORS = 2000** (G) | | | | 2000 G | 2000 G | 1000 G | 500 G | 250 G | 125 G | 125 G | 125 G |
| **REPRODUCTION IN** (LA) | | | 2000 LA | 2000 LA | 1000 LA | 500 LA | 250 LA | 125 LA | 125 LA | 125 LA | 125 LA etc |
| **FIRST 20 YEARS AVERAGES 2** (A) | | 2000 A | 2000 A | 1000 A | 500 A | 250 A | 125 A | 125 A | 125 A | 125 A | 125 A etc |
| **CHILDREN PER FAMILY** (J) | | 2000 J | 1000 J | 500 J | 250 J | 125 J | 125 J | 125 J | 125 J | 125 J | 125 J etc |
| TOTAL WORLD POPULATION | | 4000 | 5000 | 5500 | 3750 | 1875 | 1000 | 625 | 500 | 500 | 500 |
| NUMBER OF GERIATRICS | | | | 2000 | 2000 | 1000 | 500 | 250 | 125 | 125 | 125 |
| GERIATRICS-PERCENTAGE OF TOTAL POPULATION | | | | 36% | 53% | 53% | 50% | 40% | 25% | 25% | 25% |

Annotations:

- 90 YEARS - 1 CHILD POLICY
- 10 YEARS - BEFORE 1 CHILD POLICY FULLY IMPLEMENTED
- 2 CHILD POLICY TO CONTINUE INDEFINITELY
- EOL PILL NEEDED

But the chart hammers home how fast the human race could get itself into 'crisis' conditions again.

Now I will show you a second chart – of what happens when you enforce a One Child Policy soon after the Crash – which is, of course, basically, the policy that brought us to where we are today. This, as you will see, creates its own problems.

We start off again, top left, with the 2000 million survivors. Let us say the One Child Policy is not fully effective until 20 years after the end of the 'Crash' and, in that 20 years, the survivors have produced an average of 2 children per family – as before. Therefore, we are up to a world population of 4000 million before the one child policy is effective. In the next 20 years the children then produce their own children and the survivors become grandparents. The children are only allowed to have an average of one child per family so we now have a total of 2 billion grandparents, 2 billion children and 1 billion grandchildren, giving a grand total of 5 billion human beings on the earth. At this point there is no geriatric problem. In other words there is no great number of aged and infirm to be looked after.

After the next 20 years the 1 billion grandchildren have produced their 'one child' quota of 500 million. We now have 2 billion geriatrics plus 2 billion middle aged plus 1 billion adults plus 500 million children. Total 5½ billion.

However, apart from the problem of feeding 5½ billion mouths, there is now a massive burden of 2 billion geriatrics to be looked after. That is no less than 36% of the total people on the earth who are non productive and many need looking after.

After another 20 years the 500 million great grandchildren have produced their 'one child' quota of 250 million children. The original 2 billion 'Crash' survivors are gone – died out. But their 2 billion children are now geriatrics. The total world population has come down to – 3.75 billion but there are 2 billion geriatrics – which represents a massive 53%. 53% of the total world population are non productive and many need looking after.

This, Ladies and Gentlemen, is the crunch time. The 'One Child' policy is now really working and the human population of the planet is falling rapidly. However, the temptation to ditch the one child policy is almost overwhelming. A chorus of calls to abolish the one child policy are heard. "We need more young people to keep society and civilisation going," is the cry.

We must congratulate our forbears for having the determination and fortitude to keep going and get through this extremely difficult time. If you look at the chart, you will see that, in another 20 years, the total world population plummets – to a total of 1.875 billion. Again, in this 20 year period we still have a ratio of 53% geriatrics.

At the end of this period we can relax the birth control rules and allow an average of 2 children per family but it will, of course, be 20 years before the full benefits of more young people are experienced. At this stage the geriatric ratio drops slightly to 50%. Total population is now down to 1 billion.

Another 20 years of the 2 child policy and the world population has dropped to 625 million. The geriatric ratio is 40%.

Another 20 years of the 2 child policy and we are down to the target level – a world population of 500 million and the geriatric ratio has fallen to the long term figure which will apply into the far future – 25%.

This second chart, Ladies and Gentlemen, gives you a clue as to what actually happened after the Crash. A tremendous achievement by our forbears for which we should be forever grateful. The figures on the chart are only a guide as to what actually happened.

In fact, the World Government introduced the One Child Policy as early as 2141 – only 6 years after the Crash ended. It took a few years before the Policy could be fully implemented but, nevertheless, the maximum world population never reached the maximum of 5½ billion shown on the chart. The actual maximum reached was 4.7 billion and that was enough to stretch the resources of the time to the absolute limit.

The 'one child' policy never operated as efficiently as indicated on the chart. In practice it was more like a 1.2 to 1.5 child policy. This, of course, eased the geriatric problem a little but extended the time taken to get down to 500 million by another sixty years.

The geriatric problem was an immense problem and created many practical and ethical dilemmas. A number of actions were taken to try to reduce the burden. The idea of a definite end to the working life – a 'retirement age' was abolished. People were expected and, if physically fit, required to work to the age of 70. After that, encouraged to work beyond that age if fit and well but not actually required to do so. This was not as onerous as it may sound. Many, aged over 70, worked simply helping other geriatrics, less fit than themselves i.e. as carers.

The biggest problem, of course, were the legions of the senile and incapacitated. The ones who could not walk. Could not feed themselves. Could not wash themselves, were incontinent. People who needed almost continuous care.

After much debate it was decided to introduce the EOL (End of Life) pill – an extremely humane and gentle way to exit life. This was simply made available to anyone who wished to use it. Nobody was forced to take it but, it must be said, they were encouraged to do so. In practice, when it was introduced, many people were amazed at the enthusiasm with which it was received. Nearly all geriatrics, of course, knew only too well about the Crash and the need to get the world population down, the one child policy and so on. A great many had the attitude that they had been lucky to have a long life, wanted to see their descendants happy in the New Civilisation and had no desire to be an excessive burden. Many more were pleased to have the option to ease themselves gently out of this life rather than suffer years of indignity, pain and misery in old age.

To many the EOL Pill was a wonderful release. It involved no suffering whatsoever. When swallowed with a drink of water, the pill dissolved in stages. First came a mild sedative to calm and settle the person. Then a slow building of warmth and euphoria, drifting slowly into sleep. From sleep, slowly into unconsciousness and, finally, the heart slowing, slowing and, eventually, stopping. A blessed transition into peaceful tranquillity.

The success of the EOL pill was such that it was continued after the peak geriatric burden eased and remained available and, indeed, remains in use to this present day.

With the massive pressure on working adults at that time of maximum geriatric load, special consideration was given to the business of crime.

It was decided, society could not afford to have many massive jails full of criminals; could not afford to have organised crime and swarms of lifelong career criminals. A completely new approach was decided upon. A study of the cumbersome legal system of the old Civilisation showed that crime flourished. Far too much consideration was given to the rights of the criminal and far too little to the rights of the victim. Many people became career criminals. Organised crime blatantly carried on their nefarious ways – when everybody knew perfectly well what they were doing – because they had swarms of professional lawyers working for them – lawyers who knew every trick in the book to keep their clients out of jail. Petty criminals were often let off on technicalities. Jails became universities of crime – where old lags educated naive youngsters. Death sentences were abolished and maniacal killers sentenced to endless life terms in high security institutions. Many committed suicide and many more begged to be executed rather than endure a life so restricted. It was obvious to many that such life sentences were, in fact, diabolically cruel. A humane death would have been far better.

A decision was finally made. A completely new criminal code was instituted. Corporal Punishment was re-introduced. The Death Penalty was reinstated. A simple points system for criminal behaviour was introduced. For errant teenagers – a minor misdemeanour – shoplifting, vandalism, simple theft, could incur 1 point. More serious behaviour – burglary, violence against the person – 2 points. When a total of 10 points was amassed the perpetrator would be thrashed – four strokes of a device like an old fashioned birch. The ten points to stay on the record. They would also be sentenced to be fitted with a monitor for 12 months. More serious – adult crimes – serious burglary – 10 points. Burglary with violence – 20 points. Causing Grievous Bodily Harm – 20 points. Manslaughter – 50 points. Unpremeditated murder – 80 points. Premeditated or deliberate murder – 100 points. At the accumulation of each additional 10 points – four strokes of the scourge. At the accumulation of a total of 100 points – The Death Penalty.

It was decided, that if a person was to be totally eliminated – the death penalty – it should be done in as humane a manner as possible. Various methods were considered. Finally it was decided – the Pressure Chamber method would be used.

It had been found, many years ago, in training pilots to fly planes at high altitude, that a slow reduction of pressure caused no discomfort to the pilot – indeed, as the pressure dropped and deprivation of oxygen set in, the pilot experienced a feeling of relaxation and euphoria before becoming unconscious. Upon being revived they reported feeling no discomfort or distress and often were unaware they had even been unconscious.

This technique was therefore adopted.

The criminal was taken into a small, comfortable room (actually a pressure chamber) and offered a meal, a drink and a TV monitor to watch. After a while the air pressure was gradually and very slowly reduced. When the criminal eventually became unconscious, the fact was registered, the pressure rapidly reduced further and, after a few minutes, death occurred. Death was therefore induced humanely and painlessly.

Referring back to the points system – a Court could order the fitting of a monitor for 12 months or more for anyone accumulating 10 points or above. The monitor was very similar in size and shape to a wristwatch and strapped to the wrist in a similar way. It was locked in position and any attempt to remove it would be recorded and several points added to their criminal score. The electronic monitor would record conversations, log all movements and behaviour and periodically 'bleep' back the data to a master computer. It would be impossible to burgle a house or a store, for instance, wearing a monitor, since the monitor would instantly pick up the electronic building address code and record the time, the place and the burglars activities and 'bleep' an alert. The monitor even incorporated a motion sensor so that if the person became involved in a fight the exact movements and behaviour could be analysed.

Anyone going about a normal, lawful, everyday activity of any kind had nothing whatsoever to fear from wearing a monitor. In the case of career criminals and organised crime, all that was required for action to be taken was an anonymous petition of not less than 6 people requesting a monitor be fitted to a person and a court order would be made. If the person was innocent the monitor did no harm but it was almost impossible for organised crime to operate with people wearing monitors.

It was found the system worked extremely well. In most cases, teenage delinquents rapidly mended their ways. Many adult criminals decided to give up crime after amassing 70 to 80 points and incorrigible criminals and murderers were painlessly and humanely eradicated.

Special consideration was given to sexual crimes. Just one complaint of a serious sexual assault from a victim and a monitor would be fitted. If a definite serious sexual crime – such as rape – was proved or recorded, then ten points were registered and the criminal scourged. Another crime and a further 10 points registered and another scourging. A third serious crime and a further 10 points, no scourging but one testicle surgically removed. A fourth crime and the second testicle removed. This may seem very drastic but, in practice, it was rare for a second testicle to be removed. Most men, however highly sexed, seemed to be able to discover self control before that stage was reached. If it was not, then the removal of the second testicle usually solved the problem. With the source of the excess testosterone removed the criminal almost always became a more considerate, reasonable member of society.

As a result of the measures I have described, the incidence and prevalence of crime is now far less than it was in the Old Civilisation.

Some people have said that our system is more brutal than in the old days and others have ranted on about erosion of human rights. However, in this modern age, the rights of the law abiding majority take preference over the rights of criminals. Criminals, after all, choose to become criminals.

Our system is simple, straightforward and pragmatic and, above all, it works.

---

Ladies and Gentlemen. You should now have a grasp of the massive problems that faced humanity immediately after the Crash and the achievements of our forbears, leading to the remarkable New Civilisation you enjoy today.

Goodnight!"

# 2647 – PROFESSOR ROBERT SULAWESI'S LECTURE – THE APOCALYPSE

## MANDATORY CLASS A UNIVERSAL LECTURE ALL STUDENTS TO ATTEND

---

Professor Sulawesi appeared and took the stage. He was a tall, aristocratic, immaculately dressed, black man whose ancestors had come to Greenland from South Africa.

"Good Morning Ladies and Gentlemen. This lecture is concerned with the greatest biological disaster to affect this planet since the asteroid strike that wiped out the Dinosaurs. I refer to the collapse of Civilisation and the loss of eighty three percent of the entire human race in a period of only eighteen months. It is difficult to find words to really describe such a disaster. The terms Holocaust or Apocalypse come to mind but human beings have a knack of applying very simple terms to the greatest of happenings. The creation of the entire Universe has become known as The Big Bang. Similarly the immense disaster I refer to has come to be known as The Great Crash or even more simply The Crash.

I must warn you that, during the course of this lecture, we shall be showing videos and photographs of an extremely harrowing and disturbing nature. Some of the videos were taken actually during the time of the Crash, by courageous individuals, sometimes at great personal risk to themselves. Other videos and photographs were taken in the aftermath, by expeditions visiting erstwhile major cities in the worst affected areas.

We make no apology for showing these ghastly films because we feel it is absolutely vital that the people of today, and the future, should fully understand the consequences that appertain to unrestricted population growth and uncontrolled exploitation of Earth's natural resources.

The lecture will be in two parts, with an intermission between the two. The first part will deal with the root causes and run up to the

244

Crash. The second part will deal with what happened in the actual Crash and the immediate aftermath.

I strongly suggest that, in the intermission, you give very serous thought as to whether you definitely choose to see part 2 of the lecture. For those of you who do not have a triple A psychological rating for mental stability I recommend you avoid the second part and use a censored version available on video, to continue with your education.

I will mention that we shall have medical staff available, during part 2 of the lecture, to attend to students who faint or show excessive psychological stress.

I will now proceed with part one of the lecture – the Factors and Conditions leading up to the Great Crash."

---

Professor Sulawesi then proceeded to show charts and graphs showing human population levels, Atmospheric $CO^2$, Global temperature, Industrialisation levels, Agricultural land use and so on from the year 2135, back to 1000 AD.

He dealt with key political systems and events, the impact of Industrialisation and development of trade. The psychology of Industrialisation and trade. Wars. Colonisation. International travel and so forth.

Finally, at the conclusion of part 1, he did a summing up of the salient key developments and factors.

"As you will have realised, Ladies and Gentlemen, all the evidence points to the conclusion that the Great Crash, as it happened, or half a dozen different variations of it, was almost totally inevitable.

When the Industrial Revolution started, it was triggered by a few, key, great inventions, made by individuals, supported by their own or private finance. The Governments of the day, recognised this and encouraged innovation by developing the patent system, whereby inventive individuals were encouraged to create and, thereby, to become rich. The notion of personal effort, personal gain – fame and fortune – the virtues of the Private Enterprise system became embedded in the western psyche. It worked extremely well – if you wanted expansion, wealth, progress and power. And who didn't?

Increased Industrial Capacity and National Wealth rapidly translated into Military Power and an age of Conquest began. It was at this point that the modern Population Explosion started. The Nations of Europe, Britain particularly, found that wealth and power solved their food production problems. Food could be imported – particularly from their colonies. This raised the standard of living of their citizens – and enabled them to rear far more children. To Governments – this was fine – it created more workers – to further increase industrial output and also more manpower for the Military.

Competition between European Nations led to some vicious wars. Russia became a major colonial power as a Monarchy until the communist Revolution in 1918. This may have started as an idealistic movement but rapidly became a paranoid Dictatorship. The Communists did not give their colonies back to their original peoples but continued the colonial set up under a pretence. They called it the USSR – the Union of Socialist Soviet Republics. Finally they became embroiled in a militaristic arms race with the West the West being the rest of Europe and the USA. They lost and in 1990, the USSR collapsed.

Japan and South Korea had copied the Western System and been very successful.

The rest of the world looked on and concluded the only way to go was to emulate the Capitalist Free Enterprise System. The whole world, with the exception of a couple of minor states – North Korea and Cuba, set out on the road to Industrialisation on the free enterprise capitalist system. Russia, after seventy years of Dictatorial Communism, couldn't really make up its mind to fully embrace Capitalism and languished.

So, Ladies and Gentleman, at the start of the 21$^{st}$ Century, the entire world or almost the entire world, embraced Industrialisation, Capitalism and Democracy.

It was very successful. China led the way, with massive industrial expansion and, by 2025, was the greatest industrial nation on Earth. All the poor, 'Third World' (as they were called then), Nations, rushed to follow in China's footsteps. They all began to be successful – in greater or lesser degree and here we have the root of the problem. As the Third World industrialised, their peoples became more prosperous, better fed, more secure. Their populations burgeoned. Their desire for material goods increased. Therefore the demand on the Earth's natural resources increased. More food was required – from land and sea. More energy was needed, to fuel expansion and production. Much of the energy was produced by burning coal, oil and natural gas, which, of course, increased emissions of $CO^2$ – that most important greenhouse gas.

The psychology of the whole world was locked on to industrialisation, development and growth. Every stock market on Earth required growth. Every Government needed growth.

Growth gave people a better standard of living, more food in the larder, a better future for the kids. The system worked. Who, in his right mind, would vote against it?

So! By the start of the 21st Century the whole human world was locked into a policy of expansion and industrialisation, expansion of population, over exploitation of seas, land and natural resources.

A few dissenting voices were raised. It was pointed out that $CO^2$ emissions were dangerous and could lead to global warming. A few pointed out that natural resources were finite and would run out – someday.

A few – a very few – sounded the alarm over population.

At the beginning of the 21st Century, some of the already developed nations made half hearted attempts to cut greenhouse gas emissions – but they stood no chance. The undeveloped nations were catching up fast – and they were going to continue to burn coal, oil and gas in ever increasing quantities.

By 2020, global warming was a certainty. There was no way total human greenhouse gas emissions were going to be reduced at an early date. And two major positive feedback conditions had already kicked in. I refer to Arctic and glacial ice melt, which led to increased solar radiation absorption and the melting of the tundra permafrost – which created a massive additional input of greenhouse gases.

With regard to depletion of resources. When this was pointed out the optimists said . "For food we shall produce more and better crops, fertilise the land and sea – and the geologists will find more mineral and metal ore deposits. Don't worry!" And this in the face of the self evident fact that the Earth is a finite planet, and the obvious evidence that resources were already seriously depleted.

Let the good times roll! Nobody wants to think of nasty possibilities when it is all so good.

On Population! At the beginning of the 21st Century, a few said there were too many people already. (At that time it was about 6 billion). When predictions were made of 12 to 15 billion by the end of the 21$^{st}$ Century the optimists said "So What! We will feed them. No problem!"

At the end of the 20$^{th}$ Century half hearted efforts were made to educate 'Third World' countries into the benefits of reduced families and to supply contraceptives. Most of their talk fell on deaf ears and many people hated to use condoms anyway. The Roman Catholic Church still insisted contraception was against 'God's Law'.

The fact is, in 2015, statistics indicated the human population of the Earth was rising by no less than 90 million extra human beings per year.

One of the remarkable things that should be mentioned is that the Chinese actually introduced a 'One Child' policy way back in 1979. However, this was not because they were trying to show the world the way. It was to solve their own, internal, over-population problem.

In the mid 20$^{th}$ Century, millions of Chinese periodically starved to death. The Nation simply could not produce enough food to feed its people and, it didn't have the financial wherewithal to buy food from elsewhere. The Chinese population, at that time, was around 800 million.

In desperation they brought in the 'One Child' policy. At that time only a Dictatorial Government like the Chinese could have done it. Amazingly, they were condemned by the rest of the world. 'Infringement of the Human right to have Children' they called it.

The 'One Child' policy worked reasonably well.

However, the Chinese then industrialised; The standard of living went up, The Chinese could afford to buy food abroad. In 2014, the Chinese Government abandoned the One Child Policy. By 2014, the Chinese population had increased to 1300 million. The increase being mainly due to the improved standard of living and the resulting increase in the expectation of life at birth. However, the main reason the Chinese abandoned the One Child Policy is the same problem we, in the late 22$^{nd}$ Century, had to contend with. Forty to fifty years after the restricted birth rate is introduced, a situation arises where there is a preponderance of old people and a shortage of young, working age people. Looking after the old is a heavy burden and a shortage of young workers increases costs, raises wages and cramps production. The Chinese saw this coming, realised it would reduce their international competitiveness and abandoned their birth control rules. Several other countries, around the same time, with balanced or slightly reducing populations, began to encourage their people to have more children.

So! Ladies and Gentleman! By as early as the year, 2020, serious Global warming was a 'locked in' certainty.

Massive depletion of natural resources was a 'locked in' certainty.

Human Population increase to at least 10 billion and, more likely, 12 to 15 billion was also a 'locked in' certainty.

Despite the fact that any intelligent person, giving the matter a little thought, should have been able, at that time, to see where the human race was heading, very few people indeed raised any serious misgivings or sounded an alarm.

No really serious problems occurred for the next fifty years – which takes us to 2070. The human race carried on much as before. There were periods of economic boom and bust. Terrorist attacks continued, usually performed by malcontents or religious extremists. Occasional industrial strife, strikes, riots, local civil wars and, sometimes minor inter-nation wars occurred.

The Third World continued to modernise and industrialise, but not as much as they hoped – being, to a great extent, hampered by the increasing shortage of raw materials. This manifested in rapidly rising prices which effectively 'shut out' the poorer countries. Wealthy countries could afford to pay higher prices (though they did not like it) but Third World countries could not. The poor were, mainly, destined to stay poor.

Nevertheless, consumption of raw materials stayed at a high level. Coal, oil, and natural gas continued to be burned and $CO_2$ levels continued, inexorably, to rise.

By 2070, the human world population had risen to 11 billion. $CO_2$ levels were 565 ppm. Average global warming was 2.0°C above pre Industrial Revolution levels equating to an increase in temperature of 7°C in the Arctic regions and 4°C in tropical areas.

The 7°C rise in the Arctic exacerbated the melting and rotting of the permafrost and effectively guaranteed that global greenhouse gas levels would continue to rise.

The 4°C rise in the tropics meant that India, Africa, South East Asia and South America were becoming uncomfortably hot in summer time but just about tolerable.

Sleepwalking to Apocalypse

The reaching of the 11 billion population figure did provoke increased efforts to limit the birth rate, but improved medical procedures, reduced infant mortality and an overall increase in the expectation of life – particularly in third world countries, ensured the population would continue to rise – but at a decreased rate.

The first real signs of impending trouble could be said to have occurred in 2082, when African peasants rebelled, rioted, and, effectively, forced the Chinese out of Africa. (The Chinese, you may remember, had bought large tracts of land in Africa and leased even more, in order to consolidate and secure their food supplies). This caused the Chinese to re-assess their situation and, in 2086, with $CO^2$ levels at 613 ppm and temperature rise in China at 5°C above pre Industrial Revolution temperatures, they made the momentous decision to challenge Russia and demand the release of Siberia for mass immigration.

The world then managed to get by, relatively uneventfully, to the year 2128, when HIVa appeared.

However, by 2128, the world population had grown to no less than 15.2 billion. $CO^2$ levels had climbed to 739 ppm. World average temperature rise was plus 4°C translating to nearly 14°C in the Arctic and nearly 8°C in the tropics. The tropics, therefore, were almost on the brink of being unliveable. In addition, global warming had caused changes in marine and atmospheric circulation patterns. Hadley and Ferrell Cells – circulation patterns in the air – with which you should be familiar from your Meteorological lectures, have changed and adjusted, which, together with increased instability in the Jet Streams, have drastically altered precipitation patterns around the globe. Of particular importance are the changes in the Monsoons but, of course, the loss of much of America's and Ukraine's grain growing areas also drastically affected food production.

You could say, therefore, that in 2128, the world could be described as being in an explosive condition. It was just as well that, after the America/Russia confrontation of 2027 and the Sino/Russian war of 2086, nuclear weapons had been all but abolished.

To sum up then, Ladies and Gentlemen. In 2128, the human population was critically high. Food supplies were on the brink of being unsustainable. 77 per cent of the world's population were living in areas of the planet which were fast becoming unfit for human habitation. The scene was set, therefore, for some kind of disaster.

The population figures for the most important and critical areas of the world were as follows:-

| | |
|---|---|
| CHINA | 2.0 Billion |
| INDIA | 3.9 " |
| INDONESIA | 0.6 " |
| SOUTH AMERICA | 1.3 " |
| AFRICA | 3.9 " |
| TOTAL | 11.7 " |

The second part of this Presentation will take place in one hours time. Thank You! Ladies and Gentlemen!"

---

After the break Professor Sulawesi returned to the stage.

"Hello! Ladies and Gentlemen. We will now proceed with Part 2 of the Lecture. To recapitulate for a moment. In the Autumn of the year 2128, we had a situation where the world's total population was dangerously high, food supplies were seriously stretched and stocks were relatively low. Changes in climate had affected many food growing areas. Temperatures in the tropical areas had been at unprecedented highs during the summer months, leading to sustained heavy loads on power systems due to the prolonged and continuous use of air conditioning systems.

In the previous five years a number of important raw materials had been in very short supply due to exhaustion of mines, wells and other sources. This had led to violent and extreme price fluctuations which, in turn, led to economic and political instability. Many Commercial businesses went bust. Banks were bankrupted. Governments lost revenue. Many factories, even if they survived, were only operating part time because of shortage of components and materials. Production lines were almost totally robotic anyway but, nevertheless, office staff, sales staff and administrators were laid off. Unemployment rose to extremely high levels, particularly amongst the young who became increasingly disaffected, disgruntled and rebellious. We are talking about a world wide phenomenon.

Governments, everywhere, were in financial difficulties. Wages were cut. Benefits were cut. Payments to single unemployed youngsters were particularly slashed.

Petty crime was rampant. Shoplifting, mugging, burglary, vandalism and theft were everywhere. Inadequate police forces, understaffed, could not cope. Unemployed youths gathered together in street gangs and fought or terrorised many older inhabitants.

In the tropical countries, vast numbers of people were desperate to escape the heat and emigrate. But they could not. America and Europe had closed their borders. Even where access to Siberia had been gained by the Chinese action, only a relative few had managed to move North. Even the Chinese found it was not possible to transfer hundreds of millions or billions of people from one place on the Earth to another in a very short space of time. You cannot simply uproot half a billion people from their homes, traditions, workplaces and just dump them on a patch of prairie or Siberian Tundra. It takes time to build cities and infrastructure. Global Warming was advancing faster then human beings could cope – even if they had the freedom to move – which most of them did not.

Into this critical maelstrom then, came HIVa, like a bolt from the blue. It was an extremely virulent form – both from its action and its propagation. It was spread like a common cold and death from AIDS could occur as rapidly as 12 to 18 months after infection.

People have speculated on its source – as to whether it was a natural development or, perhaps, created by some insane and perverted Genetic Engineer.

However, Ladies and Gentlemen, History is, or should be, a study of facts.

The fact is, HIVa did appear and it was the final straw that caused the almost total collapse of Civilisation.

Fortunately, in some of the cooler Northern areas and aided by the frantic efforts of medical and pharmaceutical experts to produce drugs to control HIVa, control or, at least, partial control was maintained.

If it had not been, maybe we should not be here, today, in this magnificent building in the University of New Copenhagen, Greenland.

To proceed! Once it appeared – and we do not know exactly when and where it appeared – HIVa was rapidly spread over the entire planet by travellers – mainly air travellers. Whilst air transportation – flying – had been drastically reduced from it s heyday there were still substantial numbers of people travelling the world in 2128, so much so that over 30% of the world's populations was already infected before HIVa, as a distinctly different variant of the old HIV, was even discovered. Because of its mode of transmission, soon 95% of all people were infected; the remaining 5% being mainly those that were naturally immune. There are always a few who are immune to every great plague. The real collapse started 12 to 18 months later in 2130, when vast numbers of people began to go down with AIDS.

It took 6 to 9 months to create the first effective anti HIVa drugs and it was simply not possible, in the time available, to produce enough of the drugs for more than a few hundred million people. Accordingly nine-tenths of the Earth's population – mainly in the tropics and the most highly populated areas, had no defence against HIVa at all.

When young people – teenagers, 20 year olds, realise they have HIVa – realise they have no future – will be dead in 12 to 18 months time – some go into a state of apathy, some commit suicide but many are filled with rage and frustration. They lose all respect and fear of the forces of law and order. They go on the rampage – burning, looting, shooting, vandalism. They blame Society – the Civilisation in which they find themselves and which – somehow – they feel must be responsible for the plight they are in.

Their behaviour is a sort of rebellion – a search for revenge – a desire to destroy the system which they feel has somehow denied them life – has brought them to this bleak and final valley of death. So – they fire bullets into electrical systems, set fire to buildings large and small, destroy transport, destroy infrastructure, wreck communications. This – the reaction of the young to the shock of HIVa – is the main reason all the infrastructure, the services, the communications vital to the maintenance of Civilisation, collapsed so rapidly and completely over most of the world as soon as HIVa began to create AIDS and people began to die. At that point young people realised they were doomed and vast numbers went on a wrecking spree.

Only in America was it realised this would happen and only in America was a protected enclave system adopted – where everyone in the enclave received HIVa medication and everyone outside was denied. This brutal and extreme system worked and enabled Civilisation in the enclave area to survive and, later, spread back into the rest of the continent.

In most of the world the roving gangs of feral youngsters went mad in an orgy of destruction. Looting, wanton vandalism, rioting, arson, gang warfare. Most had managed to obtain fire-arms. Often they fired bullets into electrical installations simply to see the firework display. The effect, particularly in the cities, can be imagined.

The poor inhabitants, many living in skyscrapers or high rise blocks, already suffering the onset of AIDS symptoms, found themselves without food, other than the stocks they already had, without power, without air conditioning, without transport. Without water and sanitation systems. At that time all major cities had electrified all transport, to reduce congestion and eliminate air pollution and $CO_2$ emissions.

Skyscrapers were all fitted with fire control sprinkler systems, supplied from a massive header tank situated at the top of each building. Inmates, desperate for water, resorted to damaging and perforating sprinkler supply pipes. This meant the header tanks rapidly ran dry – and – with no power to run the pumps to fill them up again, left the buildings extremely vulnerable to fire. That is why, as I shall show you shortly, so many city skyscrapers burned out, and many collapsed – often with a great many occupants still in them.

As things became worse and worse, people began to die. Not in thousands but in millions, then in hundreds of millions.

At first, what remained of the Authorities did their best to cope. They tried to get food, water and supplies into the cities. They collected the bodies, buried them in enormous pits. They also set up vast funeral pyres, acres in extent. But the administrators themselves, the police, the military, the medical staff, were being decimated as people went down with AIDS.

Those that escaped from the cities, mainly young and unattached, who were still free of AIDS symptoms, joined the trek, away from the cities, into the countryside, joining the remnants of the street gangs. These usually then became scavengers, raiding and pillaging private houses, shops and stores wherever they could find them.

Life became a murderous, vicious, cut throat battle for personal survival.

It is almost impossible, to describe, in words, the hell and the horror that was created. It is reckoned that, at the height of the Crash, worldwide, no less than five hundred million human beings died in a single week. It is almost beyond comprehension.

However, the Principal and I and, indeed, the World Government, feel it is essential that you, as the students of today and the leaders and policy makers of tomorrow, should fully grasp and understand what happened so that we can make sure it never, ever, happens again.

Accordingly we shall now show still photographs and videos taken at the beginning, during the climax and in the aftermath of the Crash.

The pictures and films shown are extremely harrowing. The seats, which you will have noted, are very deep, luxurious and padded, are especially designed to capture and prevent anyone who faints from falling out and injuring themselves. They are also fitted with sensors – to monitor vital signs and signs of distress. Medical staff are on standby to tend to the distressed in case such should be needed.

Here is the first still picture."

The lights in the Auditorium went down and an enormous screen was illuminated. The first picture showed a medium sized high rise building or skyscraper, burned out and blackened but still standing. The second shot focussed on the area around the base of the building, which was littered with the bones and remains of those who had leapt from the upper floors. There were gasps and someone muttered "My God!"

The third picture showed the centre of a large city. There was total devastation. Half the skyscrapers were still standing, blackened and bare. The remainder were collapsed. Great heaps of rubble. Grey dust was everywhere. The fourth picture showed a park area, but what had been the flower beds and lawns were littered with hundreds upon hundreds of putrefying bodies.

And so it went on, Picture after picture. Each one seemed worse than the last. They saw colossal pits, dug by the bulldozers, with 100,000 bodies in each pit.

They saw immense funeral pyres, acres in extent, made up of rows of fuel and bodies, row after row after row, piled ten feet high, before they lit the fires – and the same pyres afterwards – a gigantic sea of flame and smoke.

A considerable number of students had to be treated and attended to. One young man – a burly athletic type of individual, completely broke down and had to be escorted from the Auditorium, sobbing, saying over and over – "I can't take any more of this!"

Then the videos started. The videos were even worse, if that was possible. But movement and sound emphasized the horror. There were scenes of the giant funeral pyres again – but this time accompanied by the roar and grumble of the flames and an all pervading background of wailing screaming, groaning, sobbing. The death pit scenes were live now, with the growling of the bulldozers, the tumbling of the bodies, the endless droning hum – the swirling immense black clouds of flies.

A hand, holding a small piece of food, extended in front of the camera. Instantly it was enveloped in a seething black glove of flies.

There were scenes from the cities – blazing buildings – the thunder of a falling skyscraper – the great clouds of dust.

It seemed to go on and on. An unspeakable litany of horror and disaster.

After an age there came to be what seemed to be a break.

The camera showed a tranquil scene. A long winding valley. No! Not a valley – a U shaped gorge with near vertical cliffs on one side, a steep slope on the other and a beautiful sparkling river in the bottom. A mile away from the camera the gorge and the river turned to the right so, for a distance of half a mile, the cliffs were almost face on to the camera.

For maybe a third of the distance, the exposed view of the cliffs was blocked and flanked by what looked like an enormous scree slope, extending from the top of the cliffs all the way down to the river. The bottom part of the slope had extended into the river and had been partially washed away.

The camera zoomed in, in one rapid motion – and revealed the scree slope to be one gigantic mass of jumbled human bodies.

The entire audience sucked in its breath in one great sobbing hiss.

There – was a scene far beyond the most ghastly imaginings, of Dante or any of the medieval painters. A picture so stark as to be almost beyond human comprehension.

The camera panned – from side to side and from cliff top to river.

At that point the Lecturer cut in.

"I will not tell you – exactly – where that is – except to say it is close to what was one of the great cities of the World. Initially they buried the bodies. Then they resorted to massive pyres. Still the bodies kept coming. In desperation they resorted to this, while there were still the last vestiges of control and law and order left. When that failed the remainder were left in the city, to rot where they died.

Millions were buried. Millions were cremated. It is estimated that, on this cliff face, which is over 400 feet high, there were over four million human bodies.

Millions more died in the city and remained there.

Ten years later, exploratory teams visited a number of abandoned cities.

The last videos you will see are from those expeditions."

The final videos were almost an anti climax. Horrific though they were – bleached bones and skulls do not have the impact of dead bodies. The videos showed the ruins of cities littered with human bones, everywhere. Skeletons were on the streets, on the pavements, inside the wrecked buildings. Even sitting at tables, relaxing in chairs, lying in the remains of beds; sometimes singly, sometimes in groups. It was weird. It was bizarre. But, to the students already shell shocked, almost to the limit, of endurance, these final videos almost washed over them.

The lights went up. Professor Sulawesi stood there.

"I sincerely hope we have not caused too much distress. But it was a vital and necessary part of your education. Some of you, no doubt, will, in the future, reach positions of Authority and Power. There must be an understanding and a determination that the conditions that spawned the Great Crash must never be allowed to develop again. We must work steadfastly to reduce and hold the human world population at levels that can be sustained, comfortably, for ever, in balance with the rest of the planet.

Once before, the human race was on the brink of a similar Holocaust – but of a different nature. I refer to the nuclear confrontation in 1962 between the USA and the USSR.

At that time the USA had 25,000 and the USSR about 12,000 nuclear bombs. Insane figures! Both nations capable of wiping the other out a hundred times over – and destroying the planet in the process. Such a war would have wrecked the world's weather, precipitated a nuclear winter, and contaminated the entire planet with radio activity.

The Russian President – Nikita Khrushchev – was a very aggressive, macho, bombastic character. He placed nuclear missiles on Cuba, directly threatening the USA. When the USA responded, blockading Cuba and intercepting ships, carrying more missiles, bound for Cuba, the world was on the brink of disaster. However, just before the confrontation, Khrushchev had travelled North – to personally witness the testing of a Russian multi-megaton hydrogen bomb.

When the bomb was detonated, Khrushchev watched, from a vantage point 100 miles away. He could not believe the immensity of the blast. He felt his body buffeted by the shock wave. He felt the furnace heat of the enormous fireball, scorching his face – even at that range.

Only then did he realise the hellish danger of the game he was playing with the USA. Shocked and subdued he turned to one of his Generals and is reputed to have said "We mustn't ever use these things."

Shortly afterwards, when the USSR/USA confrontation came to a head, Khrushchev backed off and the situation was defused. If he had not personally seen and experienced the H Bomb test, the world might be a very different place today. The human deaths would not have been so great – there were only three billion humans on the Earth at that time, but the entire planet would have been devastated.

Only if you truly understand a danger can you react correctly and make the right decisions.

Thank you for attending this Lecture – painful though it was. Now! You too – should really understand the dangers. Good Night! And God Bless You All!"

# EPILOGUE – THE WORLD IN 3012

It was a glorious sunny day in May in the year 3012. David Kealey parked his electric tricycle at the side of the track and lifted the lid of its little trailer to take out his fishing tackle. The tricycle could be pedalled (in emergencies or if you felt like it) but was normally driven by a small electric motor, powered from a battery pack in the trailer. There was another trailer, back home in the garage, recharging from the mains supply. Changing trailers only took seconds.

This model would bowl along merrily at 25 to 28 miles an hour for 70 to 80 miles, which David thought was fine, for local use. He could have bought a more powerful model if he had wished, with a slightly larger trailer, two seats (one behind the other to reduce air drag) and a more powerful motor, which would enable the trike to do up to 40 miles an hour for a range of 140 miles. However, for him, the single seater was quite adequate.

As he took the rod out of the trailer he paused and looked around him at the magnificent scenery. He gave a little sigh of pleasure. "What a wonderful day to be alive!"

To the South East he could see the spires and turrets of the beautiful city of New Copenhagen. Winding through the spectacular valley was the sparkling, gin clear, waters of the Namsen River, teeming with salmon at this time of the year. To the North and North West were rolling forest covered hills and far beyond them, a range of snow capped mountains.

The immense ice sheet that once covered most of Greenland and totally engulfed the mountains had almost gone now. Most of the valleys were clear but a few glaciers still ran down from the higher mountains of the interior. "Greenland today, must be like Scandinavia was a thousand years ago" he thought as he fitted the rod together and grabbed the satchel with his lunch, reels and fly boxes. It was the weekend. Three days gave plenty of scope. Yesterday he was hiking with friends, today – fishing and, if the weather forecast was correct – and it usually was – tomorrow he would be out on the hills hang gliding.

He was still in his study years – at the University of New Copenhagen, reading Architecture and Civil Engineering. He wanted to help design and build the beautiful – semi classical – buildings of the day and the slender elegant bridges that were needed to span the multitude of rivers, as new settlements spread, more and more, into the interior and to the North.

As he walked down the track to the river he reflected. What a wonderful world this had become. Nearly all the lost species had been re-instated; the forests renewed, the seas brought back, from a near wilderness to a teeming diversity of species – large and small.

The tropics had been almost entirely abandoned now. There were a few people in South Africa, the southern part of South America and in New Zealand and Tasmania but by far the bulk of the human race lived in the Northern Lands. A few hundred years ago The World Government had decided it would be better if the human population came down a bit more so – now – the world population was around 400 million. Now – everybody had good nutrition, good housing, good education, peace, security and, very importantly – good health.

All the genetically inherited defects and diseases had been eliminated. Cancer defeated and relegated to the history books – as had all the dreadful parasitic, bacterial and viral diseases that used to plague human kind. Average expectation of life, at birth, was now around 100. International wars had been abolished. There were still dissident groups and dissatisfied individuals – and always would be, but most problems were handled by the local police (some form of policing would always be necessary). Serious rioting or rebellion resulted in an investigation and the problem would be submitted to the World Arbitration Council. A small, powerful, well armed military force was available for emergencies. All energy was from renewable and natural sources i.e. wind, wave, tidal, solar and hydro power.

Most employment was of a satisfying and rewarding nature. People worked 28 hours a week, 32 weeks of the year. Nearly all heavy, repetitive boring and dirty jobs were done by robots.

Nearly all robots were old fashioned 'automation' type fixed robots, working on assembly lines or in dismantling, reclamation or recycling centres. Very few were mobile or in people's homes. In the mid 21st Century, Electronics Engineers had experimented with different circuits and components. They copied the human brains neurons, with multiple connections and artificial synapses. Parallel processing systems and so on. They created cognitive functions and, eventually, inevitably, they finally produced true consciousness – self awareness.

260

They thought they were cautious – carefully programming in Isaac Asimov's Three laws of Robotics – and a few more besides – to ensure robots could not harm people. But it was not quite as simple as that. They found that a genuinely conscious robot became distressed to find it was a machine – not truly live – and was deprived of many of the great sources of happiness and pleasure enjoyed by a truly live animal. It was called the 'Pinocchio Effect'. Also – some people became too attached to a conscious robot – as emotional as they would be to a pet Labrador dog. But dogs aged and died. Robots did not. Others treated robots as inferior – as slaves.

It was found that a maltreated conscious robot could become resentful. There was a danger they might eventually get round to modifying their own circuitry – might cut out the Laws of Robotics. A thinking, conscious robot became capable of thinking its own thoughts – becoming distressed, resentful – maybe eventually – belligerent. The dangers were recognised. Conscious robots were restricted. After the 'Crash' the World Government banned their construction and use entirely. So – today in 3012 there were no conscious robots. In many ways it was healthier anyway. People needed to do things for themselves. Use their brains. Get some exercise. Being waited on, hand and foot, by a slave, even if it is a machine, is not good for people.

David paused and thought how the human race could so easily have fallen back, after the 'Crash', into a new Dark Age – with endless strife, pestilence and famine, afflicting humanity in a ruined world. He marvelled at the foresight, the courage, the dedication and determination of the people who had started and built up The New Civilisation.

This wonderful world they had created could now go on, indefinitely, into the far future – as long as humanity adhered to a few basic, simple rules, chief of which was the control of population to sane levels.

He thought of the conditions that must have been before the Crash. "How could they have let the population run away to 15 billion? Unbelievable!" For a moment he shuddered as he remembered some of the hellish scenes from that ghastly mandatory 'Crash' lecture. "Almost too awful to be true!"

He shook his head as if to clear the awful images away and thought of more pleasant things.

On Monday evening he would go down to the Stadium and get some practice on his pole vaulting. In a month's time he would be competing in the Greenland Games. He didn't think he would qualify for the Olympics but he would certainly try.

Tuesday evening he would go to the University Dance. Old fashioned dancing to a real band, formed of University students. What they lacked in musical ability they more than made up for in enthusiasm. Maybe he would meet that fascinating Euro/ African girl again. The one with the complexion his friend had described as 'coffee with cream'. She had said she was studying Genetic Engineering and Organic Chemistry. Now – that took brains! And – she had a great figure.

"Communicators were all very well but – there was no beating a face to face chat, as you glided round the dance floor, with your arms around a girl, was there?"

Suddenly he was at the river and dragged himself back from his reverie. There were rocks, leading down to a sloping shingle bank that disappeared into the water gliding past. He put down his gear, rummaged in the satchel and sorted out his ultra light weight 'thinsulate' waders. After he had put them on he picked up a fly box and pondered. Some people used very fancy, new fangled garish flies but he preferred the old fashioned patterns. They always seemed to work for him. Like his friend said – "If you have confidence in the fly – it will work."

He picked up a 'Green Highlander', put it back in the box and then decided to start with a 'Willy Gunn' – an old favourite. He had already fitted a reel with a floating line and now he carefully tied the Willy Gunn on to the leader. Seventy yards below him, the water speeded up, cascading and rushing into a long, swirling pool.

He walked slowly down the shingle bank and waded, carefully, into the water, just above the entrance to the pool. After sorting himself out and running out a little line he cast out the Willy Gunn about 10 yards and let the fly swing round in the current. He pulled out more line, cast again, three feet further, and repeated the process. He was using a long – 15ft – rod and an old fashioned centre pin reel with a ratchet mechanism. The ratchet acted as a 'drag' and when line was pulled off, the reel made a noise like a snarl or a growl.

When his casting had reached a range of 25 yards he began to move downstream, 4ft between casts.

David noticed, below him, there was a 'boiling' patch on the surface of the moving water and knew this indicated there was a large boulder on the river bed. Such a boulder created a relatively calm pocket of water, immediately behind the boulder, and it was a favourite spot for salmon to lie and rest, protected from the flow of the river.

David lifted the rod tip, swung it in a figure 8 movement, creating a loop in the line and flicked the rod, driving the loop out across the river. He had heard this was an ancient manoeuvre called a Spey Cast, invented a thousand years ago on a river called the Spey, somewhere in Scotland.

The loop extended out across the river and finally unfurled itself, the fly travelling out across the water until the whole line was out, at right angles across the river, two feet above the water. Then it settled. Perfect! The fly sank down and then began to swing as the current pulled the line. David kept his fingers away from the reel so there was nothing to stop line being pulled off the reel except the ratchet drag.

The fly swung round, swept just behind the place where David judged the rock to be. There was a slight tug and the reel snarled briefly. He held his breath. Knew that a salmon had snatched at his fly but failed to hold. He waited a few seconds. Repeated the cast. This time, as the fly tracked round, he moved the rod, forwards and backwards about 20 centimetres, in a rhythmic movement. This trick imparted to the fly a jerky motion, giving the impression the fly, as something live, was fighting to swim against the current. Often, this would stir a salmon's curiosity and provoke an attack. The fly came round. There was a tug. The reel growled for a moment – and again. Line was pulled off the reel. David forced himself to wait – an agonising few seconds – as the fish turned down with the fly – then he clamped his hand on the line, lifted the rod, felt the weight of the fish and drove the hook home.

A moment later a magnificent salmon exploded from the water, trying to shake the hook. A beauty – about 11 to 12 Kilos. "Now – he was in for a battle for sure."

With a fish this size and David wading in the river – there was at least a 50% chance the fish would beat him and break off.

Three quarters of an hour later, breathless and with his arms aching, David stood in shallow water with the fish at his feet. It was finally exhausted.  He looked at the superb lithe body in the clear water – a perfect hen (female) fish.  Silver flanks, speckled and darker on the back, perfect fins.  It looked at him, gasping.

He reached down, removed the hook and supported her with his hands along the flanks.  Gently stroked her on the head and along the sides.  Still she lay there, gulping in oxygen, waiting for her tired muscles to recover.  After a full minute, David took his hands away, touched her on the tail.  Gave her a little push and, with a flick of her tail, she surged away and back out into the main river.

David gave a little sigh.  "Magnificent!  What an experience!"

He had no wish to kill her.  It was simply the challenge.  To tempt such a fish to take the fly.  The thrill of the 'take'.  To battle such a powerful, dynamic being and counter, or try to counter, every move, every lunge, every streaking run it made.  "So exciting!"

Some people were critical.  "Cruelty!" they said.  David knew that, basically, they were right.  But the hunting instinct in man is very powerful and, after all, he released the fish unharmed, to carry on up river to fulfil its destiny.

Two hours later, after catching, and releasing two more smaller, salmon, he went back to the tricycle and prepared to go home.

David relaxed and let the motor of his tricycle do the work.  He did not pedal but simply sat back and enjoyed the view back to New Copenhagen.  He did not go to his University rooms but carried on to his grandparents place on the outskirts of town where they were holding a dinner and family get-together that evening.  As he travelled he looked across the city and admired the many spires and high pitched roofs, reminiscent of the old Copenhagen as it was in Denmark, a thousand years ago.  The new town had indeed been modelled on old Copenhagen and even had a replica bronze statue of the famous mermaid – this time on a granite boulder in the middle of the main square.  The city of New Copenhagen was, of course, 70 to 80 feet higher than its harbour – to allow for future sea level rise.  The rows and rows of ugly, high thermal efficiency, houses, with their black south facing solar panel facades, reminiscent of rows and rows of enormous black teeth, as they had been 400 years before, were gone.

As Greenland's ice cap had steadily melted, more and more river valleys had opened up, suitable for development of hydro power.

A final technological breakthrough had been the development of 'room temperature super-conductors'. The boffins had finally 'cracked it' after hundreds of years of experimentation. They had finally developed flexible super-conducting cables that maintained super-conductivity up to 21°C – which meant that now – small diameter, below ground, cables a thousand miles long could carry enormous power loads with almost zero losses.

As a result – almost 100% of Greenland's electrical power was now generated by hydro-electric power stations – that most benign form of power generation. Long life turbines, no pollution whatsoever. The only downside was the interference with the salmon migration – and that was catered for by salmon ladders and even fish lifts. So, with the advent of the superconducting cables, Greenland finally abolished all wind powered generators and even ditched the high efficiency solar panel power farms. After all, the solar panels only worked in summer.

With plenty of cheap power, Greenland decided, with World Government approval, it could afford to drop the ultra high efficiency (but ugly) house and municipal building designs and go for a slightly less efficient but far more aesthetically appealing construction. So now, New Copenhagen looked remarkably like old Copenhagen of a thousand years ago.

---

David arrived. Parked his tricycle at the side of the house. Noted – a number of other trikes were already there, tidied himself up and walked in.

He was met by his great, great grandparents, Lucinda 92 and Joseph 94 who embraced him with enthusiasm.

Lucy stood back and appraised him.

"You are looking fit and well – as ever. They tell me you have taken up hang-gliding. Be careful! We don't want you breaking your neck!"

Joe stepped in.

"Let the boy enjoy himself! You are only young once! I hear you have been salmon fishing. Did you do any good?"

"I had a beautiful 12 kilo fish and two about 6/7 kilos." said David.

"I hope you brought one back." said Lucy. "I love fresh salmon."

"Sorry Granma. You know I don't like killing them. Afraid you'll have to get one in town."

"I'd like to come with you one of these days." said Joe. "I can still cast a good fly you know. I just don't wade quite so deep these days."

"Sure Grandpa. We must fix a date." said David.

He looked at his great grandparents. They were both clear eyed, sharp witted and standing tall. The twin ancient scourges of old age – dementia and arthritis had been all but eliminated. The incidence of cancer reduced to near zero. Stem cell and gene therapy kept all the organs working. Average expectation of life was now around 100.

A few seconds later and his older brother Rolf appeared along with his wife Datari and their children. Two year old Lakinda – a happy, bubbly little girl with wavy black hair and sparkly dark eyes with a hint of the oriental. The boy, Daniel – 4 years old. Daniel was a favourite Kealey family name. No one knew how many Daniels there had been since the first one came to Greenland. Little Daniel, remarkably, had fair hair and blue eyes.

"The old Nordic genes still showed up, now and again" reflected David.

Both children had been genetically checked at conception, in accordance with accepted practice but, in fact, 99% of the commonest defects had already been screened and eliminated in Rolf's and Datari's forbears.

When Genetic Screening was first introduced, scientists had been astounded to find out how many of humanity's health problems had a genetic link. There were the obvious ones like cleft palate, epilepsy, haemophilia, and so on but careful investigation revealed that thousands of ailments and problems had an unrealised genetic link. The defective genes themselves, often with very minor genetic changes, did not directly cause problems but often interacted with factors in the environment to create a 'predisposition' towards certain problems. There could be a predisposition towards high blood pressure. A predisposition towards cancer. Towards allergies. Towards fragile bones. Towards a thousand and one things. Arthritis, for instance, was caused by a predisposition for the immune system to malfunction slightly and attack the body's own tissues, particularly those in the joints. As were two other devastating diseases – M.S. (Multiple Sclerosis) and Motor Neurone Disease. These were both caused by a malfunction of the immune system whereby the immune system attacked and destroyed the myelin sheath (the insulation) around the nerves, leading to immobility, paralysis and pain. Both of these diseases were fundamentally caused by relatively minor genetic defects which the Geneticists were easily able to edit before the egg cell was allowed to develop into an embryo.

It was found that there were a number of minor genetic defects – they were so common they could hardly be called defects – that made the immune system prone, in later life, to attacking the body's own tissues. Gradually these slight genetic changes were tracked down, deleted or replaced with genes that boosted the immune systems recognition system. The curse of Arthritis that had plagued the human race for thousands of years, was finally overcome. Many other minor gene defects were found that merely slightly reduced the body's efficiency. This was often the cause of the difference between the performance of a superb athlete and an average person. The difference between a racing car driver's superb eyesight, lightning reflexes, judgement and even the high speed working of his brain. It had been noticed that these kinds of gifts often ran in families – giving the clue to a genetic link.

By the year 3000, the study and application of Applied Genetics had advanced to such a point that every child that was born was certain to be free of any serious genetic defects. On top of that, the child, as it grew up, was sure to have good health, a superb physique, a body working at maximum efficiency. Superb eyesight, reflexes, co-ordination, a healthy heart and organs, maximum efficiency immune system, good bone structure, good healing, mental stability, slow ageing, freedom from dementia and arthritis in old age. Better eyesight, taste and hearing in old age.

However, nothing is perfect! In old age people still did, sometimes, have strokes, have haemorrhages, have kidney failure, have heart failure, even have cancer but, by and large, the improvement in life and general well being of the people alive in the year 3012, was fantastically better because of Applied Genetics.

---

Two hours before they were due to have dinner the door chime rang. David answered it and found James M'Gombe, the 13 year old dark skinned boy from next door on the doorstep. He gave David a cheeky grin and said "Mum asked me to deliver this bag of 'greens'. You might find them useful!" and, with that, he was off, pedalling his bike furiously down the road.

David watched him go, remembering that, just two years ago, this same lad had fallen out of a tree, hit the ground awkwardly and shattered his spine, breaking the spinal cord and paralysing him from the waist down.

His parents were devastated.

He was rushed to hospital. The medics operated, sorted out his spine and then were faced with the fact the spinal cord was parted with a 7mm gap between the two ends.

The neuro surgeons then took over.

They took nerve cells from an olfactory bulb in his nose, cultured them in a nutrient solution and then grafted the resulting pulpy mass into the gap in the spinal cord. They then injected a concentrated nerve growth factor into the mass, closed him up and immobilised two thirds of his body in a cage for 3 weeks.

After a month, feeling began to come back into his feet. Six months later he was walking and now, after 2 years, no one could tell he had ever been injured.

David took the bag to the kitchen. The contents were placed on a worktop.

"Great!" said David's 49 year old mum Gwen. "These are fresher than the ones I have in the 'greens box'. Kidney beans, lettuce and tomatoes."

All three were, of course, frost resistant varieties. The beans had been sown before Christmas and were cropping already, having withstood numerous frosts after they had germinated. The old, original kidney beans wouldn't have stood a chance. Just one light frost and they would have been goners. The tomatoes too, were frost resistant. So much so that, at the end of a season, the vines were merely cut back two thirds and the stumps left. These burst into new life in the spring and produced a first crop of tomatoes far earlier than would have been possible with old 'frost sensitive' varieties. And the flavour, in the modern varieties, was superb.

Shortly afterwards David's grandparents turned up – on their trikes and there were hugs and handshakes all round.

They lived twenty miles to the north east on a farm in a beautiful little valley with a tributary of the Namsen running through it.

Lara was 72 and Nathan 75 years old, both very capable and active. The farm was part arable, part fruit and they ran it with the help of several young students, a robotic tractor and a couple of robot fruit pickers.

Everybody got together around the big table and enjoyed a good meal. There was much banter and laughter. Nathan described how, the previous week, they had gone into New Copenhagen for a night out, had a meal at an Italian Restaurant, where Nathan had managed to spill his soup over the waiter. They had then gone to a Virtual reality Travel Theatre and done a trip along the Zambezi River to the Victoria Falls.

"Fantastic!" said Nathan. "It was so damn realistic we even got wet."
David laughed "I reckon they must have turned the power station off for a while for the Video crews. Normally the power station takes 95% of the total flow over the falls these days."

After the meal they broke up into little groups, sat on the long settees and drank coffee.

David sat next to Joseph and talked salmon fishing. Joseph sipping a cherry brandy liquor – there were massive cherry orchards in Greenland now.

After a while, Joseph reminisced, talking about his days as an Engineer – building bridges and railways.

"You know!" he said "It's been a marvellous life really – and it's great to be here and see everybody happy. But 94 is knocking up the years somewhat. Nobody lives forever and the day will come when it's time to go. I remember being with my father at the end. He was 98 but had a stroke – a haemorrhage in the brain – probably over-exerted himself. The stroke damaged his brain. One side of his body was paralysed. He became incontinent. He hated being looked after, shaved, washed, bathed, having to wear diapers and so on.

He spoke to me and the doctors and told us he would prefer to go. He had had a good life and would like to just leave – quietly and without fuss. Would we mind if he took an EOL pill and said goodbye. Would we mind?" Joseph wiped his eye. "I talked to Lucy and the doctors and we went back to see him. I told him. Dad! If that's really what you want to do its OK by us, but we love you and don't want to see you go. He smiled and gripped my hand with his good hand."

"I know that, but I would prefer to go. This is no life is it?"

"We discussed it with the doctors and, next day we sat at his bedside. We talked for a while but he was very weak. He was quiet for a while then roused, smiled at us – quietly said "It's time to go!" placed the EOL pill in his mouth and washed it down with a drink of water. The doctor adjusted his pillow and made him comfortable. He looked at us and smiled, laid back and relaxed. I took his hand in mine. He squeezed it and held it loosely. After a time his eyes closed. Gradually his hand relaxed as he went to sleep. Gradually his breathing slowed. After a time his breathing slowed until you could hardly notice and then, finally, I realised he was gone. Just lying there with a little smile on his face.

David! When my time comes – I would like to go like that. Much better than long drawn out unhappiness and misery, don't you think?"

"Yes! Granddad! I do! But we aren't there yet and a couple of hours ago you asked me if you could come fishing. Let's talk about that!"